COMPREHENSIVE BIOCHEMISTRY

SOLE DISTRIBUTORS FOR THE UNITED STATES AND CANADA:
AMERICAN ELSEVIER PUBLISHING COMPANY, INC.
52, VANDERBILT AVENUE, NEW YORK 17 N.Y.

Library of Congress Catalog Card Number 62–10359

With 91 illustrations and 43 tables

PRINTED IN THE NETHERLANDS BY
DRUKKERIJ MEIJER – WORMERVEER AND AMSTERDAM

COMPREHENSIVE BIOCHEMISTRY

COMPREHENSIVE BIOCHEMISTRY

SECTION I (VOLUMES 1–4)

PHYSICO-CHEMICAL AND ORGANIC ASPECTS OF BIOCHEMISTRY

SECTION II (VOLUMES 5–11)

CHEMISTRY OF BIOLOGICAL COMPOUNDS

SECTION III

BIOCHEMICAL REACTION MECHANISMS

SECTION IV

METABOLISM

SECTION V

CHEMICAL BIOLOGY

GENERAL INDEX

COMPREHENSIVE BIOCHEMISTRY

EDITED BY

MARCEL FLORKIN

Professor of Biochemistry, University of Liège (Belgium)

AND

ELMER H. STOTZ

Professor of Biochemistry, University of Rochester, School of Medicine and Dentistry, Rochester, N.Y. (U.S.A.)

VOLUME 4

SEPARATION METHODS

ELSEVIER PUBLISHING COMPANY

AMSTERDAM · LONDON · NEW YORK

1962

CONTRIBUTORS TO THIS VOLUME

PROFESSOR P. CHOVIN, D.Sc.

Assistant Director of the Town Laboratory for Explosives, Radioactivity,
Electricity, Chemistry, Public and Industrial Health, Scientific Research,
39 bis, Rue de Dantzig, Paris 15 (France)

L. C. CRAIG, B.S., Ph.D.

The Rockefeller Institute, New York 21, N.Y. (U.S.A.)

EDGAR LEDERER, Ph.D., D.Sc.

Professor of Biochemistry, Laboratoire de Chimie Biologique,
Faculté des Sciences, Paris and Institut de Chimie des Substances Naturelles,
Gif-sur-Yvette, Seine et Oise (France)

MICHAEL LEDERER, Ph.D.

Laboratorio di Chromatografia dell C.N.R.,
Istituto di Chimica Generale ed Inorganica, Piazzale delle Scienze 5, Roma (Italia)

GENERAL PREFACE

The Editors are keenly aware that the literature of Biochemistry is already very large, in fact so widespread that it is increasingly difficult to assemble the most pertinent material in a given area. Beyond the ordinary textbook the subject matter of the rapidly expanding knowledge of biochemistry is spread among innumerable journals, monographs, and series of reviews. The Editors believe that there is a real place for an advanced treatise in biochemistry which assembles the principal areas of the subject in a single set of books.

It would be ideal if an individual or small group of biochemists could produce such an advanced treatise, and within the time to keep reasonably abreast of rapid advances, but this is at least difficult if not impossible. Instead, the Editors with the advice of the Advisory Board, have assembled what they consider the best possible sequence of chapters written by competent authors; they must take the responsibility for inevitable gaps of subject matter and duplication which may result from this procedure.

Most evident to the modern biochemist, apart from the body of knowledge of the chemistry and metabolism of biological substances, is the extent to which he must draw from recent concepts of physical and organic chemistry, and in turn project into the vast field of biology. Thus in the organization of Comprehensive Biochemistry, the middle three sections, Chemistry of Biological Compounds, Biochemical Reaction Mechanisms, and Metabolism may be considered classical biochemistry, while the first and last sections provide selected material on the origins and projections of the subject.

It is hoped that sub-division of sections into volumes will not only be convenient, but will find favour among students concerned with specialized areas, and will permit easier future revisions of the individual volumes. Toward the latter end particularly, the Editors will welcome all comments in their effort to produce a useful and efficient source of biochemical knowledge.

Liège/Rochester
March 1962

M. FLORKIN
E. H. STOTZ

PREFACE TO SECTION I

(Volumes 1–4)

Students and teachers of Biochemistry would not deny the importance of a sound understanding of at least certain areas of organic and physical chemistry in the comprehension of modern biochemistry. Toward this end the Editors have constituted the first section of Comprehensive Biochemistry. This section is intended neither as a textbook of organic nor of physical chemistry, but rather as a collection of chapters which seem generally pertinent in the interpretation of biochemical techniques and in the understanding of the chemistry of biological compounds and reaction mechanisms. Certain areas of organic and physical chemistry have been reserved for later presentation in context with specific biochemical topics, but the material of Section I seems to the authors to underlie all of modern biochemistry. The choice of material for Section I may well not agree with that of individual readers, and comments toward the construction of future volumes will be appreciated.

Section I has been subdivided into groups of topics designated as Atomic and Molecular Structure (Volume 1), Organic and Physical Chemistry (Volume 2), Methods for the Study of Molecules (Volume 3) and Separation Methods (Volume 4). It is hoped that all may find general favour, and that the individual volumes will find a special place on the shelf of the specialist.

Liège/Rochester
August 1962

M. Florkin
E. H. Stotz

CONTENTS

VOLUME 4

SEPARATION METHODS

Chapter I. Countercurrent Distribution

by L. C. CRAIG

Chapter II. Chromatography

by E. LEDERER AND M. LEDERER

Part A. Adsorption Chromatography

Part B. Ion Exchange Chromatography

Part C. Partition Chromatography

I. PARTITION CHROMATOGRAPHY ON COLUMNS

II. PAPER CHROMATOGRAPHY

Chapter III. Gas Chromatography

by P. Chovin

The other Volumes of Section 1 contain the following chapters:

Volume 1. *Atomic and Molecular Structure*

Chapter I. Atomic Structure by W. PARKER ALFORD (Rochester, N.Y.)
Chapter II. Electronic Theory of Organic Molecules by H. H. JAFFÉ (Cincinnati, Ohio)
Chapter III. The Structure of Molecules by J. D. BERNAL (London)
Chapter IV. Stereoisomerism by KURT MISLOW (New York)

Volume 2. *Organic and Physical Chemistry*

Chapter I. Mechanisms of Organic Reactions by M. L. BENDER AND R. BRESLOW (Evanston, Ill. and New York, N.Y.)
Chapter II. Behaviour of Molecules in Solution by W. D. STEIN (Cambridge, Great Britain)
Chapter III. Diffusion and Osmosis by W. D. STEIN (Cambridge, Great Britain)

Volume 3. *Methods for the Study of Molecules*

Chapter I. Crystallography by G. J. BULLEN (London)
Chapter II. X-Ray Diffraction by G. J. BULLEN (London)
Chapter III. Analysis by Emission Spectroscopy by NORMAN H. NACHTRIEB (Chicago, Ill.)
Chapter IV. Spectrophotometry in the Ultraviolet and Visible Regions by R. A. MORTON (Liverpool)
Chapter V. Infrared Spectra of Compounds of Biological Interest by L. J. BELLAMY (Waltham Abbey, Essex)
Chapter VI. Fluorescence by A. EHRENBERG AND H. THEORELL (Stockholm)
Chapter VII. Electronic Paramagnetic Resonance by S. I. WEISSMAN (St. Louis, Mo.)
Chapter VIII. Nuclear Magnetic Resonance by C. D. JARDETZKY AND O. JARDETZKY (Cambridge and Boston, Mass.)
Chapter IX. Determination of Mass, Form and Dimensions of Large Particles in Solution by CH. SADRON AND M. DAUNE (Strasbourg)

Chapter I

Countercurrent Distribution

LYMAN C. CRAIG

The Rockefeller Institute, New York

1. Introduction

Countercurrent distribution is a relatively simple extraction process which is specifically designed for the purpose of separating relatively small amounts of mixtures of solutes under the mildest conditions in the laboratory. It is a logical extension of one of the oldest known separation methods; simple partition between two immiscible solvents. Since it is a multiple partition process, entirely discontinuous and stepwise in nature, it permits a rigid systematization with division and subdivision of the solute exactly according to the binomial theorem. This permits a useful mathematical interpretation, more exact than that possible for any other known countercurrent separation process. It is, therefore, ideally suited for analysis and for the establishment of the purity of a given preparation, particularly one of interest in biological chemistry where the experimenter can ill afford to lose any of a very valuable sample.

Countercurrent distribution can be applied to any solute which can be partitioned between two immiscible phases. It is, therefore, not restricted to molecules of a certain size or type. The immiscible phases can be mixtures of solvents, buffers, salts and various complexing agents. This makes it have a very wide applicability. Although more often used as a small-scale preparative or analytical method, it can be used for micro separations or can be modified for large-scale preparative work.

With these advantages and others not mentioned it is only fair to ask why this form of multiple extraction has not been more widely used when indeed many of its advantages were fully realized by Jantzen[1] thirty years ago. Two considerations are probably responsible for the fact that it did not begin to be popular until about ten years ago. One was the labor involved together with the view that the same or a superior separation could be achieved by a continuous extraction process with much less labor. The

References p. 31

equipment available today makes this view questionable and greatly reduces the labor of the discontinuous process. The second point deals with the problem of suitable systems. Great improvement along this line now has resulted from the publication of partition data for the separation of nearly every type of solute known. A discussion of equipment and systems will form a considerable part of this chapter.

The literature dealing with extraction is enormous and widely scattered among many papers dealing with all kinds of chemical subjects. All too often an observation of interest to partition forms only a small part of a long paper. Partly for this reason and partly because an attempt at complete coverage would be too unwieldy for this chapter, no claim for completeness will be made. For a more complete coverage, see Craig and Craig[2], Hecker[3] or Weisiger[4].

In countercurrent distribution nearly all separations will be made using conditions which give complete equilibrium between the two phases. Thus the simple partition law is satisfied. As used in this work, C_1 is the concentration

$$K = C_1/C_2 \tag{1}$$

of the solute in terms of weight, or something proportional to it, in the upper phase; C_2 is the concentration in the lower phase. This designation will hold whether or not the polar phase is the heavier. C_1 and C_2 include all the solute of interest in the respective phases whether or not it exists in more than one readily interconvertible form.

It is interesting to think of simple partition in terms of a certain probability since this naturally leads to the mathematics to be used later in the interpretation of the results. K for a given concentration level and temperature will be very constant because of the very high number of molecules involved but as the population density of the molecules increases it will show a certain shift. The effect of this in countercurrent distribution will be discussed later in connection with non-ideal distributions.

In spite of this latter complication slight differences in the probability, here expressed as K, can be exploited better if repetitive extractions are made so that the mathematics of the binomial theorem or its approximation can be directly applied.

The systematization which will permit this is given schematically in Fig. 1. Here each contacting phase is represented by a rectangle and numbered serially starting with 0. The stages or transfer numbers are on the left. The top row gives the state of affairs after equilibration at 0 transfers. Unit quantity of solute is assumed in this scheme and a K of one. The phase volumes are all equal. At transfer 1 after equilibration, the fraction of the solute in each of the four phases in contact is represented by the decimal inside the appropriate rectangle. Similarly, the distribution of fractional parts at transfer 2, 3 and 4 is shown.

It is obvious from Fig. 1 that the solute will spread equally to the right and to the left if the upper and lower phases are moved alternately, equilibrating at each stage. It is equally apparent that the same distribution of

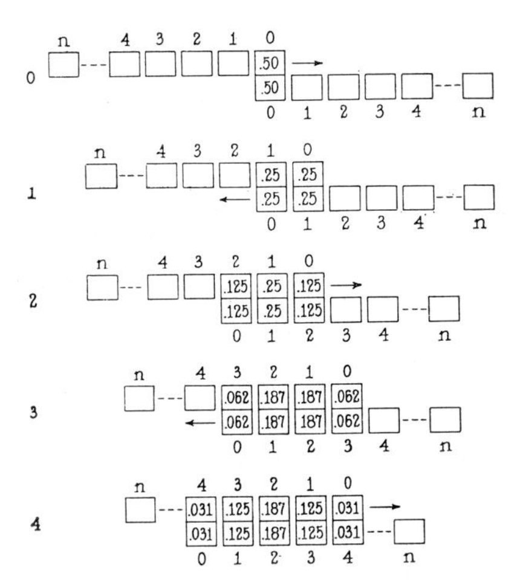

Fig. 1. A systematic extraction scheme. (Taken from *Techniques of Organic Chemistry*, Vol. III, A. WEISSBERGER (Ed.), Interscience, New York, 1950.)

fractional parts will result if only one phase is moved at each equilibration. Here the solute will migrate as it spreads. In the development to follow, the lower phase will remain stationary.

A further simplification results if the total fraction in each unit in both upper and lower phase is combined. When the scheme of Fig. 1 is treated in this way, the figures given in Table I are obtained. Here the scheme is expanded to 8 transfers.

Mathematically the development of the fractions in each contacting unit, each fraction in Table I, is given by the simple binomial in eqn. 2 where

$$(x + y)^n = 1 \tag{2}$$

x is the concentration in the lower phase and y that in the upper. The exponent n is the number of transfers. Since the fraction in each phase at equilibrium is fixed by K, it follows that eqn. 2 in terms of K and n is given in eqn. 3.

$$\left(\frac{1}{K+1} + \frac{K}{K+1}\right)^n = 1 \tag{3}$$

References p. 31

TABLE I

DISTRIBUTION OF FRACTIONAL PARTS FOR A SOLUTE WITH A K OF 1

Transfer No.	Tube No. 0	1	2	3	4	5	6	7	8
0	1.000								
1	.500	.500							
2	.250	.500	.250						
3	.125	.375	.375	.125					
4	.062	.250	.375	.250	.062				
5	.031	.156	.313	.313	.156	.031			
6	.015	.093	.234	.313	.234	.093	.015		
7	.008	.054	.164	.274	.274	.164	.054	.008	
8	.004	.031	.109	.219	.274	.219	.109	.031	.004

(Reprinted with permission from *Analytical Methods of Protein Chemistry*, Pergamon, London, 1960.)

The most practical way of showing the distribution of fractions along a train of contacting units (separatory funnels or tubes) is by a plot of the fraction or of something proportional to the amount in each unit against the serial number of the unit. Fig. 2 is such a plot at 8 transfers. The central curve would be that obtained with a K of 1. The right dashed curve would be that obtained with a K of 3 while the left would result from a K of 0.30.

If a mixture of two solutes with K's of 3 and 0.30 had been taken, the sum of the two curves would have resulted and the chart would give an excellent overall analytical picture with a certain amount of overlap in tubes 3 to 5. With the application of higher numbers of transfers, this overlap area would decrease but never completely disappear in the absolute sense. It is entirely practical to perform 10 to 12 transfers with individual contacting units but becomes progressively less practical for higher numbers unless a train of contacting units is used which enables many simultaneous extractions to be made. Since equipment for accomplishing this is now

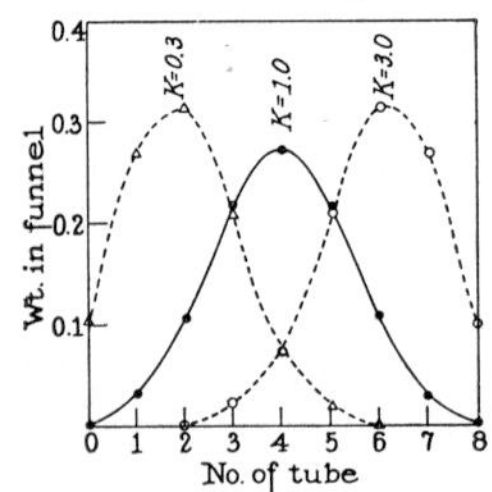

Fig. 2. Countercurrent distribution patterns with partition ratios of 0.3, 1.0 and 3.0. (Taken from *Techniques of Organic Chemistry*, Vol. III, A. WEISSBERGER (Ed.), Interscience, New York, 1950.)

readily available, the mathematics and reasoning will be further developed.

Let us assume that the scheme of Fig. 1 had been continued until 25 units filled with both phases were in the contacting train. Thus 24 transfers would have been applied. With a mixture of two solutes with K's of 0.707 and 1.414, the binomial of eqn. 3 would permit calculation[5] of the respective

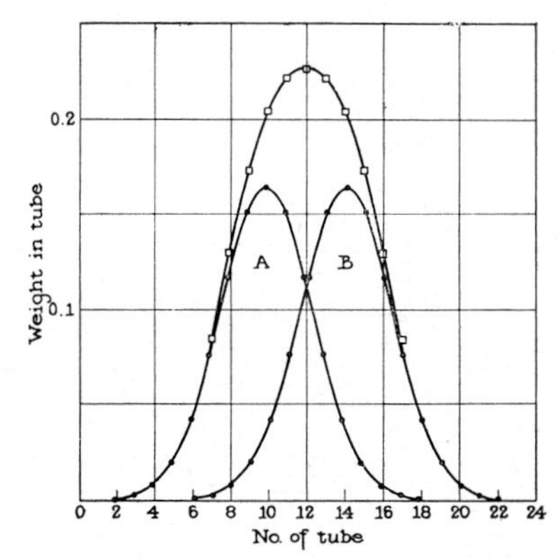

Fig. 3. Countercurrent distribution patterns at 24 transfers for two solutes with K's of 0.707 and 1.414. (Taken from *Techniques of Organic Chemistry*, Vol. III, A. WEISSBERGER (Ed.), Interscience, New York, 1950.)

two lower curves shown in Fig. 3. The sum of these two curves would give the upper curve which would be the curve experimentally found with such a mixture if the two solutes behaved ideally.

In order to calculate a curve such as A or B or for smaller numbers of transfers, eqn. 4 is very convenient. It is arranged to calculate each

$$T_{n,r} = [n!/r!\,(n-r)!]\,[1/(K+1)]^n\, K^r \tag{4}$$

term of the binomial directly[5]. In this equation r is the tube number and $T_{n,r}$ is the fraction for a given number of transfers and tube number.

Even this becomes laborious when n, the number of transfers, becomes much higher than 20. However, in this case an approximation can be used which gives values well within the experimental error. The form of this approximation in terms of the partition ratio, K, and of the numbers of transfers, n, is given in eqn. 5. Here y is the total fraction of solute in the

$$y = 1/\sqrt{2\pi nK/(K+1)^2}\cdot \exp - x^2/[2nK/(K+1)^2] \tag{5}$$

xth tube either to the right or left from the maximum of the bell-shaped curve. This equation is not as complicated as it appears to be and can be

References p. 31

Fig. 4. A 30-tube countercurrent distribution train.

rearranged so that a theoretical distribution can be calculated in about 10 minutes with the aid of a slide rule. In countercurrent distribution work, this equation is very much used, but a discussion of its application will be postponed until the experimental procedures of countercurrent have been described. These will now be considered.

A simple distribution train for accomplishing the scheme depicted in Fig. 1 is the 30-tube hand operated train shown in Fig. 4. The glass cells fitted closely together are held in place by an aluminium frame supported at each end by bearings so that all the cells can be tipped forward and back as a unit.

The design of each cell is shown schematically in Fig. 5. The dimensions given in cm are for 10-ml lower-phase volumes and up to 15-ml upper-phase volumes. Each cell carries a flat butt joint held in place by a spring so that liquid can be added or removed at will, usually with a syringe to be described later. These joints are designed for the greatest speed in removal and will not leak. The solute is brought to equilibrium with the two phases in each tube by rocking the train forward and back as from A to B in Fig. 5 about six times. This will nearly always be sufficient for the purpose. For a theoretical discussion of the reason a longer time is not needed (see the Chapter in Weissberger by Craig and Craig[2]). The phases are permitted to separate with the cells in position B and the train then tipped to C. Here the upper phase decants through tube c into d leaving behind the lower phase.

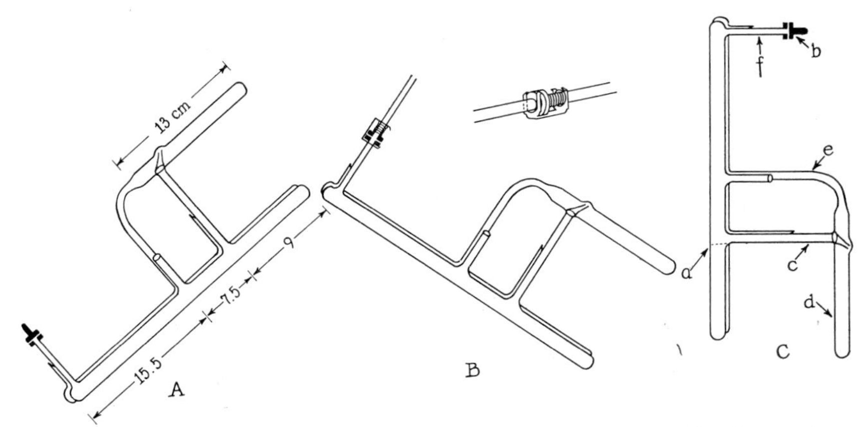

Fig. 5. Schematic drawing of individual units of a countercurrent distribution train. (Taken from *Techniques of Organic Chemistry*, Vol. III, A. WEISSBERGER (Ed.), Interscience, New York, 1950.)

On tipping back to A, the upper phase in d cannot flow back into the equilibration cell from which it has come because of the extension of the tube c but instead runs through e to the next cell of the series. Thus a single tipping operation causes each of the upper phases to advance one tube in the train where they are again equilibrated. Each time the tubes are tipped to C, a transfer is accomplished. The whole operation of equilibration, settling and transfer, usually will require 1 to 2 minutes.

The first step in starting a distribution after a suitable system has been selected, as discussed later on, is the equilibration at the temperature to be used of a quantity of the two phases sufficient for the whole run. A large separatory funnel is most convenient for this purpose. Sufficient of the lower phase is then placed in the train so that each cell will have the required amount. This operation can be accomplished rapidly by tipping the train from position B of Fig. 5 almost to C. A small funnel supplied with the apparatus is fitted with a flat joint so that it can be attached in place of b to tube f. Approximately 170 ml of the lower phase can be run into the train through this funnel at tube 5 and another 170-ml portion at tube 15. After replacing the closures, the phases are rapidly distributed through the train by tipping from A to C the required number of times.

With each transfer during the run, the upper phase in tube 0 moves to tube 1 and must be replaced by a fresh phase. This can be done by hand or more easily with a simple filling device shown in Fig. 6. A standard Erlenmeyer flask with a 24/40 joint is fitted with a laboratory dispensing head which can be purchased in 15, 10, 5, etc., ml sizes from apparatus supply houses such as Scientific Glass Inc., Bloomfield, N.J. The Erlenmeyer can be mounted with a clamp in the appropriate position on the train support in front of tube 0 so that the head will fill when the train is tipped to the decant position. The outlet from the head is connected to tube 0 either by a glass tube or perhaps more conveniently by a plastic (polyethylene or Kel-F) tube so that the contents of the head will flow into tube 0 in the transfer position.

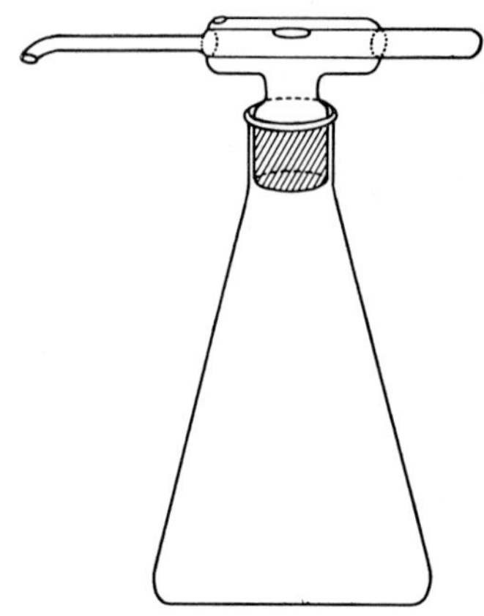

Fig. 6. A simple filling device. (Reprinted with permission from *Analytical Methods of Protein Chemistry*, Pergamon, London, 1960.)

The sample to be distributed is placed in tube 0 along with the two phases in an amount not greater than that which goes into solution or seriously upsets the phase relationships of the system. With many solutes it is possible to use up to 1 g. For a larger load, the sample may be scattered in several of the first tubes, a possibility to be considered later on in connection with a discussion of non-ideal solutes. It will be well to place several upper phases in tubes 1, 2, 3 in front of the solute so that there will be no distortions due to evaporation or a slight change in temperature.

After 29 transfers have been applied, the train of 30 cells would still contain all the solute but the few conditioning upper phases together with any excess lower phase would have migrated from the train at tube 29. Even for a pure single solute each cell at this point would contain some fraction of the original although for many of the cells this fraction would be so small that it could be neglected. No fractionation process ever gives complete separation in the absolute sense. The procedure up to this point is called the "Fundamental" procedure. If the distribution has been made on an unknown solute or mixture, it will be desirable to analyse a sufficient number of the tubes for solute content so that a distribution curve can be plotted.

From the plot the presence of more than a single component may be obvious, but the interpretation is greatly aided by the calculation and proper matching of a theoretical curve as described later on. In case only a single component is suggested by perfect agreement of the calculated curve with the experimental one, a mixture still may be present provided the components of the mixture have very similar or identical partition ratios. This possibility may be greatly reduced by continuing the process to very high numbers of transfers with the mechanical equipment described later on (even this is of no avail with identical partition ratios) or by changing systems.

When the calculated curve is only slightly different from the experimentally determined one, the correct interpretation is made more certain by determining partition ratios across the band. An actual purity study, shown in Fig. 7, with a sample of penicillin[6] will serve as an example. Here the

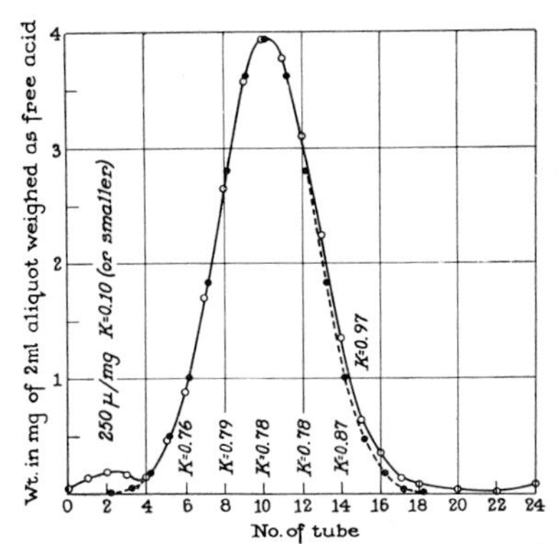

Fig. 7. A purity study of a penicillin. (Taken from *Techniques of Organic Chemistry*, Vol. III, A. WEISSBERGER (Ed.), Interscience, New York, 1950.) ● = calculated; ○ = experimental.

experimental and calculated curve are slightly different. That the divergence is caused by impurity is shown by the fact that the partition ratios in tubes 14 and 15 are significantly higher than the others. This impurity would be separated by continuing to higher numbers of transfers.

The requirements which will always give satisfactory matching of theoretical and experimental curves are: (1) Only one operating partition ratio due to a single solute (or very similar partition ratios due to several solutes). (2) A partition ratio reasonably constant with different concentrations. (3) True equilibrium conditions at each transfer. The two latter possibilities can be easily recognized as will be seen from a discussion to be given later.

2. The various operational procedures of a distribution train

In the foregoing treatment, the simplest approach has been described briefly to introduce the reader to the equipment and the most basic operation.

References p. 31

Several ways of extending the method have been found even more useful and efficient, depending on the type of mixture at hand and the purpose of the distribution. The most useful ones are given below:

1. Fundamental
2. Single withdrawal
3. Completion of squares
4. Recycling
5. Partial withdrawal

No further discussion of the Fundamental procedure need be given except to say that it always must be accomplished before going to the other variations. If enough is known about the mixture, it may not be necessary to stop for an analysis at this stage.

(a) *Single withdrawal*

Upon completion of the maximum number of transfers possible in the fundamental process with the train at hand, *e.g.* all the cells with both upper and lower phases in them, further transfers can be applied by permitting the upper phases to emerge from the last cell in serial fashion into test tubes which are set aside properly numbered in the order of emergence. The procedure is analogous to effluent chromatography with the distribution train

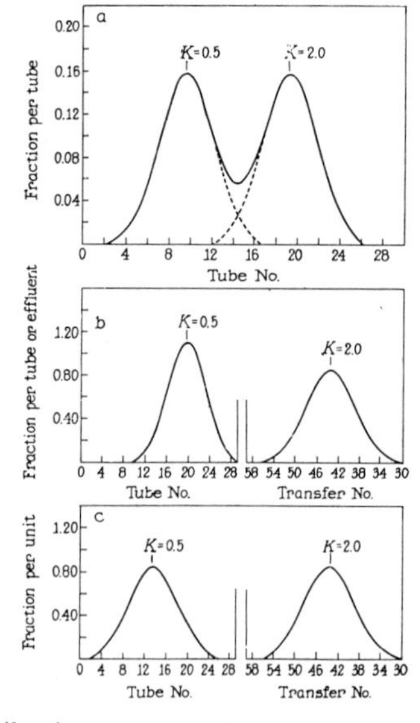

Fig. 8. Calculated distribution patterns for various procedures. (Reprinted with permission from *Analytical Methods of Protein Chemistry*, Pergamon, London, 1960.) (a) Fundamental 30-tube train; (b) single withdrawal from 30-tube train; (c) completion of squares.

taking the place of the column. The analogy, however, must end here since the distribution process is strictly discontinuous and never can become the equivalent of a continuous process no matter how many transfers are applied. Extrapolations to the contrary can be very misleading.

In order to illustrate the single withdrawal procedure, we can arbitrarily choose a mixture of equal amounts of two solutes with K's of 0.5 and 2.0 with the distributions performed in the 30-tube train of Fig. 4. Analysis at the Fundamental stage would give the upper pattern of Fig. 8. Now if the distribution were continued to 59 transfers, 30 effluent fractions would have been collected and analysis of both the effluent fractions and the cells of the train would permit construction of pattern b of Fig. 8. Here the curve of the train is constructed as for the Fundamental series and placed on the left. That for the effluent series is on the right with the last effluent to emerge nearest the highest tube number. The transfer number on which it emerged from the train is assigned to each effluent fraction. Analysis of the effluent phase is simpler since here only the upper phase is to be considered while in the train the solute in both phases should ideally be considered. However, analysis of only the lower phases will usually suffice since most of the solute will be there anyway and a correction can be applied from the K values estimated from the position of the band.

(*b*) *Completion of squares*

This is a variation first fully appreciated by Bush and Densen[7] and one often presenting a number of technical advantages. After the Fundamental stage is reached, the distribution is continued by serial collection of the effluent as above but without addition of upper phase to the train. With the train of 30 cells, the distribution would be complete at 59 transfers because all the upper phases would then be stripped from the train. Analysis would permit construction of pattern c of Fig. 8. Here the right hand curve is identical to that of pattern b but that of the left is from the lower phases only, those remaining in the train. Analysis in this case is often much simpler. In the right curve of both patterns, b and c, each effluent phase to emerge has had one more transfer applied to it than the previous one. Similarly in the left curve of pattern c, the phase in a given tube has one less transfer applied than the next higher tube. It is also quite practical to follow the single withdrawal procedure for a time and then complete the distribution as for the completion of squares. The effect of this is to lengthen the series on the right of pattern c.

(*c*) *Recycling*

The above discussed procedures are most useful for relatively short trains

References p. 31

up to 50 or 60 tubes. When longer trains are to be used, the recycling and partial withdrawal procedures become the most practical and should be considered when the separation involves a mixture of solutes with small differences in their K values.

For instance with a mixture of two solutes with K values of 0.8 and 1.2 in a train of 100 cells there would not be appreciable solute in tubes 80 to 99 at 99 transfers. Pattern a of Fig. 9 shows the separation which would be

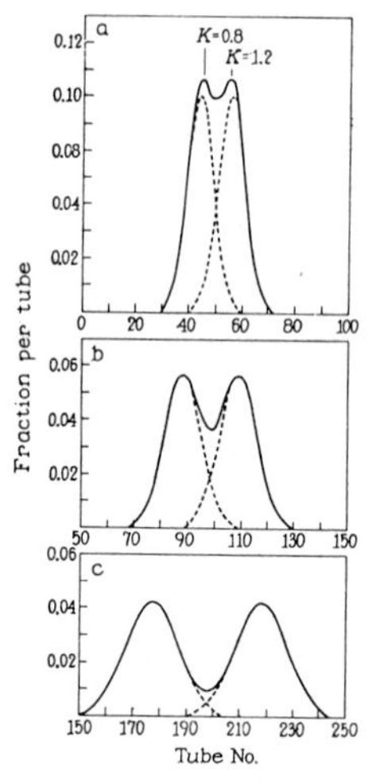

Fig. 9. Calculated distribution patterns for a train of 100 cells. (Reprinted with permission from *Analytical Methods of Protein Chemistry*, Pergamon, London, 1960.) (a) 99 transfers; (b) 199 tranfers; (c) 399 transfers.

obtained. If the distribution were to be continued, the upper phases emerging from the end of the train therefore would not contain appreciable solute and could be re-introduced into tube 0 by connecting a tube across the train. This connection is made much easier, especially for the longer trains if they are arranged in two rows as in Fig. 10. Here the transfer tubes of the cells of the lower row lead toward the left which makes the upper phases move from right to left. The highest tube in the train is, therefore, directly under the 0 tube and in a position conveniently permitting the effluent to flow into 0.

If the distribution shown in pattern a of Fig. 9 were continued to 199 transfers by recycling, pattern b would be obtained. In plotting this tube 0 becomes tube 100 on the chart. In fact the process could just as well be continued to 399 transfers since this would give pattern c. Here tube 0 has become 200 on the chart. Obviously, this is the highest number of transfers practical by recycling in a 100-tube train since going further would bring

Fig. 10. A countercurrent distribution train arranged in two rows. (Reprinted with permission from *Analytical Methods of Protein Chemistry*, Pergamon, London, 1960.)

the front edge of the most rapidly migrating band into the rear edge of the slowest.

The separation in c is obviously much better than the others and this has been accomplished without using any more solvent than in a. Only labor and time are required. This is minimized by a mechanical robot to be described later. With longer trains of the order of several hundred tubes, the recycling process becomes even more important and effective.

(*d*) *Partial withdrawal*

In many cases the distribution will be concerned with a more complex mixture than in Fig. 9. For instance, several bands may have appeared in tubes 0 to 30 and 70 to 100 in pattern a in addition to the two main ones. Here whatever tubes containing solute in the series 0 to 30 could be removed and replaced with fresh solvent. The same could be done with the contents of tubes 70 to 99 before recycling or these could be permitted to emerge by single withdrawal until the band of $K = 1.2$ was about to emerge, at about 150 transfers. Recycling could then be started. Analysis at 199 transfers would show whether any other impurities were emerging from the two bands of interest and if so, a second withdrawal might be required before proceeding to higher numbers of transfers.

An inspection of Fig. 9 will reveal that at no time is the mixed solute, the central overlapping portion of the two curves, greater than 20 tubes. Thus it would be theoretically possible to separate the mixture in a 25-tube train by withdrawing each solute, one from the right and the other from the left, as soon as it was free of the other. This could be done by alternate with-

References p. 31

drawal of first one side on a transfer and the other side on the next transfer or two tubes, one from each side, could be withdrawn on every second transfer. For a more detailed account of Alternate and Double Withdrawal, see Craig and Craig[2]. These techniques are effective for binary mixtures but are difficult to interpret with more complex mixtures and with systems that do not behave ideally. The use of longer trains is to be recommended wherever possible.

3. Calculation of theoretical curves

From Fig. 5, it is obvious that the fraction of solute in each cell which moves forward on each transfer is that in the upper phase. In terms of the partition ratio, it is $K/(K+1)$ for equal volumes of the phases or $vK/(vK+1)$ for unequal volumes where v is the ratio of the upper to the lower phase volume. This is true only for ideal conditions, *i.e.* linear partition isotherms and true equilibrium. The rate of migration of solute through the train is controlled by the fraction which moves forward on each transfer. Therefore, for a given number of transfers the maximum of the band M will be that given in eqn. 6 for equal volumes of the phases or eqn. 7 for unequal volumes.

$$M = nK/(K+1) \tag{6}$$

$$M = nvK/(vK+1) \tag{7}$$

With eqns. 6 and 7, the operating partition ratio can be derived very simply from an experimental distribution pattern. For example, in pattern a of Fig. 8 the maximum of the first band is at tube 9.7. There are of course no fractional tubes but the mathematics work out ideally if it is assumed that there are. Use of this value and 29 for n in eqn. 6 gives 0.5 for the partition ratio. This ratio is used in calculation of the curve even though actual determination of the K may give a slightly different value due to temperature shifts. Where the volumes of the phases are not equal this would of course give Kv, which then should be used in place of K in the following development.

Eqn. 5 repeated again here will be used to calculate the theoretical curve.

$$y = 1/\sqrt{2\pi nK/(K+1)^2} \cdot \exp - x^2/[2nK/(K+1)^2] \tag{5}$$

y is the value of the ordinate, y_0 is the value at the maximum and x is the number of tubes either to the right or left on the abscissa for the tube in question. Since at y_0 x is 0, the value of y_0 is given by eqn. 8.

$$y_0 = 1/\sqrt{2\pi nK/(K+1)^2} \tag{8}$$

The other y values are calculated from the y_0 value by substituting appropriate values of x in eqn. 5. Since usually an experimental curve will already be available, the y_0 value from this can be taken and eqn. 8 neglected. Thus eqn. 5 becomes eqn. 9 and may be expressed also as in eqn. 10.

$$y = y_0 \cdot \exp - x^2/[2nK/(K+1)^2] \tag{9}$$

$$y_x = y_0/\text{antilog } 0.434\, x^2/[2nK/(K+1)^2] \tag{10}$$

The ratio $0.434/[2nK/(K + 1)^2]$ is thus a constant used in calculating all the y_x values required for the curve. Where K is 0.5 and n is 29 as in Fig. 8, pattern a, the ratio would be $0.434/[2 \cdot 29 \cdot 0.5/(1.5)^2]$ or 0.0336. Substituting this in eqn. 10, one obtains eqn. 11. y_1 would be $0.156/\text{antilog } 0.0336 = 0.146$.

$$y_x = y_0/\text{antilog } 0.0336\, x^2 \tag{11}$$

Four more such points, y_2, y_3, etc., quickly calculated on the slide rule will give sufficient points to draw the curve. Since the maximum in this case does not fall exactly on a tube, none of the other points will either, but will be 1, 2, etc., tubes removed from 9.7.

After a little practice with this equation, a theoretical curve can be calculated for any band regardless of the number of transfers. Of course, with the higher numbers of transfers, the curve is broader but in spite of this only about 5 points are required on each side of the maximum, sufficient to draw the curve accurately.

Several other ways of calculating curves have been proposed by other workers. See Weisiger[4], Way and Bennet[41], Von Tavel and Signer[8], Hecker[3], Alderton[42] or Borsch-Supan[43]. Extensive binomial tables have been published by The Bureau of Standards (1950) and The Harvard University Computation Laboratory (1955).

For calculation of curves in Single Withdrawal, the left-hand curve is calculated as above since this is a Fundamental series. The right-hand curve for the withdrawn series requires a similar but modified equation.

From eqns. 6 and 7, it is obvious that the transfer number n_m on which the upper phase of maximum concentration emerges from the train is also the number of transfers required to move the band the length of the train. K is given by eqn. 12 where L is the length of the train and v is the ratio of

$$Kv = \frac{L}{n_m - L} \tag{12}$$

References p. 31

the volumes of the two phases. As before, the following development will be for equal phases were $v = 1$ but Kv in place of K would be more general.

Eqn. 13 can be derived from eqn. 5. It can be applied in much the same

$$y = 1/\sqrt{2\pi n_m/K} \cdot \exp - x^2/(2n_m/K) \quad (13)$$

manner as given above for the fundamental series in the form of eqn. 14. In these equations y and x are again the ordinate and abscissa.

$$y = y_0/\text{antilog } 0.434\, x^2/(2n_m/K) \quad (14)$$

In calculating curves for the Completion of Squares procedure, the right-hand curve is calculated as above for the withdrawn series. The left-hand pattern, however, requires different equations. Here the partition ratio is calculated by eqn. 15 where t_m is the tube number at the maximal concentration.

$$Kv = t_m/(n + t_m - L) \quad (15)$$

For equal phase volumes, eqn. 16 then becomes the equation to use for

$$y = 1/\sqrt{2\pi(n + t_m - L)K} \cdot \exp - x^2/2(n + t_m - L) \quad (16)$$

calculating the curve. Again Kv can be substituted for K where there are unequal phase volumes.

4. Non-ideal distributions

In the majority of cases with mixtures, when a run has been made and theoretical curves matched, it will be found that one or more of the experimental bands do not agree with the calculated. This can be due to (1) insufficient fractionation, (2) non-linear partition isotherms and (3) failure to reach equilibrium on each transfer. The latter two may be considered non-ideal distributions. The first, although not in this category, is considered together with the other two because it occurs with the second in so many cases and proper interpretation requires an understanding of how to differentiate one from the other.

When the partition ratio is not constant at different concentration levels, the partition isotherm is said to be non-linear and the distribution bands resulting are skewed as shown in Fig. 11. The dashed curves are the symmetrical calculated curves. With increasing load the deviation can be toward a higher partition ratio as shown in pattern a or less frequently in the reverse direction as shown in pattern b. A plot of the partition ratio across a band which does not agree with the theoretical is always helpful in interpreting the reason for the disparity as can be seen from the patterns. In a the K increases with the load but falls again on the other side of the band. The reverse is noted in b.

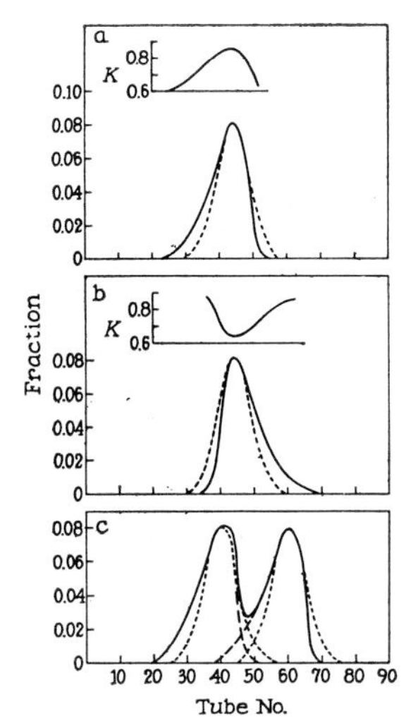

Fig. 11. Hypothetical skewed distribution patterns. (Reprinted with permission from *Analytical Methods of Protein Chemistry*, Pergamon, London, 1960.)

If the further complication of a mixture were present, then the K on the right limb of the band would not return to the value at the same concentration on the left limb. Continuation of the distribution to higher numbers of transfers would be all that is needed to confirm this interpretation.

Thus a certain amount of skewing does not interfere seriously with precise interpretation of distribution data unless two or more solutes with similar partition ratios are present. This could result in the difficulty shown in pattern c of Fig. 11. Here the trailing rear of the right-hand band extends too far into the left-hand band. An increased yield of pure product in the right-hand band is possible but at the expense of the left. The state of affairs is analogous to that of azeotropy in fractional distillation (see Craig and Craig[2]) and may be troublesome but also can be used to advantage for separation of the leading band or the trailing one where the deviation is that of pattern b.

A skewed distribution is usually wider than a normal one and is to be avoided where possible except under certain circumstances. Partition isotherms may also be more complicated than those considered here and can produce very narrow, yet almost symmetrical, distribution bands as was found by Hausmann and Craig[9].

References p. 31

Skewed distributions are nearly always caused by the tendency of solutes to associate into dimers, trimers, etc. This tendency can be overcome by the choice of solvents which themselves strongly associate with the solutes of interest. This was first clearly shown by Ahrens and Craig in the distribution of long-chain fatty acids[10] and bile acids[11]. Components of the solvent system which are most useful for this purpose are strong hydrogen binding agents such as acetic acid, formamide, urea, etc. Even detergents in buffered systems may be useful. The phenomenon of association is highly dependent on pH and ionic strength. Therefore buffers can be very important in the systems. Pyridine–acetate buffers are often helpful.

In crude mixtures that are difficult to separate, it is often worth while to do a preliminary distribution of up to 15 or 20 transfers under very high load. Here distribution patterns are useless but analysis of individual tubes may reveal a surprising separation from certain other components of the system. Such a preliminary separation can only be fully exploited by subsequent use of an entirely different separation technique.

The third consideration mentioned at the beginning of this section is that of the failure to reach true equilibrium at each transfer. Seldom is this encountered since the apparatus provides optimum conditions for reaching equilibrium[12]. This is generally true even for very large and complicated solutes, but certain solutes are anomalous in this regard. Lack of equilibrium may result in skewed distribution patterns similar to those found with non-linear partition isotherms. The effect can be discovered and corrected by repeating the distribution with several times the number of tips for equilibration. As in the skewed distributions discussed above there is the possibility of achieving improved separations by using a certain stage of disequilibrium. Exact conditions for this could be difficult to find but may be discovered inadvertently.

Where there is a strong tendency of a solute to deviate from a linear partition isotherm, the relative volumes of the two phases may become distorted to a greater or less extent. The effect of this is cumulative and may swell the upper phases in advance of the band but deplete those behind it. In part this can be compensated for by adding a small volume of the lower phase to tube 0 on each transfer along with the upper phase. The distribution is run co-current to this extent. The mechanically operated trains described later on are equipped to do this automatically. Such a correction is most important in the earlier stages of the distribution where the concentrations are highest. Later on, the volume of the co-current addition can be reduced or eliminated if it is not required to keep the lower phases leveled off. Distributions which seem to be very much distorted at first often give patterns which agree very well with calculated curves. In such cases it is advisable to plot concentration or something proportional to it against tube number rather than the total fraction in the tube.

5. Emulsions

One of the annoying difficulties often encountered in any type of liquid–liquid extraction is the formation of emulsions which separate only very slowly. These are the result of surface active components which, in biological work, are often the solutes of interest themselves. In spite of this, suitable systems can be compounded for nearly every solute regardless of its surface activity, as the tables of systems for various solutes given later on will show.

Emulsions result from the formation of stable, often solid, films at the interface. Not only does this keep the phases from separating but it interferes with the proper interchange of solute between the two phases and may prevent establishment of true equilibrium. Systems that separate too slowly are to be avoided, if possible, for several reasons. A number of comparatively small changes in the system may remove the difficulty.

If the solute is not sensitive to lower or higher pH, adjustment of the pH to a different value may be sufficient. A lower pH often is the more helpful. Often the same system may be usable if the phase containing more of the organic solvent is increased in volume relative to the other phase. If the system does not contain salt or buffer, a trace of a salt added to the system may suffice. Addition of a little of an alcohol soluble in both phases may shift the equilibrium sufficiently to break the emulsion.

The emulsion may be caused by an impurity in the preparation. Often it may be removed by a quick dialysis in a film dialyzer[13]. If the distribution has already been started, the first few transfers may be accomplished by centrifuging the contents of each tube. Here the upper and lower phases are returned to the tubes carefully leaving the interface in the centrifuge tube. After a number of preliminary transfers have been reached, it may be found that the tube or tubes causing the trouble contain little of the solute of interest. They can, therefore, be withdrawn and the distribution continued.

Occasionally a distribution may appear at first to proceed satisfactorily and then a few tubes, usually at the front or rear of the band of interest, begin to cause trouble. An impurity which associates with the solute of interest may at first prevent the formation of an emulsion but as it becomes pulled away the somte exhibits its emulsifying capabilities. The best remedy for this is to find solue known component to add to the system which can later be removed. Of course with solutes of a size sufficient to exhibit denaturation phenomena the formation of an emulsion may be indicative of a type of transformation.

6. Loading the sample in more than one tube

The complications resulting from non-ideal behavior and emulsions are considerably reduced if at the start of a run the sample is placed in more

References p. 31

than one tube. The reasoning for this can be seen from the patterns in Fig. 12. Here is shown the distribution curve to be expected with a K of 1 at 100 transfers. Curve A would be found if the sample were all initially placed in tube 0. If the sample were divided into 7 parts each placed in tube 0, 1...6 initially, seven overlapping curves separated by a distance of one tube

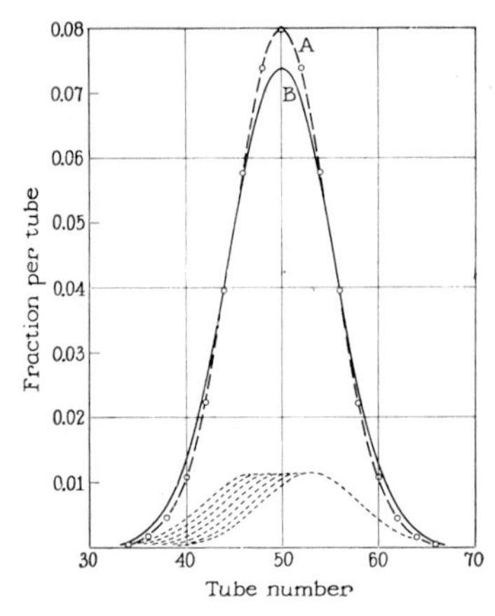

Fig. 12. Hypothetical distribution pattern showing the effect of multiple loading.

should be considered. The sum of these curves would yield the experimental curve B which does not differ too seriously from A. The difference between A and B would steadily decrease with higher numbers of transfers.

The total load in both cases is the same, yet in B the initial concentration is only one seventh that of A. Thus a shorter segment of a curved partition isotherm for non-ideal solutes is involved and the distribution curve obtained would be nearer the symmetrical ideal curve. With longer trains it is possible to scatter the sample sufficiently so that the maximum tube at the finish of the distribution has almost the initial concentration. In general, one may scatter the sample in a number of tubes up to 5% of the total number of transfers without much loss of separating power. Thus for a 1000-tube apparatus and 1000 or more transfers the sample could be scattered in the first 50 tubes without serious impairment as far as spreading is concerned but with considerable advantage otherwise.

7. Types of countercurrent distribution trains

Many different types of distribution trains are described in the literature. A few will be mentioned here, although the majority of the separations reported in the literature have been accomplished with the design already

Fig. 13. Photograph of a 1000-tube automatic distribution train.

described in this chapter or an earlier version of it[14]. All sizes of these trains are made commercially by the H. O. Post Co., 6822 60th Road, Maspeth, New York. Either hand-operated or completely automatic trains equipped with fraction collectors can be purchased. A model commonly used in this country is one which contains 200 tubes of 10/10 ml capacity arranged in two rows. Another of similar design but arranged in four rows of tubes with 2/2 ml capacity is shown in Fig. 13. The total of 1000 tubes need not all be used since it is provided with two filling devices and the fraction collector can operate from any point in the train. Thus two or more simultaneous runs can be made.

Countercurrent distribution trains are manufactured and sold by the E–C Apparatus Co., 538 Walnut Lane, Swarthmore, Pennsylvania. These trains operate as in the above case by decantation but the construction of the tube is entirely different. It is an ingenious design of Raymond[16].

The space planned for this chapter does not permit a complete description of this and other apparatus reported in the literature. The reader is referred

References p. 31

to the original literature or to the more comprehensive reviews[2-4]. Various designs have been reported by Jantzen[1], Tschesche and Konig[17], Lathe and Ruthven[18], Craig and Post[14], Hecker[19], Grubhofer[20], Von Metzsch[21] and Verzele[22].

(a) *Choice of systems*

Even though adequate equipment is now available commercially for refined separations by countercurrent distribution and even though the procedures are well described, the method cannot be used successfully without a good understanding of the solvent systems available and the art of shifting their properties by addition of another solvent or by changing the proportions. Systems are chosen or compounded with a number of considerations in mind, among which are the following:

1. Solubility of the solutes to be distributed.
2. Selectivity.
3. Stability of solutes.
4. Rate of separation of dispersions (emulsions).
5. Range of partition ratio.
6. Deviation from ideality.
7. Analysis complications.
8. Recovery.
9. Toxicity and volatility of solvents.
10. Cost.

Since few solvent systems will rate well on all these points, a compromise must usually be made and the system chosen with the minimum of disadvantage.

Point 1 requires no discussion, but point 2 requires definition in addition to a short discussion. The selectivity of a system is a measure of its ability to provide as great a difference in the partition ratios of the different components in a given mixture as possible. Obviously if the selectivity of a system is great enough, a distribution train would not be needed. Selectivity is often spoken of in terms of β values for binary mixtures. Here $\beta = K_1/K_2$ where K_1 and K_2 are the respective partition ratios in the system of the two components to be separated. Where automatic trains of considerable length are available, a system of moderate selectivity may be quite acceptable provided the other points are favorable.

In general, the greatest selectivity will be found in systems providing the greatest differences in polarity or solvent contrast between the two phases. Thus, addition of a solvent completely miscible with both phases will make them more nearly alike and with more of the solvent finally reach the critical point where only one phase exists. Usually, but by no means always, this tends to reduce the selectivity. Often adequate selectivity is retained until just before the critical point, with a decided improvement in some of the other factors listed above.

If the solutes are acids or bases, the use of buffers usually will improve selectivity[23]. Various combinations of pyridine and acetic acid are useful as buffers. The combination of ammonia and acetic acid also is good. These buffers can be removed by direct evaporation under reduced pressure.

A practical question relating to selectivity concerns the number of transfers required for given β values. Although this can be answered precisely only where the recovery, yield and purity required are specified, a rough estimate can be made to guide in the choice of equipment. Where values are of the order of 5 or more, individual extraction units such as separatory funnels or test tubes will be sufficient for reasonably good separations. If the β values are of the order of two or more, hand-operated trains will suffice. Automatically operated trains of approximately 200 tubes in length will be required if β values are of the order of 1.2.

Point 3 requires little comment except to say that systems containing buffers or salt often provide an environment providing more stability than pure volatile solvents. Complexing agents may also be useful in this connection.

As regards the remainder of the points, 4 and 6 have already been discussed briefly. The others scarcely require discussion except possibly 5. The best system is one which will give a partition ratio in the range of 1 for the solute of interest. With mechanized trains, this becomes less important and a range of partition ratio between 0.1 and 10 becomes quite acceptable. The reason for this is that the greatest spread between two bands on a pattern for a given number of transfers occurs when the geometric mean of the partition ratios of the two solutes is 1, *e.g.* $\sqrt{K_1 \cdot K_2} = 1$. A degree of compensation can be made by changing the relative volumes of the two phases so that $\sqrt{K_1 V \cdot K_2 V} = 1$ where V is the ratio of the volumes of the two phases. However, with an automatic train a better spread of the two bands can be obtained easily by simply applying more transfers. Here the apparatus does the work. In fact in this case, it is often better to adjust the geometric mean of the K values to the range of 0.2 to 0.3 so that more transfers can be applied before the bands migrate from the train.

Recovery of the solute following a distribution is best accomplished in a rotatory evaporator[24]. The apparatus was originally designed for this specific purpose but has now become very popular for many other purposes and is sold commercially in modified versions under various names such as "Roto-Vap", "Flash Evaporator", etc.

In order to assess the various factors as quickly as possible in a preliminary way, a rapid two-transfer distribution is to be recommended. This can be done easily in three graduated centrifuge tubes. Transfers can be made

References p. 31

individually with a suitable hypodermic syringe fitted with a short length of plastic tubing of appropriate diameter (preferably Kel–F).

After the second transfer and equilibration of the tubes, analysis will permit the partition ratio in each tube to be tabulated. Thus a single pure solute with a K of 1 would give the amounts and partition ratios in each tube (Table II).

TABLE II

Tube	*K*	*% of sample*
0	1	25
1	1	50
2	1	25

On the other hand, if a mixture of equal amounts of two solutes with $K = 0.5$ and $K = 2.0$ were present, the data would be as listed in Table III.

Since partition ratios often can be determined with considerable accuracy, small divergences detected as above can be very helpful in deciding how to proceed and whether a mixture or a solute which deviates from ideality is present (or both). If deviations from ideality are suspected, repetition of the two-transfer distribution at one tenth the load will confirm the deviation.

TABLE III

Tube	*K*	*% of sample*
0	0.67	27.8
1	1.0	44.4
2	1.48	27.8

Table IV is a list of the solvents most commonly used in countercurrent distribution.

The solvents in Table IV are place din the order of increasing polarity. Many other possibilities could be considered and have been used successfully. In addition, interesting solubility and selectivity effects can be derived by various proportions of either three, four or even five different solvents so long as they furnish two clearly separable phases with sufficient difference in density to enable separation of a dispersion in no more than a few minutes. All solvents should of course be freshly distilled before use and residue-free.

No attempt will be made in this short chapter to cover all of the many systems used so successfully in the literature for a wide variety of solutes. This type of coverage can be found in other reviews and chapters[2,3,8,25–28].

TABLE IV

SOLVENTS COMMONLY USED IN COUNTERCURRENT DISTRIBUTION

n-heptane
2,2,4-trimethylpentane
cyclohexane
benzene
methylethyl ketone
chloroform
acetonitrile
n-butanol
2-butanol
propanol
ethanol
methanol
phenol
pyridine
formamide
acetic acid
water
aqueous salt and buffer solutions

However, discussion of some of the systems most useful for a few classes of substances may prove helpful.

Basic substances, including alkaloids, quinoline derivatives, amines, etc., usually are best separated by an aqueous buffer solution, such as phosphate, equilibrated against an organic solvent[3,23] such as heptane, cyclohexanes, chloroform or *n*-butanol. Mixtures of heptane and butanol are good for providing intermediate properties. Benzene is a good solvent but may interfere with analysis by optical density at the shorter wavelengths. The use of buffers becomes less helpful if the base contains many polar groups. In this case, systems near the critical point, such as 2-butanol–water, will be better.

The same systems employed for bases also will be most useful for acids unless they are large enough to have surface active properties. In this case, systems made without water[10,11], such as one containing *n*-heptane, methanol, glacial acetic acid and acetonitrile, are most useful. Others of this type include one made from *n*-heptane, methanol, formamide and glacial acetic acid or one made from *n*-heptane, methanol and formamide. Dinitrophenylated amino acids[29] can be separated nicely in a system made from benzene, glacial acetic acid and water or one made from chloroform, glacial acetic acid and water.

The hydrochlorides of amino acids can be separated[8] in 2 *N* HCl and phenol or *n*-butanol and 5% aqueous HCl. A system made from *n*-propanol, 2-butanol and a concentrated aqueous solution of ammonium acetate gives

References p. 31

a good spread of K values with the free amino acids. A system made from n-butanol, pyridine and 0.1% acetic acid (volume proportions 11:5:3) can also be useful.

The choice of systems for peptides will depend on their polarity. For the less polar ones combinations of methanol, chloroform and water[30] are good. If the partition ratio is too high in this system, one made from ethyl acetate, n-butanol and water or n-butanol and water may have the right properties. The n-butanol–pyridine–1% acetic acid system in the last paragraph is often selective. For the most polar peptides, systems made from 2-butanol and water or perhaps propanol added to a point short of the critical point may be tried. A system made from phenol and water may be very selective.

Thus far the method has been used in a rather limited way in the sugar field. It would seem that the same systems useful for peptides would also be those which might be suitable for sugar work. An interesting system for this class of substance is one made from butyraldehyde and aqueous HCl[31]. Systems for separating flavon glucosides and aglycones have been reported[44].

Much effort has been expended in trying to develop suitable systems for purifying and characterizing proteins[8]. The most promising thus far are of four general types: (1) the pyridine system given above[15,32], (2) systems made from propanol, ethanol and ammonium sulfate solution[33] and (3) systems made from n-butanol or 2-butanol with various concentrations of aqueous trichloro- or dichloro-acetic acid. The latter has been widely used for isolation and characterization of insulin[8], the hormones of the pituitary[34], angiotensin[35], parathyroid hormone[32] and others. The fourth general type, (4), has no organic phase in the sense of the first three systems. The two phases are formed by relatively dilute aqueous solutions which strangely enough are immiscible. This ingenious system is being developed by Albertsson[36,37]. It seems to offer considerable promise even though separation of the phases is very slow.

The effect of the chloroacetic acids seems to be due to the fact that they reduce the charge and polarity of the protein. Certain other solutes also have this effect, for example toluene sulfonic acid or the long-chain fatty acids or amines. These have been called "carriers"[38] because they have a marked effect in shifting the partition ratio of certain solutes from a value strongly in favor of the aqueous phase to one favoring the organic phase. Systems of this type have been studied for the separation of sugar phosphates, proteins, protamines and many other solutes[2,3].

(b) *Analytical methods*

Almost any really precise fractionation method requires a considerable amount of analytical control if it is to be used to its ultimate capabilities.

Countercurrent distribution is no different from other approaches in this regard. In fact the analysis following a run often may require more time and effort than the run itself.

From the overall analytical standpoint and for empirical work on an unknown mixture, countercurrent distribution offers the possibility of determining percentage composition by direct weight analysis. Other methods of analysis such as titration or spectroscopic study superimposed on weight analysis then will go far toward characterization. A variety of colorimetric tests, in particular the ninhydrin determination[39], can then be put on a more quantitative and meaningful basis. Bio-assay scanning can be very definitive. Of the various possibilities, only weight analysis (ref. 2, p. 321) will be treated here.

In the author's laboratory, the most rapid and reliable way of determining residue weight is shown in Fig. 14. The evaporation and weight determination is done on very thin-walled platinum shells which hold a little more than 1 ml. These can be purchased from The American Platinum Works and are built according to the specifications given by the Rockefeller Institute. Each shell weighs approximately 1 g, as little as possible for rapid heating and cooling so that weights on a microbalance can be taken without delay. In fact they are so thin walled that they cannot be handled by forceps. Instead an especially designed fork is used.

The fork is made from a piece of glass tubing fire polished at both ends and about 1 foot in length. A platinum wire, No. 21, about 12 cm long is doubled and hooked over a length of somewhat smaller copper wire also doubled and pulled through the glass tube until one third of the platinum wire has passed into the tube. The copper wire is then secured on the other end of the glass tube and the platinum wire bent into a fork of the proper width as shown in Fig. 14. The prongs of the platinum fork bend easily, thus protecting the shells.

The holder for the shells is made from a stainless steel strip as shown in Fig. 14 with each end bent downward to provide rather shallow feet. Each shell rests in a cut-out portion of the strip. The shells are tared to within 0.050 mg of each other by dropping tiny pieces of platinum in the lighter shells. This facilitates rapid weighing of the series since only a single counter-balance weight is required.

For the evaporation the shells are placed in the holes of the boiler shown in Fig. 14. The latter is a stainless steel pan heated by a hot plate. Holes of the appropriate size are cut in the cover of the pan to receive the shells. Each hole has a vertical glass tube above it with the other end extending into a movable manifold. Air, filtered by passing through a wide tube packed with cotton, is led into the manifold. The speed of the air passing into the glass tubes is barely sufficient to cause a slight movement on the surface of

References p. 31

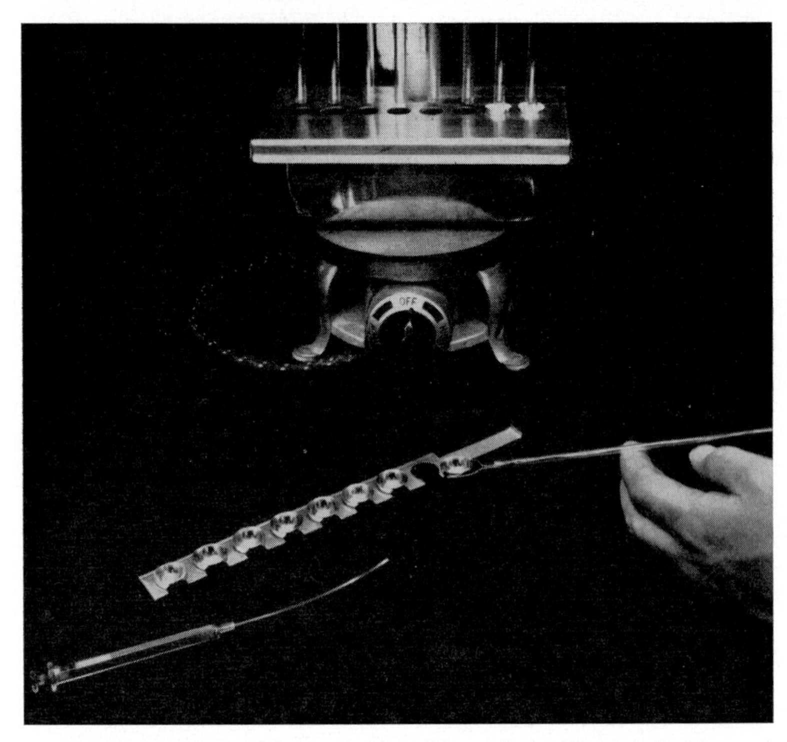

Fig. 14. Platinum shells and evaporator for weight analysis. (Reprinted with permission from *Analytical Methods of Protein Chemistry*, Pergamon, London, 1960.)

the solution but not enough to blow any solid residue from the shell. A water manometer is helpful in adjusting the air pressure to this point. The air current causes a surprisingly rapid evaporation without spitting or bumping. The liquid in the boiler is usually water but for lower temperatures methanol or ethanol can be used. A reflux condenser is attached to the boiler.

The aliquot to be evaporated can be obtained best with a syringe fitted with a plastic tube for a needle (preferably of Kel-F). Such syringes will be found useful for many purposes in the laboratory aside from nearly all the analytical operations connected with countercurrent distribution.

Following the evaporation step, the drop of water clinging to the bottom of each shell is removed by partial submersion in acetone, the acetone touched off on filter paper and the shell placed on the holder. The holder is inserted into a drying tube at 100° under 0.2 mm vacuum for about 5 min before weighing.

A sufficient aliquot to provide a residue of the order of 0.5 mg is advisable. Rather rapid weighings can be made which are reproducible to $\pm$ 0.010 mg or with careful checking of the 0 point to $\pm$ 0.003 mg.

The platinum shells can be cleaned by burning in a low flame. With inorganic residue-free solvents and solutes, the shells return to their original tare weight. If not, an easy way to estimate the inorganic salt is provided. However, this must be correlated with the behavior of the particular salt on burning.

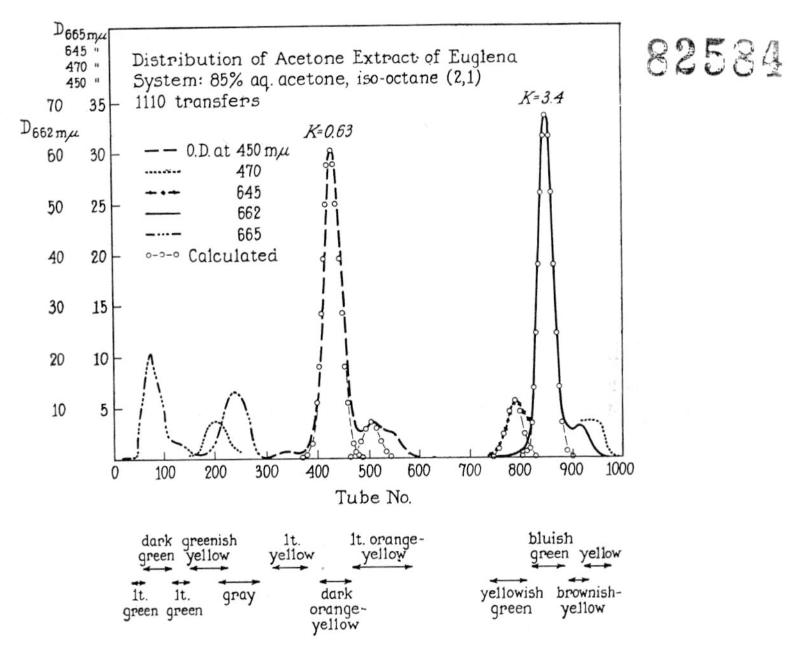

Fig. 15. Distribution pattern of an acetone extract of Euglena.

Countercurrent distribution is a separation method which lends itself to the most inclusive type of analysis. An example of this is shown in Fig. 15 which is the pattern obtained with an extract of a Euglena mutant. The various colored bands could be plainly seen in the 1000-tube machine with the naked eye. Analysis at more than one wavelength with a spectrophotometer gave a more complete picture of the separation. Weight analysis would permit extinction coefficients to be calculated directly.

8. The integration of countercurrent distribution with other separation techniques

In concluding a short chapter of this type, a few remarks about the place of countercurrent distributions in the array of separation tools now available would seem appropriate. Although it is a procedure with obvious wide applicability both in regard to the type of compounds and the amounts of

References p. 31

material at hand, it is certainly not the tool of choice for every separation.

Up to the present, it has usually been given a serious trial only after other separation methods have failed. This is due to the fact that other methods, such as chromatography, were developed to a higher degree somewhat earlier. Even so, many successes have been scored and there is a steadily growing demand for the equipment. It must be admitted that acquisition of the required apparatus and the analytical tools to support it appear somewhat formidable to the novice. As compared to other separation tools, even this is not always true; but even so, once it has been acquired the labor is not excessive, often less than with other methods.

Countercurrent distribution is best suited for the preliminary investigations in the isolation of a new active principle. It has often been used this way in the fields of antibiotics, hormones[3,32], carotinoids[40], plant estrogens[40], etc. The information and preparations so obtained give a good base from which to apply other separation techniques. Danger of loss or of transformation is minimal. Then, as more becomes known about the substance, it is certainly one of the tools of choice for proving final purity. In fact, it has perhaps had more application to this problem than for the many other purposes for which it can be used.

REFERENCES

[1] E. JANTZEN, *Das fractionierte Distillieren und das fractionierte Verteilen*, Dechema Monographie, Vol. V, No. 48, Verlag Chemie, Berlin, 1932, p. 81.
[2] L. CRAIG AND D. CRAIG, *Extraction and Distribution* in A. WEISSBERGER (Ed.), *Technique of Organic Chemistry*, Vol. III, *Separation and Purification*, Part 1, 2nd ed., Interscience, New York, 1956, p. 149.
[3] E. HECKER, *Verteilungsverfahren im Laboratorium*, Monographien zu Angewandte Chemie, Verlag Chemie, Weinheim/Bergstr., 1955.
[4] J. R. WEISIGER, *Countercurrent Distribution in Organic Analysis*, Vol. II, Interscience, New York, 1954, p. 277.
[5] B. WILLIAMSON AND L. C. CRAIG, *J. Biol. Chem.*, 168 (1947) 687.
[6] L. C. CRAIG, G. H. HOGEBOOM, F. H. CARPENTER AND V. DU VIGNEAUD, *J. Biol. Chem.*, 168 (1947) 665.
[7] M. T. BUSH AND P. M. DENSEN, *Anal. Chem.*, 20 (1948) 121.
[8] P. VON TAVEL AND R. SIGNER, *Advances in Protein Chemistry*, Vol. XI, Academic Press, New York, 1956, p. 237.
[9] W. HAUSMANN AND L. C. CRAIG, *J. Am. Chem. Soc.*, 80 (1958) 2703.
[10] E. H. AHRENS JR. AND L. C. CRAIG, *J. Biol. Chem.*, 195 (1952) 299.
[11] E. H. AHRENS JR. AND L. C. CRAIG, *J. Biol. Chem.*, 195 (1952) 763.
[12] G. T. BARRY, Y. SATO AND L. C. CRAIG, *J. Biol. Chem.*, 174 (1948) 209.
[13] L. C. CRAIG, T. P. KING AND A. STRACHER, *J. Am. Chem. Soc.*, 79 (1957) 3729.
[14] L. C. CRAIG AND O. POST, *Anal. Chem.*, 21 (1949) 500.
[15] L. C. CRAIG AND T. P. KING, *Federation Proc.*, 17 (1958) 1126.
[16] S. RAYMOND, *Anal. Chem.*, 30 (1958) 1214.
[17] R. TSCHESCHE AND H. B. KONIG, *Chem. Ingr. Tech.*, 22 (1950) 214.
[18] G. H. LATHE AND C. R. J. RUTHVEN, *Biochem. J.*, 49 (1951) 540.
[19] E. HECKER, *Chem. Ingr. Tech.*, 25 (1953) 505.
[20] N. GRUBHOFER, *Chem. Ingr. Tech.*, 22 (1950) 209.
[21] F. A. VON METZSCH, *Chem. Ingr. Tech.*, 25 (1953) 66.
[22] M. VERZELE, *Bull. soc. chim. Belges*, 62 (1953) 619.
[23] L. C. CRAIG, C. GOLUMBIC, H. MIGHTON AND E. TITUS, *J. Biol. Chem.*, 161 (1945) 321.
[24] L. C. CRAIG, J. D. GREGORY AND W. HAUSMANN, *Anal. Chem.*, 22 (1950) 1462.
[25] L. C. CRAIG, *Anal. Chem.*, 26 (1954) 110; 28 (1956) 723.
[26] F. A. VON METZSCH, *Angew. Chem.*, 65 (1953) 586.
[27] R. COLLANDER, *Acta Chem. Scand.*, 3 (1949) 717; 4 (1950) 1085.
[28] E. HECKER, *Chimia*, 8 (1954) 229.
[29] W. HAUSMANN, J. R. WEISIGER AND L. C. CRAIG, *J. Am. Chem. Soc.*, 77 (1955) 723.
[30] A. R. BATTERSBY AND L. C. CRAIG, *J. Am. Chem. Soc.*, 74 (1952) 4019.
[31] R. R. TINK, A. C. NEISH, E. Y. SPENCER AND J. M. ROXBURGH, *Can. J. Chem.*, 29 (1951) 243, 250.
[32] H. RASMUSSEN AND L. C. CRAIG, *J. Am. Chem. Soc.*, 81 (1959) 5003.
[33] T. P. KING AND L. C. CRAIG, *J. Am. Chem. Soc.*, 80 (1958) 3366.
[34] C. H. LI, *Advances in Protein Chemistry*, Vol. XI, Academic Press, New York, 1956, p. 101.
[35] L. T. SKEGGS, JR., J. R. KAHN AND N. P. SHUMWAY, *J. Exptl. Med.*, 103 (1956) 301.
[36] P. Å. ALBERTSSON, *Nature*, 182 (1958) 709.
[37] P. Å. ALBERTSSON AND E. J. NYNS, *Nature*, 184 (1959) 1465.
[38] A. E. O'KEEFFE, M. H. DOLLIVER AND E. T. STILLER, *J. Am. Chem. Soc.*, 71 (1949) 2452.
[39] S. MOORE AND WM. H. STEIN, *J. Biol. Chem.*, 211 (1954) 907.
[40] C. R. THOMPSON, A. L. CURL AND E. M. BICKOFF, *Anal. Chem.*, 31 (1959) 838.
[41] E. L. WAY AND B. M. BENNET, *J. Biol. Chem.*, 192 (1951) 335.
[42] G. ALDERTON, *Anal. Chem.*, 31 (1959) 625.
[43] W. BORSCH-SUPAN, *Z. Naturforsch.*, 14 (1959) 56.
[44] L. HORHAMMER AND H. WAGNER, *Arch. Pharm.*, 289 (1956) 532; 290 (1956) 15.

Chapter II

Chromatography

E. LEDERER

Laboratory of Biological Chemistry, Faculty of Sciences, Paris and Institute for the Chemistry of Natural Substances, Gif-sur-Yvette, Seine et Oise (France)

AND

M. LEDERER

Laboratorio di Cromatografia dell C.N.R., Istituto di Chimica Generale ed Inorganica, Roma (Italy)

Literature on chromatography

The 2nd edition of *Chromatography, a Review of Principles and Applications*[1] is still the only comprehensive book covering the whole field of organic and inorganic chromatography. Two recent volumes in French, *La chromatographie en chimie organique et biologique*[2], give in great detail the principles of the various experimental chromatographic methods and many details of separations in all fields of organic chemistry and biochemistry.

The yearly reviews of Strain[3] in *Analytical Chemistry* as well as the review articles of *Chromatographic Reviews*[4] may be also recommended for information on recent developments.

The *Journal of Chromatography* can be consulted for reviews and for all recent applications of chromatographic techniques.

History of chromatography

Accounts of the early history of chromatography have been given by Weil and Williams[5,6], Farradane[7] and Zechmeister[8]. While it seems certain that different authors have observed separations of substances by filtration through columns of finely divided adsorbents, it is evident that the Russian botanist Tswett[9] was the first to be aware of the great possibilities of chromatography. He described in detail the separation of pigments and colourless substances by filtration through columns, followed by development with pure solvents. The edition by Richter and Krasnosselskaja[10] of selected papers of Tswett will be welcomed by those who are interested in this subject.

The first paper of Tswett, published in 1903, contains a study of more than 100 adsorbents used in conjunction with several different solvents and a comparison of the efficiencies of column and batch adsorption. The chromatography of a leaf extract on a column of inulin is described as follows: "The adsorption phenomena observed during filtration through the powder are particularly interesting. The liquid emerging from the lower end of the funnel is at first colourless, then yellow (carotene) whilst at the top of the column of inulin a green ring is formed below which there soon appears a yellow band. When pure ligroin is filtered through the column, both bands start spreading and move down the column" (translated from p. 21 of the selected papers of Tswett[10]).

The following account was given by Tswett of the purification of lecithin: "A few cm^3 of the solution (from egg yolk) were filtered through a column of inulin. The filtrate was at first colourless, then yellow, and contained much fatty material. Filtration of ligroin through the column was continued until no transparent spot was obtained when a drop of the filtrate was allowed to evaporate on tissue paper. A mixture of ligroin and alcohol was then passed through the column. The filtrate, which was pale yellow, afforded on evaporation a wax-like solid having the characteristic properties of the lecithin complex." (Translated from p. 25 of the selected papers of Tswett[10]).

Further descriptions of chromatographic techniques are contained in a paper published by Tswett in 1906 and in his book *The chromophylls in the plant and animal world* (1910)[9]. Tswett died prematurely in 1920 (for a biographical sketch, see Dhéré[11], and Zechmeister[12] and his method was used only very rarely during the following years.

It was only in 1931, when Kuhn and Lederer[13] separated the carotenes and xanthophylls on a preparative scale on columns of alumina and calcium carbonate, that the possibilities of Tswett's method were fully realised. Rapid development of the new field by workers such as Brockmann, Karrer, Winterstein, Zechmeister, etc. soon enabled the organic chemist to apply this technique to the separation and isolation of a wide variety of compounds. In 1938, Reichstein[14] introduced the liquid, or flowing chromatogram, thus extending the applicability of the method to colourless substances. During the years 1940–1943 Tiselius[15–20] worked out the techniques of frontal analysis and displacement development. Partition chromatography on silica gel, introduced by Martin and Synge[21] in 1941 further extended the scope of chromatography to a great range of biologically important substances. Paper chromatography was first described by Consden, Gordon and Martin[22] in 1944 and has become a major tool for biochemical analysis and

References p. 97

research. The development of gas–liquid chromatography, by James and Martin[23] in 1952, has opened a new field in analytical chemistry which promises to have a wide application, both in research and in industry.

Prominent contributions to the theory of chromatography were made since 1940 by Wilson[24], De Vault[25], Martin and Synge[21], Glueckauf[26–33] and Weiss[34,35]. In 1947, a series of articles released by the U.S. Atomic Energy Commission, notably by Boyd[36–38], Spedding[39–41] and Tompkins[42–44] described the use of ion exchange chromatography for the separation of fission products and rare earth mixtures. The use of paper chromatography in inorganic chemistry was introduced in 1948 by M. Lederer[45] and Linstead *et al.*[46]. Chromatography has thus become an important technique in inorganic chemistry as well.

Chapter II

PART A

Adsorption Chromatography

1. General chromatographic techniques

(*a*) *Introduction*

In its classical form, as described by Tswett[9], chromatography consists in separating substances by filtering their solution through a column of a finely powdered adsorbent, filled into a glass tube, and then washing (*developing*) the column with a solvent. Tswett and the early workers after 1931 were mostly concerned with pigments and thus observed the formation of coloured zones on the column of adsorbent, each zone corresponding to a pure pigment. The developing of the column with the pure solvent was clearly an important step in the fractionation process, as the zones were seen to separate more and more from one another during the development. As soon as separation was judged to be sufficient, development was stopped and the zones containing the adsorbed pigments were separated mechanically with a spatula, either with or without extrusion of the whole adsorbent column from its tube. Each portion of adsorbent was then treated separately with an appropriate solvent for elution of the adsorbed pigment.

This simple and very effective procedure is still used extensively in work with pigments. When working with colourless substances, the column can be cut up arbitrarily in several portions, each being eluted separately.

(*b*) *Liquid or flowing chromatogram*

The above mentioned technique has been superseded for the separation of colourless substances by the method introduced by Reichstein and his school[14,47,48] known as the *liquid* or *flowing* chromatogram. The method consists in washing the column successively with a series of solvents of stronger and stronger eluting power (*e.g.* light petroleum, benzene, ether, acetone, alcohol or appropriate mixtures of these solvents), each filtrate

References p. 97

being collected separately. For details of this method which is very largely applied, see under *Elution*, p. 67. An important modification, *gradient elution* is discussed on p. 69.

(c) *Frontal and displacement analysis*

Tiselius, Claesson and their collaborators[15-20,49-62] invented a modification of adsorption chromatography which they called *frontal analysis*. A solution of the substances to be studied is forced continuously through a column and their concentrations on leaving the column are measured by the use of an optical system registering changes in refractive index based on the "Schlieren" method due to Toepler.

The measurement of concentration gradients by optical methods is practised also in sedimentation studies (ultracentrifuge), diffusion and electrophoresis. Numerous optical instruments are used in addition to the aforementioned "Schlieren" method and these are adequately treated in most accounts of electrophoretic methods. Svensson[63-65], in describing a new interferometric method has also surveyed the available techniques. Other instruments have been described by Holman[66] and by Hellström and Borgiel[67].

The degree of adsorption of different substances is expressed as the *specific retention volume* (or retardation volume), that is the volume of liquid passing through the column per g of adsorbent before the substance in question leaves the column. Table I shows the retention volumes of amino acids and

TABLE I

RETENTION VOLUMES IN ml/g OF CHARCOAL (Tiselius[68])

Alanine	0.3	Histidine	15.0	Leucyl-glycine	18.2
Hydroxyproline	2.0	Arginine	40.4	Leucyl-glycyl-glycine	29.8
Proline	2.5	Tryptophan	76.5	Valyl-alanine	22.0
Valine	3.2	Phenylalanine	62.5	Alanyl-leucyl-glycine	34.4
Leucine	7.7	Glycyl-glycine	3.5	Glycyl-leucyl-alanine	42.5
Isoleucine	9.2	Glycyl-alanine	4.0	Glycyl-leucyl-glycine	38.0
Methionine	12.4				

peptides (in ml/g of adsorbent). These figures allow the characterisation of the affinity of a variety of substances for a given adsorbent. It can be seen that aromatic amino acids have much higher retention volumes than aliphatic amino acids and that tripeptides are more strongly adsorbed than dipeptides, etc.

Claesson[52] showed that in an homologous series the degree of adsorption can be correlated with the boiling point, always rising with increasing boiling point. Hall and Tiselius[69] have confirmed this for the case of isomeric compounds with similar functional groups. Thus the boiling points of 2-methyl-2-butanol, 3-methyl-1-butanol and 1-pentanol are respectively 101.8°, 130.5° and 138°. The retention volumes observed were 76, 97 and 113 ml. Table II shows the same phenomenon for isomeric butyric and

TABLE II

CORRELATION OF BOILING POINT AND RETENTION VOLUME

(Hall and Tiselius[69])

Substance	*B.p. °C*	*Retention volume*
2-Methylpropionic acid	154.4	9.0
n-Butyric acid	163.5	18.5
3-Methylbutyric acid	176.7	20.1
n-Valeric acid	187.0	27.5
4-Methylvaleric acid	207.7	42.0

valeric acids. This correlation can be very useful for choosing the proper *carrier* in *carrier displacement* (see p. 41).

Fig. 1 shows the frontal analysis curve for a mixture of four substances *A*, *B*, *C* and *D*. The point at which each substance leaves the column is indicated by a step, the number of steps indicates the number of substances in the mixture. This *frontal analysis* does not, however, allow the separation of the substances.

In order to obtain a separation it is necessary to wash the column with pure solvent. Fig. 2 shows the case of *elution development* of a mixture *E*, *F*, *G* and *H*. It can be seen that substance *E* leaves the column free from

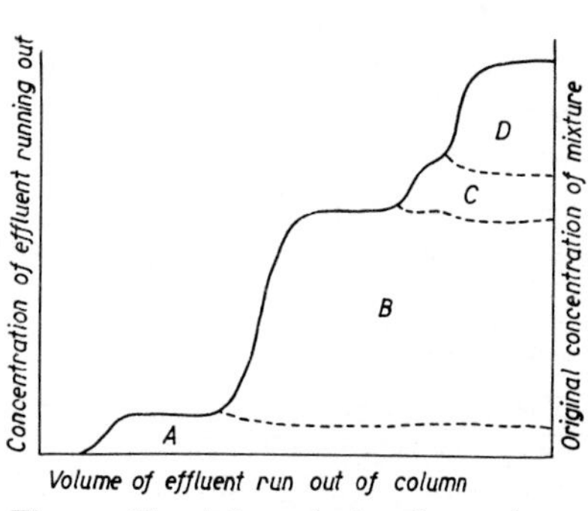

Fig. 1. Frontal analysis of a mixture A + B + C + D, according to Tiselius (from ref.[72]).

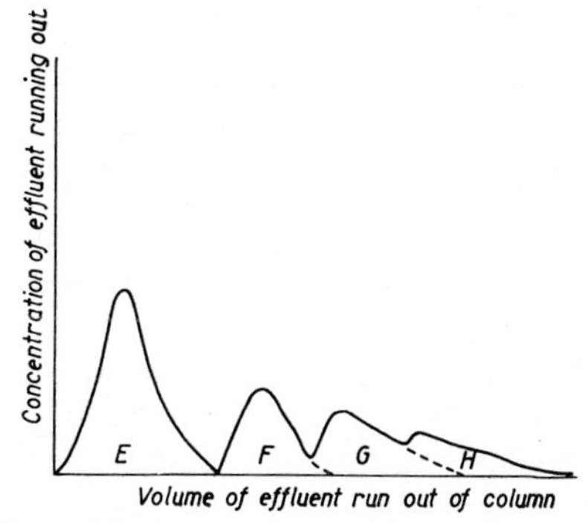

Fig. 2. Elution development of a mixture E + F + G + H, according to Tiselius (from ref.[72]).

the others and is immediately followed by *F*. Complete separation of *F*, *G* and *H* is however impossible as *G* begins to leave the column before *F* is completely eluted, the same phenomenon being repeated in an exaggerated form for *G* and *H*. This difficulty, found very often in chromatography, is due to the fact that many substances are adsorbed more strongly from dilute solution; quantitative elution thus becomes more and more difficult, as the substances *tail* through the column.

Tiselius[20] has since shown that it is advantageous to develop the chromatogram with a solution of a substance more strongly adsorbed than the substances to be separated. This method is called *displacement development*. The band of the substance the least adsorbed leaves the column, followed immediately by the next, one displacing the other, the last being displaced by the substance chosen for the displacement (*e.g.* phenol for peptides, ephedrine for polysaccharides, Fig. 3 and Table III). The advantage of this

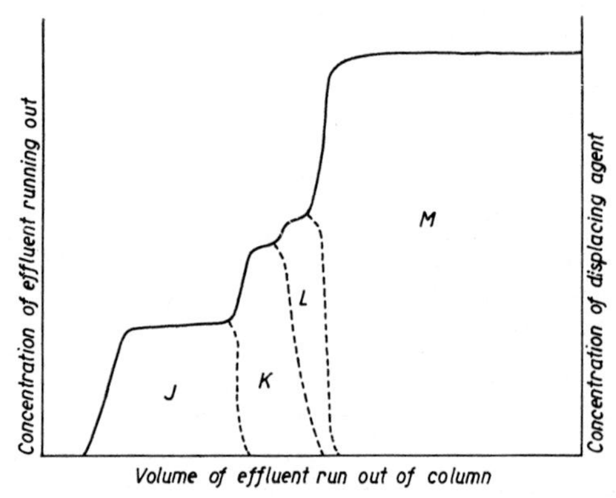

Fig. 3. Displacement development of a mixture J + K + L with displacing agent M, according to Tiselius (from ref. [72]).

method is that the back of the zone remains sharp and does not tail through the column (being continuously displaced by the following zone). Difficulties do arise, however, as is shown by the work of Holman and Hagdahl[71] on the separation of fatty acids by displacement. The disadvantage of the method is that the zones leave the column immediately behind one another without being separated by a zone of pure solvent. This difficulty has been overcome by the use of *carriers* (see p. 41).

The phenomenon of displacement of one band by another is often observed during the chromatographic separation of a mixture. The band moves through the column as a sharp zone whereas the same substance when run by itself on a similar column would show a diffuse tailing band on elution.

Tiselius has shown that in the course of displacement development the

TABLE III

RETENTION VOLUMES OF DISPLACING AGENTS (IN ml/g CHARCOAL)
(Tiselius[60])

Saccharose	23	Raffinose	46
Methyl propyl ketone	31	Phenol	53
Ethyl acetate	32	Ephedrine	83
Pyridine	33	Picric acid	83

substances rapidly attain a stationary concentration which is expressed in the elution curve as a step whose length is dependent on the quantity of the substance. This stationary concentration (the height of the step) enables the characterisation of the eluted substance to be carried out (Fig. 3). Tiselius has reviewed his methods in several papers[18,59,60,72].

Drake[73] has studied some factors governing frontal sharpness in adsorption analysis; various methods of packing and various shapes of columns affect the sharpness of the fronts. The superiority of long, narrow columns and of low pressure heads was shown.

The scaling up of a separation previously carried out on a milligram scale is often difficult as the zones show many irregularities of shape. The front of a zone instead of being horizontal can assume the shape shown in Fig. 4a. Claesson[55] has invented a means of correcting this fault. It consists in joining

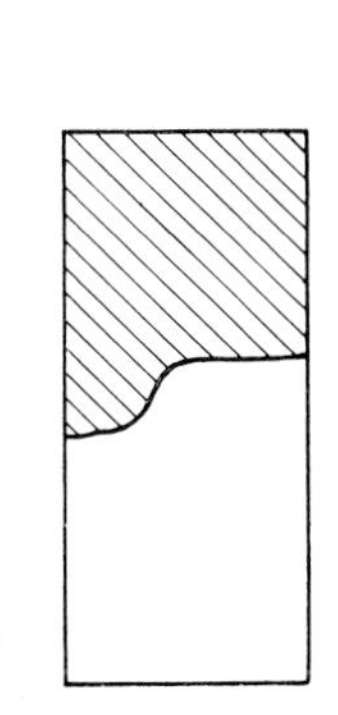

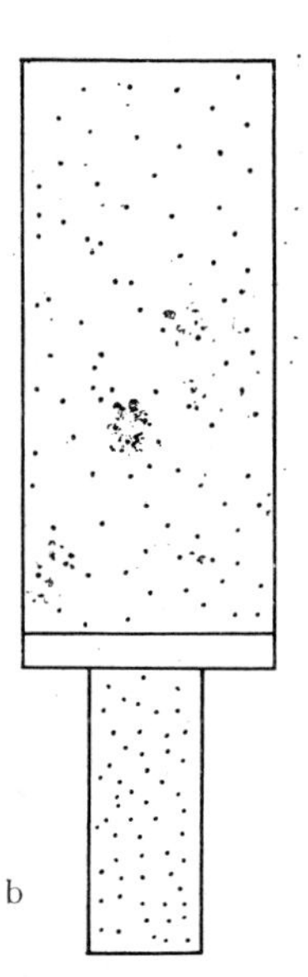

Fig. 4. (a) Irregular zone front in a large column. (b) A double sectioned column (Claesson[55]).

two or three columns of decreasing diameter together. A column of large diameter possesses at its base a compartment containing no adsorbent and is mounted on a second smaller column (Fig. 4b). When the hump in the front of the zone enters the compartment, mixing occurs with the pure solvent already there and the diluted solution enters the second column. As in general the more dilute part of a zone is held back more strongly than the concentrated part of the zone, it is rapidly caught up by the region of higher concentration leaving the large column. In this way a uniform horizontal front is formed in the second column. Fig. 5 shows the result obtained with and without Claesson's modification.

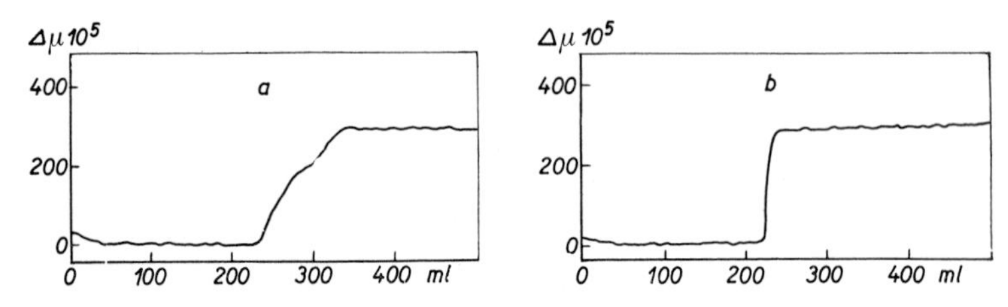

Fig. 5. Frontal analysis of 2% sucrose in water. Filter (a) 20,000 π, (b) 20,000 π + 5,000 π (Claesson[55]).

Claesson recommends the use of a series of columns each of which is one-fifth of the size of the one preceding (*e.g.* from top to bottom: 40 × 100 mm, 20 × 50 mm, and 10 × 50 mm). The same effect is not obtained either by placing an empty compartment between two columns of the same diameter, or by using a conical column.

Hagdahl[74] has also shown that with frontal analysis and displacement development a series of filters of diminishing size connected by narrow tubes greatly improves the sharpness of separation, the irregularities of the front in one section being more or less corrected in the succeeding section. Such composite columns are available from LKB-Produkter, Stockholm (Hagdahl[75]).

Some applications of the Tiselius techniques may be cited here: Wetterholm[76] has studied the frontal analysis of glycols and glycerols, Holman[77] has examined in detail the displacement analysis of lipid-soluble substances, such as hydrocarbons, alkyl iodides, bromides, chlorides, mercaptans, nitriles, esters, and Holman and Williams[78] have described the displacement analysis of unsaturated acids on charcoal (with aqueous ethanol as solvent). Li, Tiselius *et al.*[79] examined ACTH peptides on Carboraffin Supra + Hyflo Supercel (1:9) by displacing with 0.4% Zephiran chloride. Porath and Li[80] have described elution and displacement analysis of insulin and adrenocorticotropic peptides on pre-treated charcoal (Darco

G-60, see p. 53). For frontal analysis and displacement analysis of acids, sugars and gases, see also Claesson[52].

(d) *Carrier displacement*

Tiselius and Hagdahl[81] have invented an improvement on displacement development called *carrier displacement*. In ordinary displacement development the zones are in close contact, thus effective quantitative separations are rendered difficult. By interposing a number of substances of intermediate adsorption affinities (carriers) between the substances the zones can be separated successfully from each other.

In a preliminary communication[81] the separation of a number of amino acids and peptides by interposing aliphatic alcohols was described using activated charcoal containing equal parts of Super Cel. The amino acids and peptides in such a chromatogram collect at the boundaries of the alcohols and the following sequences of amino acids with homologous alcohols as carriers were reported:

Valine: *tert.*-butanol/water.
Leucine: *sec.*-butanol/*tert.*-butanol.
Methionine: *sec.*-butanol/*tert.*-butanol.
Leucyl-glycyl-glycine: isoamyl/*n*-butyl alcohol.
Phenylalanine: *n*-amyl/isoamyl alcohol.
Glycyl-tryptophan: benzyl alcohol/*n*-amyl alcohol.

Very successful separations of the homologous fatty acids were also obtained with methyl esters as carriers[82] (see Fig. 6). Similar work on the C_{18} fatty acids was carried out by Kurtz[83], who terms the process *amplified chromatography*. The carrier displacement of peptides, using normal alcohols with 8 to 10 carbon atoms as carriers has been described by Porath[84] and Li *et al.*[85].

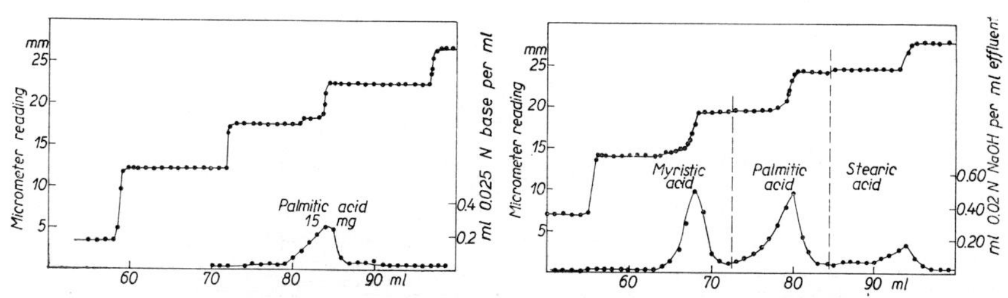

Fig. 6. Carrier displacement separation of myristic, palmitic and stearic acids in a carrier system of methyl esters of these acids; filter–column capacity 40 ml, solvent 95% ethanol, carriers 50 mg methyl laurate, 80 mg methyl myristate, 120 mg methyl palmitate, displacer 1.0% methyl stearate. Acid quantities indicated on curves (Holman[82]).

(*e*) *Continuous chromatography*

An extensive report on the development of a continuous chromatographic apparatus was made by Svensson *et al.*[86,87] giving references to relevant preliminary work on this question.

The principle of the apparatus (Fig. 7) described by these authors is best understood by considering two concentric cylinders with plane bottom, the annular space between the cylinders being filled with the sorbing agent, and the bottom being equipped with a number of equidistant outlet tubes. The mixture to be separated is continuously fed from one fixed point above the upper surface of the sorbent bed (Fig. 7, No. 6), while an eluting agent is fed

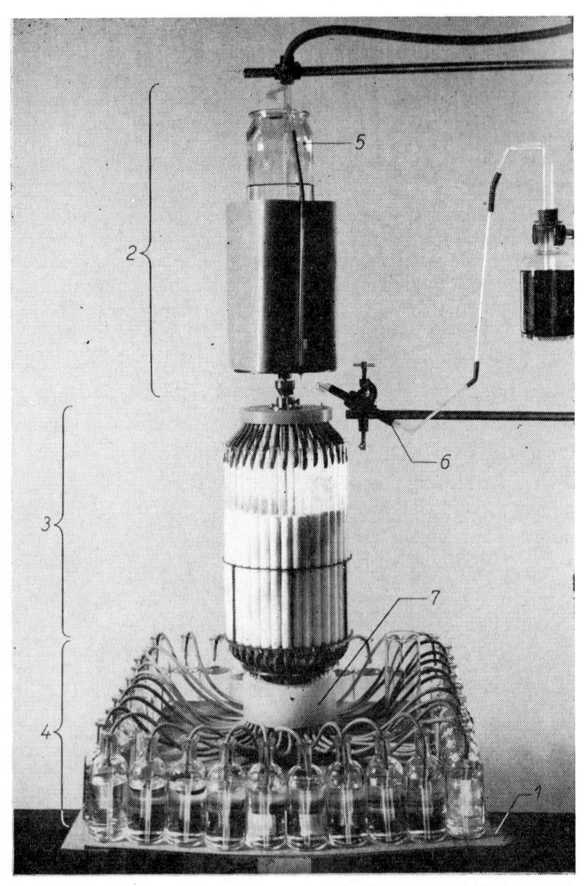

Fig. 7. Experimental apparatus for continuous chromatographic separation. 1, Wooden frame; 2, Feeding arrangement; 3, Rotating chromatographic column; 4, Fraction collector (Svensson *et al.*[87]).

to the entire remaining part of the same surface (Fig. 7, No. 5). Both solutions are fed slowly enough so that each drop has time to drain into the column before the next drop falls at the same spot; yet the rate of flow has to be fast enough to keep the upper surface constantly wet. Below the cylindrical column there is a fraction collector with many compartments, the inlet holes of which are arranged in a circle of the same radius as that of the column (Fig. 7, No. 7). The column is slowly rotated, while the feeding arrangement and the fraction collector are kept stationary. Every solute will then acquire the same tangential speed, which is determined by the angular velocity of the column. Each solute will have a specific rate of vertical migration, however, which depends upon its strength of sorption. Consequently, each solute will acquire its own flow spiral in the rotating column. Components without any sorption will form the steepest spiral, while for a sorbed component, the steepness of the spiral will be smaller the stronger the sorption of the component. Since the sample feeding arrangement and the fraction collector are fixed, each component will continuously run out into one or in a few adjacent compartments of the collector.

One model in which the sorbent container is sectioned, *i.e.* consists of a series of separate columns, is shown in Fig. 7. The above authors report satisfactory performance during one month's uninterrupted separation.

Solms has constructed a continuous apparatus using essentially the same principles as above and employing a paper curtain[88]. See also the patent by Olsen[89].

(*f*) *Inverse chromatography*

Fieser *et al.*[90] have described a method used for the separation of cholesterol from accompanying steroidal diols, which they call *inverse chromatography*: "a solution of the material in ether is stirred with two or three successive, relatively small, batches of alumina, and these are collected, washed extensively with benzene, dried, and made into a chromatograph column. Elution with suitable benzene–ether mixtures removes residual cholesterol and readies the column for delivery of more strongly adsorbed companions, or for stripping with ether–methanol for recovery of the total diol fraction for chromatography after acetylation. Selective adsorption of this fraction into alumina seems to effect separation as efficiently as the conventional, far lengthier process of chromatography and greatly facilitated the processing of batches of several hundred grams".

(*g*) *Chromatography on thin layers*

(*i*) *Chromatostrips and chromatoplates*

Kirchner *et al.*[91] have prepared fluorescent "chromatostrips" by coating a glass strip with a slurry of silicic acid, mixed with starch as binder and

References p. 97

$ZnCdS_2$ and Zn silicate as fluorescing agent. The dried strips are spotted with a terpene mixture and a solvent (*e.g.* 15% ethanol in hexanol) is allowed to ascend the strip in a test tube. Kirchner *et al.*[91] also described the preparation of non-fluorescent strips with various adsorbents. An apparatus for the preparation of chromatostrips was described by Miller and Kirchner[92].

Reitsema[93] has used larger strips, called "chromatoplates" for the analysis of essential oils; the use of plates allows the simultaneous running of known substances with the unknown.

Non-fluorescing chromatoplates (of silicic acid containing 5% starch) have proved very useful for the separation of diterpenes (Demole and Lederer[94], Fig. 8) carotenoids and porphyrins (Lederer[95]) and benzoquinones (Barbier[96]).

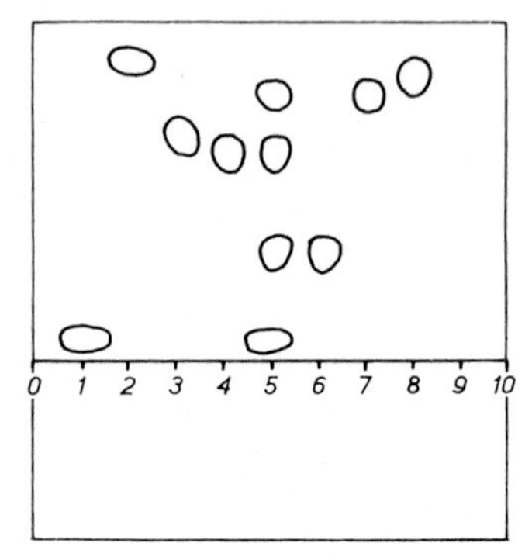

Fig. 8. Separations of bile pigments and porphyrin methyl esters on a chromatoplate (Demole[97]). (1) biliverdine, 3 µg; (2) bilirubine, 7 µg; (3) coproporphyrine I ester, 7 µg; (4) coproporphyrine III ester, 15 µg; (5) biliverdine + uroporphyrine I ester + coproporphyrine III ester + deuteroporphyrine ester; (6) uroporphyrine I ester, 9 µg; (7) deuteroporphyrine ester, 3 µg; (8) protoporphyrine ester, 5 µg. Solvent: benzene 90–ethyl acetate 20–ethyl alcohol 7.5 (v/v). 15-min run, distance 5 cm. Adsorbent: silicic acid, thickness 1/3 mm.

Such chromatoplates are very useful for control of column eluates; development of the strips or plates takes only 30 min. Most substances can be detected on the strips or plates by placing them in a jar with iodine vapours or by a treatment with dilute permanganate or other specific reagents. For detailed reviews, see Demole[97], Stahl[98,99] and Wollish *et al.*[99a].

Thin layer chromatography is also mentioned in the parts on ion exchange (p. 132) and partition chromatography (p. 161).

(ii) Chromatography on glass fiber paper

Glycerides and steroids[100], phospholipids[101] and sugars[102] have been separated on glass fiber paper impregnated with silicic acid, potassium silicate or potassium phosphate.

2. Apparatus

(a) *Chromatographic columns*

Chromatographic tubes are usually made of glass, drawn out at one end, sometimes fitted with a porous plate at the bottom and carry a tap on the exit tube so that the filtration can be stopped if desired. Bigger columns usually carry a separating funnel to hold the solvent. The height of the column should be 4 to 10 times the diameter. The reviews of Lederer[103], Strain[104], Williams[105] and Zechmeister and Von Cholnoky[106] contain a number of illustrations of columns (Fig. 9).

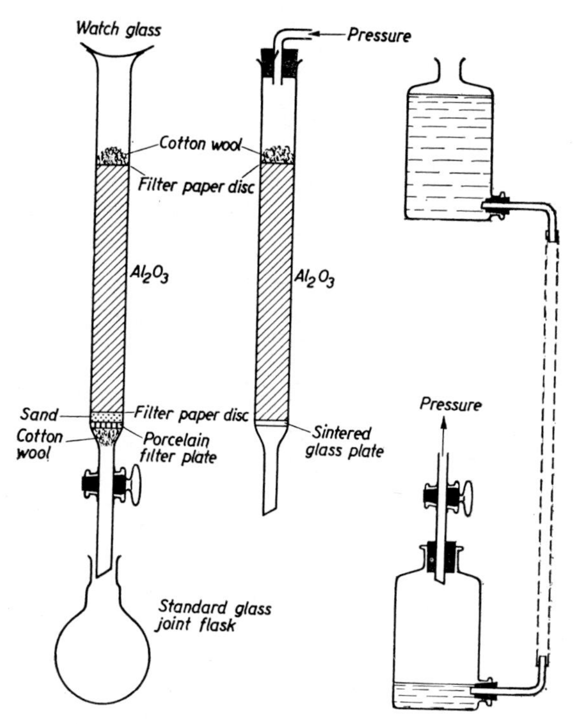

Fig. 9. Columns and pressure device for chromatography with fractional elution (Reichstein and Shoppee[107]).

The sizes of tubes listed in Table IV are recommended by Reichstein and Shoppee[107].

The tube is selected so that, when the appropriate quantity of adsorbent has been introduced, it is about half full.

Georges *et al.*[108] used tapered tubes which facilitated the extrusion of the

References p. 97

TABLE IV

SIZES OF CHROMATOGRAPHIC TUBES (Reichstein and Shoppee[107])

Amount $Al_2O_3(g)$	*Internal diam.* *(mm)*	*Usable length* *(mm)*	*Bore of tap* *(mm)*
1	8	110	3
2	10	130	3
4	13	160	4
8	16	200	4
15	20	250	4
30	25	300	6
60	32	400	6
125	40	500	6
250	50	600	8
500	65	750	8

columns for application of streak reagents. Gault and Ronez[109] have described tubes consisting of sections with interchangeable ground glass joints; the column can thus be opened at different heights.

Tiselius[15-20,59-62,72], Claesson *et al.*[49-58] have described in detail the elaborate apparatus necessary for their *frontal analysis*. Tiselius' columns are made in the form of cells or rectangular cuvettes of transparent plastic (Perspex, Lucite, or Plexiglass) or of glass or metal and have diameters of 20, 10 and 5 mm and heights of 40, 20, 10 and 5 mm[18]. Tiselius *et al.*[110] used

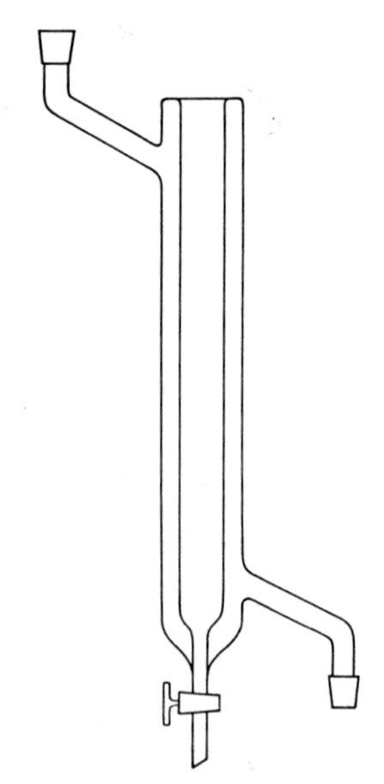

Fig. 10. Chromatographic tube with heating mantle.

a demountable apparatus of three columns for the separation of the amino acids into a number of groups. Composite columns have been mentioned on p. 40.

Huisman and Prins[111] have used flat Lucite (Perspex) cuvettes (20 × 3 × 0.5 cm inside dimensions) placed in a rack for serial separations of hemoglobins on ion exchange columns (see also the review of Prins[112]).

For chromatography at higher temperatures tubes with heating mantles can be used (Fig. 10).

Miller and Kirchner[113] have described a modification of the usual column technique; they mix the adsorbent (*e.g.* silicic acid) with plaster of Paris and pour it, after addition of water, into a suitable mould; they thus obtain a *chromatobar*, a self-supporting column, on which the zones can be located by streaking with a reagent. They have used the chromatobar for separations of terpenes.

(*b*) *Pressure devices*

In working with volatile solvents (light petroleum, ethyl ether, etc.) it is preferable to apply pressure to the top of the column instead of vacuum to the receiver. In this way evaporation of the filtrate and uneven flow-rate is prevented. The small air compressors used for the production of air bubbles in aquaria are useful in this connection. An apparatus utilising a bicycle pump has been proposed by Williams[105]. Booth[114] has described an apparatus for pressure and suction regulation (see also Fig. 9). Mowery[115] has described an apparatus for chromatography at pressure of up to 120 lbs per square inch; thus one can attain much higher flow rates than usual. This apparatus has been used for the separation of D-glucose and D-fructose on Florex XXX[115].

(*c*) *Industrial apparatus*

Mair *et al.*[116] have described a 52-foot *laboratory* column. A patent of Meng[117] describes an apparatus consisting of separate zones of adsorbent in which eluting solvent and eluate can be fed into and withdrawn from any selected adsorbent zone independently of the other zones and without any break-up of the adsorption unit. Lynam and Weil[118] suggest that the numerous valves necessary for elution, backwash etc. can be dispensed with, if a movable column is used, which can be shifted for each step.

A centrifuge packed with the adsorbent (called the *chromatofuge*) was first suggested by Hopf *et al.*[119,120]. This chromatofuge, however, is unable to cope with more than pilot-scale amounts of adsorbents. Thus the idea was modified by having a stationary disc of adsorbent and centrally feeding it with solution and eluant under a small central pressure and peripheral suction[121,122]. Numerous advantages are claimed for such radial development.

References p. 97

An adsorbent disc 3 feet in diameter and 1 foot deep is claimed to be equivalent to a column 7 feet high and 1 square foot in section. By designing a container, which is sectioned with perforated partitions it is possible to separate zones cleanly. If a number of interchangeable adsorbent containers are used for one chromatographic plant, a semi-continuous scheme may be adopted.

Williams and Hightower[123] describe an industrial installation for the purification of streptomycin on columns of alumina of 80 cm diameter and 4 m high. The industrial chromatography of carotene from alfalfa on columns of charcoal (60 cm diameter and 2 m high) has been described by Shearon and Gee[124] (see also ref. 125). For a review on industrial chromatography, see Weil[126]. Swinton and Weiss[127] criticise chromatographic development as industrially unfeasible and suggest counter-current adsorption with a fluidised bed of adsorbent moving against a stream of solution. In further papers the properties of the adsorbents to be used in such systems[128,129] are examined, also its application to the purification of a crude penicillin extract[130]; a froth flotation process based on the same principle is also discussed[131]. Froth chromatography of colloids is also studied by Mokrushin[132].

(d) *Apparatus for control of eluates*

Clear-cut separation of eluted colourless substances can often be achieved by measurement of physical constants of the eluates. Claesson[50] employed an automatic apparatus for the determination of the refractive index of the eluate. Further recording interferometers and refractometers were designed by Holman and Hagdahl[133], Kegeles and Sober[134], Glenn *et al.*[135], Trenner *et al.*[136], McCormick[137] and Hellström[138]. Jeffrey[139] uses a pH meter for continuous recording of the pH of the effluent. Conductivity recording has been frequently employed, especially in ion exchange chromatography (James *et al.*[140], Partridge and Westall[141], De Verdier and Sjöberg[142]).

Automatic photometry of column eluates has been described by Heimburger[143] and by Verzele[144]. Porter[145] describes a simple device for cutting fractions using a photoelectric cell. Johansson *et al.*[146] let the effluent pass a cell which forms a part of a high-frequency resonance circuit; changes in the conductivity are recorded as a function of time. For the simultaneous measurement of ultraviolet absorption and radioactivity in eluates see Bradley[147].

3. Adsorbents

(a) *Particle size*

Table V shows the particle size of different adsorbents (after Zechmeister and Von Cholnoky[106]). Before using a non-standardized adsorbent it is recommended to rub it through a 150-mesh sieve and collect the part retained by the 200-mesh sieve.

TABLE V

AVERAGE PARTICLE SIZE OF SOME ADSORBENTS

Adsorbent	*Particle size (μ)*
Alumina Merck (standardized Brockmann)	7
Acid clay	10
Calcium carbonate precipitated	1.5
Calcium hydroxide	2.5
Calcium sulphate (hydrated)	10.5
Magnesium oxide	1.5
Fuller's earth	3
Floridin	1.5–7
Floridin XXF	1.5–6

Mowery[115] has described a method for blowing air through adsorbents to remove the finer particles so as to accelerate the flow rate. The measurement of flow rates has been described by Hesse *et al.*[148] and by Mowery[115].

(b) *Description and use*

(i) *Inorganic adsorbents*

Alumina (Al_2O_3) is one of the principal adsorbents used in chromatography. It often contains sodium carbonate and bicarbonate[149] whose presence exerts a marked effect on its adsorptive properties. The alkali of alumina often causes secondary reactions (see p. 90); this can be prevented by washing with dilute acid or with water (followed finally by methanol), then by reactivation [107,150] at 200°. Heating alumina above 500° should be avoided; Krieger[151] has stated that the surface of alumina remains constant up to 528°, then decreases by 15% at 734° and by 40% after heating at 938°. Russell and Cochran[152] have studied the influence of temperature, atmosphere and duration of heating on the surface of various forms of α- and β-aluminium mono- and tri-hydrates and of an amorphous alumina. Usually 1 g of alumina for chromatography has about 90 square metres surface; an alumina having less than 6 square meters per g is useless as an adsorbent (Jutisz and Teichner[153]).

Preparation of alumina for chromatography. We quote in detail a procedure for the preparation and regeneration of alumina recommended by Reichstein and Shoppee[107] (p. 55). Dupont *et al.*[154] have described the preparation of alumina by calcination of the hydrate at 500° followed by activation with concentrated HCl. Fuks[155] has also described the preparation and standardization of alumina. The preparation and use of *fibrous* alumina was described by Wislicenus[156]. This is a very active but rather costly adsorbent, obtained by treating aluminium amalgam with water. A patent by Stewart[157] describes the preparation of alumina for chromatography; for older references see Krczil[158]. Quite recently, a German firm (Woelm, Eschwege) has begun producing a standardized alkali-free alumina which is obtained by treating pure aluminium with water. The preparation and properties of amorphous alumina have been described by Imelik *et al.*[159]. Alumina may be treated by stannous chloride to prevent the oxidation of autoxidizable substances (Kofler[160]; Stoll[161]).

Acid alumina. For adsorption in aqueous media, the properties of alumina can be modified by washing with acid. This activation, used by Kuhn and Wieland[162] for the adsorption of pantothenic acid, transforms the alumina into an ion exchanger (Wieland[163]); the adsorbent takes up chloride ions which can be exchanged for mineral or organic anions. This *acid alumina* was used for the adsorption of the dicarboxylic amino acids and acidic peptides.

Basic alumina. On heating technical alumina, the alkali carbonate which it contains forms active centres of sodium aluminate; the sodium ions of these centres can be exchanged against inorganic or organic cations (Wieland's *basic column*[163]); the capacity of this column is, however, quite low.

Bauxite, $Al_2(OH)_4$, has been used by Zechmeister *et al.*[164] for the separation of enzymic hydrolysates of chitin. LaLande[165] recommends it for the refining of sugar.

Aluminium silicate allows the adsorption of sterols[166] and sterol glycosides[167] from oils without the use of solvent.

Magnesia (MgO) often advantageously replaces alumina[168,169]. As it is often too finely divided to allow a satisfactory filtration, it can be mixed with a filter aid (Celite, Hyflo Supercel, etc., see p. 54). For the preparation of a suitable magnesia, see [170]. The most active magnesia is obtained by dehydration of the hydroxide.

Magnesium silicate. Magnesol ($MgO \cdot 2.5\ SiO_2 \cdot H_2O$) has been used for the separation of sugar acetates[171]. Magnesium trisilicate (No. 34 of the Philadelphia Quartz Co., Berkeley, Cal.) has been extensively used by Liebermann *et al.*[172–174] for the separation of steroids; it is less active than alumina. Reichstein *et al.*[175,176] use magnesium trisilicate (Siegfried, Zofingen) for the chromatography of acetylated glycosides. This adsorbent is better than alumina for the purification of easily saponifiable substances, such as esters, glycerides and lactones (see also p. 90). The effect of moisture on the chromatographic properties of synthetic hydrated magnesium silicate has been studied by Wolfrom *et al.*[177]. Adsorptive capacity increases with decreasing water content.

Calcium hydroxide. The adsorption of the carotenoids on calcium hydroxide has been specially studied by LeRosen[178] as well as by Bickoff[179]. Karrer and coworkers[180–183] have often used it for the separation of carotenoids. Williams[105] recommends, in the case of a difficult elution, that the calcium hydroxide be suspended in water through which CO_2 is bubbled; the calcium carbonate formed is a much weaker adsorbent. A mixture of calcium hydroxide and magnesia allows the separation of the di- and tri-nitro-toluenes[184].

Calcium carbonate is used in the chromatography of xanthophylls[106,185], of naphthoquinones[186–188] or other pigments[189]. The elution of adsorbed substances can be carried out by dissolving the carbonate in dilute acid. Stolkowski[190] has shown that the adsorptive capacity of calcium carbonate depends on its crystalline form; vaterite, the unstable crystalline modification, is a much stronger adsorbent than aragonite or calcite. (See also Mathieu[191] for the relationship between adsorption and crystalline structure.)

Dicalcium phosphate ($CaHPO_4$) has been used for the purification of carotene[192].

Tricalcium phosphate ($Ca_3(PO_4)_2$) is a good adsorbent for enzymes[193,194].

A special preparation of *hydroxylapatite* (brushite, $Ca_5(PO_4)_3OH$) can be used with success for purification of proteins (Swingle and Tiselius[194]). It is readily prepared in a reproducible form with desirable physical characteristics and showing reversible adsorption for many proteins. Tiselius[197–199] has described the preparation of the adsorbent and several applications of this method; amongst these the separation of the chromoproteins phycocyanin and phycoerythrin is the most conspicuous; elution is effected by phosphate buffers of increasing concentration. Phycoerythrin is eluted with 0.005–0.008 *M* Na_2HPO_4, phycocyanin with 0.03–0.04 *M* Na_2HPO_4. The separation of colourless proteins (serum albumin, egg albumin) can be observed by using a quartz column and photographing the column in reflected ultra-violet light. CO-haemoglobin, haemocyanin and tobacco mosaic virus could also be purified by the calcium phosphate column.

Calcium oxalate can be used for the chromatography of anthraquinones and substances related to hypericine[200,201].

Zinc carbonate has been recommended for the chromatography of carotenoids[202] and for coloured derivatives of amino acids[203].

Glemser *et al.*[195,196] recommend *ferric hydroxide* for chromatography with hot solvents. Ferric hydroxide seems to be an excellent adsorbent, surpassing alumina by its selectivity and adsorption capacity. It can even be used for separating such unstable compounds as the chlorophylls *a* and *b* (Glemser and Rieck[195,196]).

*Silica gel** has been used for adsorption of sterols[204], of fatty acids and

* The terms *silica gel, silica* or *silicic acid* refer to hydrated silica precipitates the composition of which varies somewhat according to the precipitation method used.

References p. 97

glycerides[205-207], waxes[208], azoated carbohydrates[209,210], sugar acetates[171] and amino acids[211,212]. The effect of high pressures on catalytic and chromatographic properties of silica gel was studied by Freĭdlin *et al.*[213], the role of *porosity* in silica gel by Neĭmark *et al.*[214].

Stöber *et al.*[215] have studied the superficial structure of silica gel in relation with the adsorption of alcohols; hydrogen bonding with $-OH$ groups of the adsorbent seems to play an important role. During the action of alcohols on silica gel, partial esterification of the $-OH$ groups of the adsorbent has been observed. The fixation of aromatic compounds on silica gel has been studied by Kiselev[216].

The use of silica gel for *partition chromatography* is discussed on p. 154. For the preparation of silica gels, see refs. [211,217-221].

The relation between water content and adsorptive strength of silicic acid–celite mixtures has been studied by Trueblood and Malmberg[222] and by Kay and Trueblood[223].

Greater adsorptive strength was associated with lower content of *free water*. When all the *structural water* (*i.e.* water removable only by ignition) is driven off, the adsorptive power disappears almost completely.

The effect of particle size on the efficacy of silicic acid for the separation of 2,4-dinitrophenylhydrazones of lower aldehydes has been studied by Malmberg[224]; a procedure for obtaining a satisfactory adsorbent from commercially available silicic acid is described.

Fuller's earth. The natural clays called fuller's earth are chiefly hydrous magnesium aluminosilicates and are widely used in the petroleum industry for the decoloration of oil. The name fuller's earth is derived from their early use in fulling, the operation of removing grease from woollen goods. For details on the properties and uses of these clays, see Mantell[225].

Various brands of fuller's earth (some called *Filtrol* or *Filtrol-Neutrol**) have been used for the chromatography of basic hydrosoluble substances (amino acids[226,227]; pteridines: Forrest and Mitchell[228]).

Bentonites are also hydrous magnesium aluminosilicates of the montmorillonite group and can be activated by treatment with acid (whereas fuller's earth is not activatable). *Superfiltrol** is such an activated bentonite. Bentonite has been used for chromatographic separations of vitamin D from vitamin A and sterols[229] and for separation of 2,4-dinitrophenylhydrazones of aldehydes and ketones[230].

An acid calcium silicate (silene EF) has been found useful for the chromatography of carbohydrates and polyalcohols[108].

Water soluble salts have also found use as adsorbents.

Brockmann[231] has separated azobenzene derivatives on anhydrous copper

---

* Filtrol Corp., Los Angeles 14, Calif. (U.S.A.).

sulphate; substances which could not be separated on alumina were easily separated on $CuSO_4$. Other water-soluble salts, such as anhydrous zinc, manganese, aluminium and magnesium sulphates can also be used to separate azobenzene derivatives. Aluminium sulphate was also used by Brockmann for separations of hydroxyanthraquinones. Elution of strongly adsorbed compounds is easily achieved by dissolution of the adsorbent in water. Vitamin A has been adsorbed on sodium carbonate[232].

(*ii*) *Organic adsorbents*

Charcoal has been extensively used by Tiselius for frontal analysis of sugars, amino acids and other substances[15,16,60,110]. Charcoal has the specific property of adsorbing strongly aromatic substances (*e.g.* amino acids)[211,233]; this can be explained by the fact that the —C—C— spacings in graphite are of the same order as those in benzene. Cassidy[234,235] and Claesson[49] have used charcoal for adsorption of fatty acids (see also[236]). Benzene elutes from charcoal a "petroleum-like" material (Cassidy[237], Cason and Gillies[238]). For details of charcoal as adsorbent see Mantell[225], Cassidy[234,235] and Weiss[239–241]. Emmett[242] has reviewed in detail the adsorptive properties of charcoal and the methods used for pore size measurements.

Weiss[239–241] has described activated carbon whose adsorptive properties were modified by depositing on it a film of a non-electrolyte or a fatty acid. The coating of the surface of an adsorbent by a film of some other substance may be a useful way of preparing adsorbents with special and uniform properties.

Powdered *sucrose* is the best adsorbent for the separation of the various chlorophylls[103,106,243–245].

Polyamides (such as perlon) are good adsorbents for polar substances (Carelli *et al.*[246]), phenols such as chalcones, flavanones and flavonols (Neu[247]) and 2,4-dinitrophenyl-amino acids and -peptides (Hörmann and Portatius[248]).

(*iii*) *Mixed adsorbents*

Carlton and Bradbury[249] have studied the use of *mixed adsorbents* in chromatography. Their data show that either the mixture behaves as one of the two adsorbents in the pure form, the second acting simply as diluent, or, adsorption is shared between the two adsorbents, in which case adsorption varies almost linearly with percentage composition of the mixture. An exception was observed with boron oxide mixed with silicic acid, or Florisil, or alumina, where certain amines were more strongly adsorbed than by either of the pure adsorbents.

References p. 97

(*iv*) *Classification of adsorbents*

Strain[104] has classified adsorbents on the basis of their adsorptive capacity; this list (Table VI) is reproduced in the form given by Williams[105].

TABLE VI

ADSORBENTS CLASSIFIED ON THE BASIS OF THEIR ADSORPTION CAPACITY
(after Strain[104])

	Weak	*Medium*	*Strong*
Increasing activity ↓	Sucrose	Calcium carbonate	Activated magnesium silicate
	Starch	Calcium phosphate	Activated alumina
	Inulin	Magnesium phosphate	Activated charcoal
	Talc	Magnesia	Activated magnesium oxide
	Sodium carbonate	Precipitated calcium hydroxide	Fuller's earth

This order, however, must not be considered as applying in every case; it does not take account of the special affinities and incompatibilities which often occur or the possibility of increasing or decreasing the activity of various adsorbents (especially alumina) by appropriate treatment.

Hesse *et al.*[148] have studied the saturation with dyestuffs of different adsorbents, under standardized conditions and found the following order of activity of adsorbents:
activated charcoal > silica gel > franconite > floridin > acid alumina > basic alumina > Cr_2O_3 > ZnS > sugar charcoal > Al_2O_3 (Merck) > CaF_2 > CaO.

Mantell[225] in his book on adsorption gives useful information on the principal adsorbents and their industrial uses. Deitz[250] has published a list of adsorbents produced in the U.S.A. with an indication of the size of their surface. For the electronic structure of some adsorbents see Meunier and Vinet[251].

(*v*) *Filter aids*

The filter aids, generally diatomaceous earths (Kieselguhr), are usually mixed with those finely divided adsorbents which when used by themselves prevent sufficiently high rates of flow. The preparations often used are Hyflo Supercel and Celite[252,253]. These powders serve sometimes as adsorbents for proteins (Clauser and Li[254]) or pigments[255-257]. Martin[258] recommends kieselguhr as perfectly inert support for the stationary phase in partition chromatography.

(*c*) *The preparation of some adsorbents*

Neutral alumina. Commercial alumina (Alumina Prolabo for Chromatography, Merck alumina Brockmann, Neuhausen alumina, or alumina of the Aluminium Ore Co. Ohio etc.) is covered with distilled water and a slight excess of 0.5 *N* HCl is added with stirring. After standing for an hour the liquid is decanted and the alumina repeatedly washed with distilled water until the washings are free from chloride ions. It is then dried at 100–150° for at least 12 hours.

Preparation of Al_2O_3 after Reichstein and Shoppee[107]. "Activated and partly standardized Al_2O_3 is available commercially. Equivalent and very active preparations are obtained by heating technical pure $Al(OH)_3$ for about three hours with stirring at 380–400°; such preparations always contain free alkali (or sodium carbonate) which, however, is usually not deleterious, and in general gives the best separations. In certain cases these preparations are too active and lead to condensation of ketones or aldehydes, elimination of alcoholic hydroxyl groups, etc., but by homogeneous addition of moisture their activity can be reduced and standardized (*e.g.*, by the use of selected dyestuffs under defined conditions)."

"For sensitive substances (ketones, lactones, readily hydrolizable esters, etc.) neutralized aluminium oxide is used. Aluminium oxide, prepared in the laboratory by activation at 380–400° or obtained commercially, is boiled repeatedly with distilled water until the extract is neutral; the filtered material is then washed with methanol and reactivated at 160–200° (internal temperature) at 10 mm pressure. Preparations reactivated at 200° are too active for many purposes and a temperature of 180° is generally sufficient. The product still contains traces of alkali, which are not harmful and is rather less effective than the alkali containing oxide in regard to separation."

"Neutralization is more rapidly achieved by neutralization of the first aqueous suspension with dilute nitric acid (use of hydrochloric, sulphuric or acetic acid is rather more dangerous) followed by boiling with distilled water, treatment with methanol and reactivation as above. The product contains nitrate ions, which are not always harmless."

Regeneration. "Used aluminium oxide is repeatedly extracted, first with boiling methanol and then with boiling water (with addition of some sodium hydroxide if necessary) and subsequently treated as described above. Slight discoloration of the regenerated material is of no importance."

Acid alumina (after Wieland[162]). Commercial alumina is mixed with 3 or 4 volumes of *N* HCl, the mixture is well stirred and the suspended particles are decanted a number of times. The alumina is washed with water until the wash water is feebly acid to litmus paper. Drying is carried out at 100°.

References p. 97

Charcoal (after Schramm and Primosigh[233]). The charcoal (Carbo activatus granulatus Schering) previously ground and sieved, is boiled for some minutes with 5 to 10 parts of 20% acetic acid in order to remove nitrogen-containing impurities, then centrifuged hot and washed with hot water. It is then suspended in water and treated for a few minutes with 50 mg of KCN per 100 g of charcoal. After centrifuging, it is washed many times with hot water. Fromageot *et al.*[211] treat the charcoal (Activite 50X P from la Compagnie Activite, 66 rue d'Auteuil, Paris) with 2 mg of ephedrine per 0.5 g of charcoal (instead of KCN) and carry out the adsorption in solutions saturated with H_2S to prevent any oxidation.

(*d*) *The standardization of adsorbents*

Many methods of standardization of the activity of *alumina* have been proposed. Brockmann and Schodder[259] measure the activity of alumina by the behaviour on the column of a number of azo-dyes. These dyes, in order of increasing adsorbability, are: azobenzene, *p*-methoxyazobenzene, benzene-azo-2-naphthol (Sudan yellow), Sudan red (Sudan III), *p*-aminoazobenzene and *p*-hydroxyazobenzene. Table VII shows the behaviour of these dyes on alumina columns more or less deactivated by water (*e.g.* alumina of activity I adsorbs methoxyazobenzene at the top of the column, and azobenzene at the bottom; with alumina of activity II, azobenzene passes out in the filtrate, methoxyazobenzene is retained at the bottom of the column, etc.). Alumina I is completely activated by calcination, whereas the others are more or less deactivated by a prolonged exposure to damp air. According to Boissonnas[260] the addition of 3.3% of water to a completely activated alumina gives an alumina of activity III. See also Boutillon and Prettre[261].

Hesse *et al.*[148] have measured the activity of alumina preparations by saturating them with azobenzene. Table VIII shows their figures relating water content of alkali-free alumina with its activity and *azobenzene index*.

TABLE VII

STANDARDIZATION OF ALUMINA (Brockmann and Schodder[259])

Activity	I	II		III		IV		V
Mixture	1	1	2	2	3	3	4	5
Adsorbed at top of column	methoxy-az.		S. yellow		S. red		amino-az.	hydroxy-az.
Adsorbed at bottom of column	azobenzene	methoxy-az.	methoxy-az.	S. yellow	S. yellow	S. red	S. red	amino-az.
Filtrate	—	azobenzene		methoxy-az.		S. yellow		

az. = azobenzene S = Sudan

TABLE VIII

ACTIVITY OF ALUMINA IN DEPENDENCE OF WATER CONTENT (Hesse *et al.*[148])

% Water added	Activity (Brockman and Schodder)	Azobenzene index (10^{-5} mol/g)
0	I	26
3	II	21
6	III	18
10	IV	13
15	V	0

Azobenzene index (Hesse *et al.*[148]). 0.5 g of the adsorbent are mixed with 3.00 ml of a 0.1 *M* solution of pure azobenzene in pure cyclohexane in a small flask fitted with a ground-in stopper and shaken several times.

After about one hour the supernatant liquid is centrifuged off and a portion poured into a cuvette of a Pulfrich step-photometer and covered immediately. The extinction is measured against pure cyclohexane with a L II Filter and the loss of azobenzene is determined with the aid of a previously prepared calibration curve.

The adsorbed quantity in moles per gram adsorbent (x) is then calculated with the formula

$$x = \frac{a}{m}(C_1 - C_2)$$

where a = volume of the dye solution in ml,
m = grams of adsorbent taken,
C_1 initial and C_2 the final concentration of the dye solution in mole/ml.

For the standardization of acid alumina, Hesse *et al.*[148] use the saturation with naphthol orange or Orange GG Cassella; for the standardization of alkaline, cation exchanging alumina, they use methylene blue. Valentin and Kirchübel[262] determined the activity of alumina by passing a 0.1% light petroleum solution of Sudan red onto the column and measuring the width of the coloured zone, which varies inversely with the activity of the adsorbent.

Müller[263] has developed a very precise method for measurement of the activity of alumina (or any other adsorbent) by measuring the heat evolved by contact between the solvent and the adsorbent. The heat evolved is proportional to the activity of the adsorbent. The activity of the adsorbent is characterised by the heat (Q) evolved in contact with purified light petroleum. Müller has given evidence for the fundamental role played by water adsorbed by the adsorbent. The addition of 1% of water to a maximum activated (dried) alumina diminishes markedly its adsorbing capacity (Fig. 11). Müller[263] prepared alumina of any desired degree of activity by the addition of definite amounts of water. (Water is added with a pipette to a known weight of alumina contained in a flask fitted with a ground stopper and shaken for many hours to ensure an even distribution of the water.)

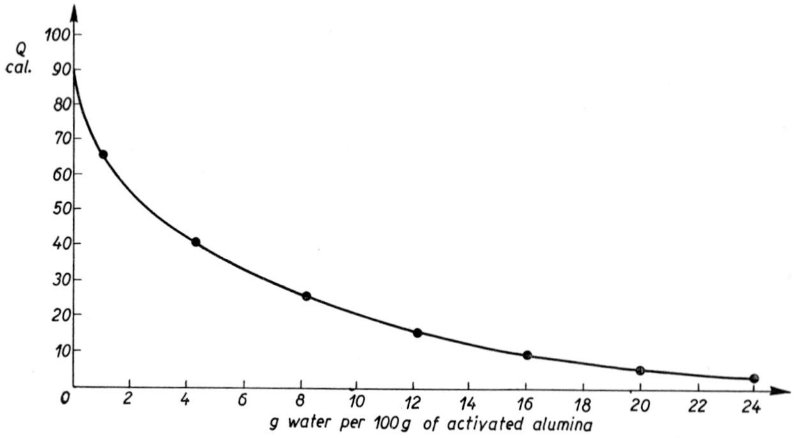

Fig. 11. Heat evolved in relation to water content of alumina (Müller[263]).

For the chemical estimation of the esters of vitamin A, Müller[264] used a column containing three different grades of alumina.

For the separation of vitamins A and D and the esters of vitamin A and of carotene, Müller[265] has used columns in 5 parts containing from top to bottom alumina of activities Q4, 11, 50, 56.5 and 83.5 (the latter representing an alumina completely activated). As an alternative for the calorimetric method Müller recommends the standardization of the alumina with the aid of carotene before carrying out such separations. Kofler[266] has proposed a simple and rapid method of measuring the activity of alumina: the colorimetric estimation of the amount of *p*-hydroxyazobenzene not adsorbed by a known quantity of alumina (after shaking in a closed system).

Magnesia and carbon can be standardized by known methods (*e.g.* by the *iodine index*, see Mantell[225]).

Wilkie and Jones[267] have determined the adsorbent strength of magnesia and magnesia-celite mixtures (used for chromatography of vitamin A) in terms of g of Butter yellow No. 4 adsorbed per g of adsorbent. Brockmann[231] has obtained various grades of bentonite, silica, $CaSO_4$, and $CaCO_3$ by varying the water content. For the standardization of silica gel for adsorption chromatography, see Sen Gupta and Gupta[268].

For a precise standardization of adsorbents it is preferable to use compounds which are chemically as similar as possible to the substances to be separated. Thus specific influences of adsorbent properties (acidity, alkalinity, pore size, impurities, etc.) can be eliminated. This principle is adopted by Keuning *et al.*[269] who use a *shake test* for the determination of the activity of adsorbents; it consists in shaking a weighed sample (2 g) of the adsorbent with a measured volume (10 ml) of the elution solvent in which the substance to be eluted (*e.g.* 1000 I.U. of vitamin A) has been dissolved. The activity is suitable if about 50% is adsorbed. The quantity of unadsorbed compound can of course be rapidly determined by spectrophotometry (see Table IX).

TABLE IX

ADSORPTION AND WATER CONTENT OF Al_2O_3 (Keuning *et al.*[269])

% of water added to the Al_2O_3	% of vitamin A adsorbed
0	73
0.5	69
1	53
1.5	49
2	32.5
2.5	23

(*e*) *Packing adsorbents in chromatographic columns*

Even the best adsorbent becomes useless if it is filled into a column in a non-uniform way. Most authors seem to agree that the easiest way to obtain an even packing and to avoid air bubbles, is to fill the empty column first half way with the first solvent to be used in the separation and then to pour either the dry adsorbent or the adsorbent slurried with the same solvent into the column. After the adsorbent has been transferred to the column, the solvent is allowed to drain, while the side of the tube is tapped with a rubber mallet or a large rubber stopper. The column should always be kept covered with solvent to prevent cracking. It is advisable not to continue a separation if a column has gone dry for some time, because of irregular cracking and channelling.

(*f*) *The characterization of adsorbents by the methods of LeRosen*

A series of papers by LeRosen *et al.*[178,270–275] deal with attempts to correlate the structure of the compounds chromatographed with the rate of movement on the chromatogram. The treatment is essentially similar to that used in paper chromatography (see p. 165) and can only be applied when substances move with constant rates and have linear isotherms.

The paper by Sporer and Trueblood[276] summarises much of this work and gives the results of such a theoretical treatment in the case of the separation of aromatic substances (with nitro, amino, aldehyde, hydroxyl and methoxy groups) on silicic acid–celite. As in the work of LeRosen very good correlation between calculated and measured rates of movement were obtained.

(g) *Specific adsorbents*

(i) *Silica gel with "specific holes"*

A promising new approach to the preparation of very specific adsorbents has been tried by Dickey[277] following a proposal of Pauling. It consists in preparing silica gel in presence of the molecules (for instance methyl orange) for which specificity is desired. Then the adsorbed substance is extracted and leaves the silica gel with *specific holes* favouring the preferential adsorption of the molecule used in the preparation of the gel. Bernhard[278] has recently expanded the experiments of Dickey[277]. The results obtained are best expressed in terms of *adsorption power* =

$$\frac{\text{moles of dye adsorbed/g of gel}}{\text{moles of dye in solution/g of solution}}$$

or of "% excess adsorption" =

$$\frac{\text{adsorption power of gel} - \text{adsorption power of control}}{\text{adsorption power of control}}$$

Tables X and XI show a very definite preferential adsorption by *specific gels*; the specificity for methyl orange and for the sulphonamide III are closely parallel; it is evident that a negative charge at the *p*′-substituent is not a requirement for specificity. Dickey[279] has studied the preparation and properties of *specific* silica gel.

Curti and Colombo[280] report an enrichment of 30% *l*-camphorsulphonic acid by percolation of the racemic compound through a column of silica gel prepared in presence of *d*-camphorsulphonic acid. With mandelic acid an enrichment of only 10% was obtained.

(ii) *Adsorbents containing complexing agents*

Polycyclic hydrocarbons have a great tendency to form crystalline complexes with polynitro-aromatic compounds, such as trinitrobenzene, picric acid, etc. This property was used first by Godlewicz[281] to separate hydrocarbons from lubricating oils on silica gel impregnated with trinitrobenzene; the various aromatic hydrocarbons give yellow to violet zones due to the formation of trinitrobenzolates. Aliphatic or alicyclic hydrocarbons are not retained.

Klemm *et al.*[282] have used silicic acid impregnated with picric acid or 2,4,7-trinitrofluorenone to study the relation between coplanarity and chromatographic adsorbability of isomeric naphthylcyclo-alkenes and poly-

TABLE X

ADSORPTION POWER OF SPECIFIC SILICA GEL (Bernhard[278])

$R_2N—C_6H_4—N=N—C_6H_4—SO_3^-$
I R= CH_3—
II R= CH_3CH_2—
III $(CH_3)_2N—C_6H_4—N=N—C_6H_4—SO_2NH_2$

Gel prepared with	*Adsorption power for*		
	methyl orange	*ethyl orange*	*III*
0	18	9.2	31
Methyl orange (I)	100	32	144
Ethyl orange (II)	90	74	120
p-Dimethylamino-*p'*-sulphonamido-azobenzene (III)	106	34	168

TABLE XI

% EXCESS ADSORPTION OF SPECIFIC SILICA GEL (Bernhard[278])

Gel prepared with	*% Excess adsorption of*		
	methyl orange	*ethyl orange*	*III*
Methyl orange (I)	450	250	370
Ethyl orange (II)	380	700	290
p-Dimethylamino-*p'*-sulphonamido-azobenzene (III)	480	280	450

cyclic aromatic hydrocarbons. In these impregnated silicic acid columns the polynitro complexing agent, A, is thought to be adsorbed *flatwise* and monomolecularly at selected spots of the surface of the silicic acid. Each such molecule constitutes an *active site* upon which only one molecule of hydrocarbon substrate may be adsorbed; adsorption is thought to be, in this case, analogous to molecular compound formation, like that which occurs in solution, rather than like that which occurs in the crystalline state.

(*iii*) *Urea columns*

Cason *et al.*[283] have separated straight chain and branched chain fatty acids on columns of urea; the former are adsorbed, the latter not. This separation is based on the well known property of urea to form crystalline *clathrate* complexes with straight chain substances only; the molecules of the branched chain homologues are too large to fit in the *holes* in the interior of the urea crystals.

(*iv*) *Histone columns*

Brown and Watson[284] have described the chromatographic fractionation of deoxyribonucleic acids on columns of kieselguhr covered with histone

References p. 97

(the basic protein which is combined with the nucleic acids in the cells). Figs. 12 and 13 show the elution curves obtained by stepwise elution, or by

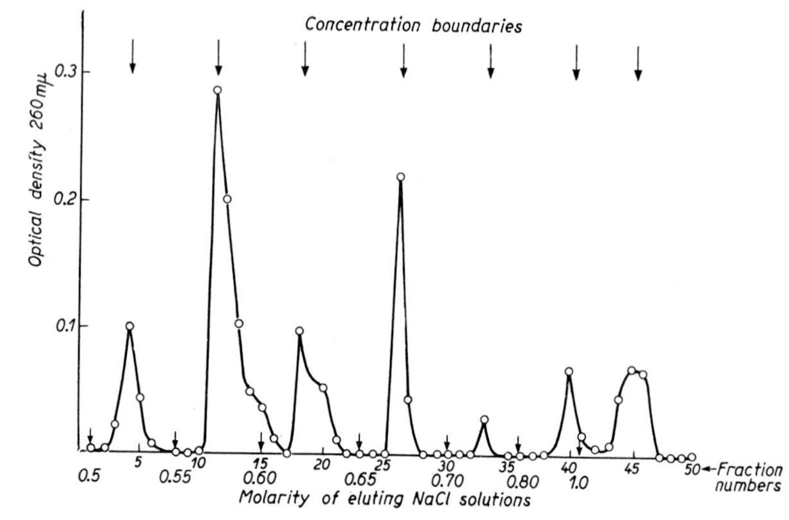

Fig. 12. Stepwise elution of calf-thymus deoxyribonucleic acid from a column of histone-coated kieselguhr with solutions of sodium chloride (Brown and Watson[284]).

gradient elution. The specificity of the histone columns is shown by the fact that ribonucleic acids are not retained by them and that deoxyribonucleic acids of different origin give different elution curves (Fig. 13).

(*v*) *Separation of enzymes*

Hockenhull and Herbert[285] had already shown that amylase is strongly adsorbed on starch columns; French and Knapp[286] have thus separated amylase from maltase. Lerman[287] has used a similar principle for the purification of tyrosinase; it is known that this enzyme is specifically inhibited by azophenols; Lerman prepared columns of cellulose combined with azophenols (for instance cellulose—$OCH_2C_6H_4N{=}NC_6H_3(OH)_2$) for the enrichment of tyrosinase. Ghuysen[288] has purified lytic enzymes from culture filtrates of Actinomyces on columns of sand covered with *E. coli* or with staphylococci. These experiments suggest a general method of purification of enzymes by adsorption on their substrates or on specific inhibitors.

(*vi*) *Purification of antibodies*

Lerman[289] has described the purification of antibodies on immunologically specific adsorbents.

An adsorbent specific for antibodies homologous to the simple hapten, *p*-azobenzenearsonate, was prepared from powdered cellulose (Solka-Floc BW200) by coupling diazotized *p*-(*p*-aminobenzeneazo)benzenearsonic acid with cellulose which had been partially etherified with resorcinol. The arsonate cellulose thus obtained binds about 3 mg of antibody protein per

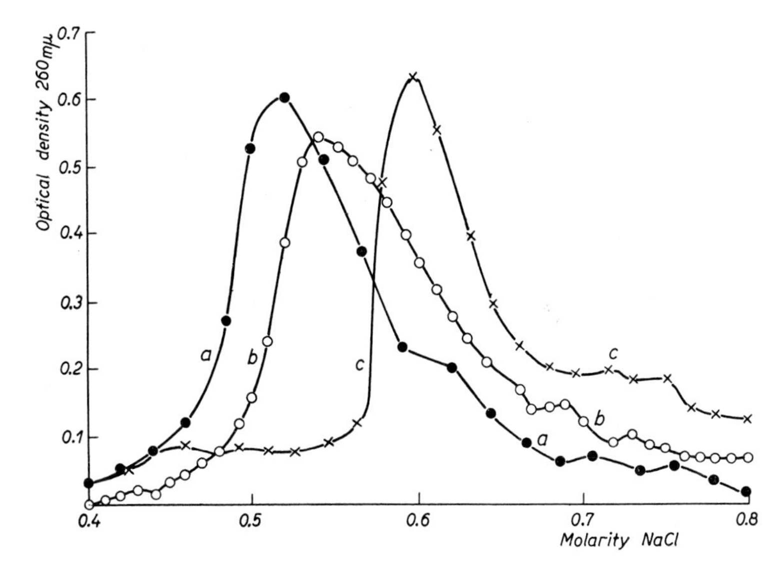

Fig. 13. Elution diagrams of some deoxyribonucleic acids obtained by eluting with continuously increasing salt solutions (Brown and Watson[284]). Curve a—deoxyribonucleic acid from *E. coli*; Curve b—idem from calf thymus; Curve c—idem from human white blood cells.

ml of packed moist adsorbent. An analogous cellulose preparation in which *p*-azobenzenesulphonate was substituted for the homologous hapten was found not to adsorb detectable amounts of antibody. Separation of two distinctly different fractions of antibody was achieved by gradient elution with a specific hapten solution (sodium arsanilate) (Fig. 14). When a heterologous hapten (sodium sulphanilate) was used instead of sodium arsanilate, no protein could be eluted.

(*h*) *Modified adsorbents*

The success of chromatographic separations depends amongst other factors on the uniformity of the adsorbent. Most of these contain a certain amount of impurities which may constitute more or less active centres causing irreversible adsorption or trailing of part of the substances to be separated.

References p. 97

This is especially true for charcoal, which has been extensively used for separations of carbohydrates, peptides, antibiotics, etc.

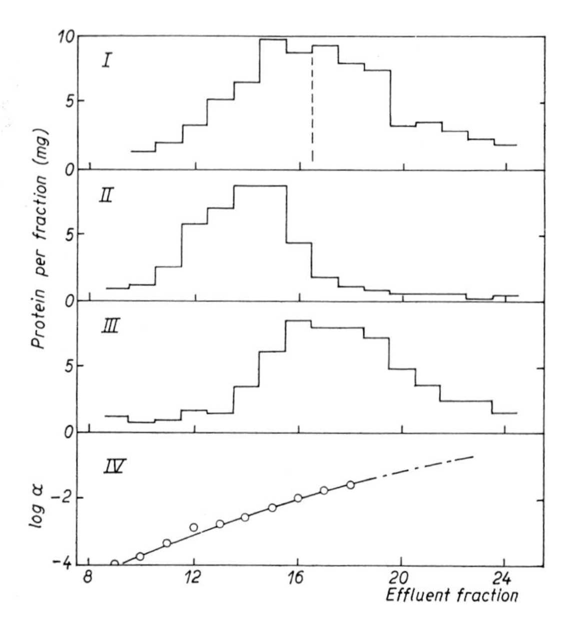

Fig. 14. Gradient elution chromatograms: I, whole serum; II, pooled eluate fractions 13–16 from I; III, pooled eluate fractions 17–24 from I. The arsanilate concentration, (measured in *M*), appearing in each fraction is shown in IV (Lerman[289]).

Porath and Li[80] explain part of the irreversible adsorption encountered with high molecular weight substances by the simultaneous anchoring of part of the molecules at several points of the surface of the adsorbent. The tendency to irreversible adsorption is greatly reduced by mixing the charcoal with some inert or weak adsorbent, such as diatomaceous earth.

Better separation seems, however, to be obtained by pretreating the adsorbent with a substance (*saturator*) which itself is strongly adsorbed. This technique, introduced by Tiselius and collaborators[71,290] (see also Weiss[239–241]) blocks especially the strongest adsorption centres. The charcoal modified in this manner is a much weaker adsorbent, exhibiting new adsorption characteristics. Hagdahl *et al.*[291] have made a study of the influence of pretreatment of charcoal for the separation of low molecular compounds. Working with insulin and adrenocorticotropic peptides and *n*-decanol as saturator Porath and Li[80] have studied the degree of saturation necessary for the attainment of optimal separation.

At a low concentration of a strong saturator, such as *n*-decanol, the adrenocorticotropic peptides studied could not be eluted completely, even with a strong displacer (saturated decanol solution). At higher concentrations of the saturator, the recovery of the peptides by displacement was enhanced and finally was quantitative. At an even higher concentration of the saturator, not far from the point of saturation concentration where practically complete recovery is obtained, a part of the peptides was easily eluted, even without displacement. The limit of concentration of the saturator at which elution of the active substance occurs in this manner is determined by the kind of charcoal used, the ratio of charcoal/diatomaceous earth, the concentration of substance, etc. This limit is called the *critical saturation point*. Porath and Li point out that for the separation of peptides, chromatography ought to be performed on charcoal saturated as near as possible to the critical saturation point. See also Williams *et al.*[292]. Porath[293] has described a *step-graded adsorption column*, which consists of segments filled with charcoal of different degrees of saturation (for instance from the top to the bottom: charcoal with 25%, 10%, 3%, 1%, 0.3%, 0.1% stearic acid). It is claimed that this arrangement allows chromatography of a mixture consisting of components of widely differing adsorbability with high total yield, in one single chromatogram and that efficient separations are obtained.

Asatoor and Dalgliesh[294] have reported that charcoal which has been deactivated by pre-treatment with various long-chain aliphatic compounds will selectively adsorb aromatic substances from aqueous solution, allowing a simple separation from aliphatic and inorganic contaminants, even if the latter are present in large excess. Aromatic adsorbates can be displaced from deactivated charcoals by aqueous phenol, and the phenol is removed (by steam-distillation) on subsequent concentration. Recoveries depend on the degree of deactivation of the charcoal, but are usually good, and the method is rapid and simple. With stearic acid as deactivating agent, the method is applicable to benzene derivatives, pyrroles, pyridine derivatives, indoles, purines and pyrimidines, but not glyoxalines. With aqueous phenol as eluant, and charcoal deactivated with stearic acid, octadecane, or paraffin wax as adsorbent, there is only a low recovery of substances with basic amino-groups, though high recoveries can be obtained by using acidified phenol as eluant. On the other hand, basic substances can be readily displaced by aqueous phenol if the charcoal has been deactivated with octadecylamine.

(*k*) *Salting-out adsorption*

The difficulties encountered in the chromatography of proteins are in the main due to the slowness of equilibration, to the frequent existence of irreversible adsorption, or of denaturation following elution. Tiselius[61] found

References p. 97

one solution to the problem by showing that many proteins were more strongly adsorbed in the presence of salts at concentrations lower than those necessary for precipitation; this phenomenon is called *salting-out adsorption*. In the absence of salts, 1 g of silica gel adsorbs only 0.5 mg of ovalbumin, but in the presence of 1.2 M ammonium sulphate, 9 mg of the protein are adsorbed. Salting out of ovalbumin does not occur below an ammonium sulphate concentration of 2.5 M. Details of this technique have been given by Shepard and Tiselius[295].

Mitchell *et al.*[296] showed that considerable enzyme resolution could be attained by use of the filter paper *chromatopile*; variations in salt concentration and pH have a great influence on the behaviour of the proteins on the paper column. See also Kritsman and Lebedeva[297].

Brandenberger[298] has studied the adsorption of blood plasma proteins on cellulose powder columns, in presence of salt. Schwimmer[299] has described column procedures for salt fractionation of enzymes: the mixture of proteins is precipitated with ammonium sulphate, then mixed with Celite and filled into a column which is then eluted by ammonium sulphate; alternatively a solution of the proteins can be filtered in presence of ammonium sulphate on a column of $CaSO_4 \cdot \frac{1}{2}H_2O$, which hydrates itself and thus increases the salt concentration in the solution.

Riley[255] has shown the effect of salt concentration on the chromatography, on Celite, of the virus of the Rous sarcoma. In this and subsequent papers[300–302], Riley has shown that chromatography can be extended to the separation of particulates ranging from viruses to mitochondria and bacteria. Riley *et al.*[303] have reversibly adsorbed melanized granules (size 0.2 to 0.6 μ or more) of mouse melanomas on Celite columns. Other constituents of the tumour homogenates were not adsorbed. The particulate elements separated by chromatography were found to be very homogeneous under the electron microscope, and to possess high dopa-oxidase and succinoxidase activities. Adsorption was proportional to the salt concentration; elution was effected with distilled water.

Riley[301] has described in detail salting-out adsorption for the purification of the virus from chicken tumours on Celite columns. A 20-fold increase in purity was obtained in a single adsorption. Leyon[304] has shown that Theiler's virus could be adsorbed on filter paper at a concentration of ammonium sulphate too low to precipitate the virus and that it could be eluted with distilled water. Shepard[305] has studied the chromatographic behaviour of *E. coli* phages in HCl-treated paper strips (solvent: 0.1% bovine plasma albumin + 0.1 M NaCl). More recently, Albertsson[306] has described experiments of chromatography of *Chlorella* cells on calcium phosphate and has separated cell walls and starch grains of *Chlorella* in a specially constructed apparatus.

4. Elution

(a) *Purification of solvents*

The purity of solvents is extremely important in chromatography as impurities can influence markedly the course of development. All organic solvents used should be dried and redistilled. Müller[263] has indicated a method for the purification of light petroleum (with concentrated sulphuric acid) which increases markedly the heat evolved in contact with alumina. Dasler and Bauer[307] recommend that solvents that might contain peroxides should be purified by passage through an alumina column, the peroxides being quantitatively retained.

When esters are used, great care must be taken to remove the traces of acids and alcohols formed by hydrolysis, as these impurities increase the eluting power. Halogen-containing solvents (chloroform, trichlorethylene, etc.) must be kept over sodium or potassium carbonate in order to remove any free HCl formed.

(b) *Elution*

The elution of colouring matters is usually carried out on zones that have been isolated mechanically and so presents no difficulty in principle. With the *liquid chromatogram* the choice of a convenient series of solvents is more important. For example, the series of solvents used by Steiger and Reichstein[14] for the fractionation of steroids is pentane, benzene–pentane 1:4, benzene–pentane 1:1, benzene, ether and acetone.

Trappe[308] has established an *eluotropic series of solvents*, useful for the fractionation of lipids (see Table XII). Strain[104] has suggested an analogous series. Jacques and Mathieu[309] have stated that the eluting power of solvents is proportional to their dielectric constant ε; they have verified that the eluants function by being themselves adsorbed. In a mixture of two eluants, the solvent with the highest eluting power (having the higher value of ε) is the most strongly adsorbed.

Section 5 (p. 78) shows that such definite series cannot be established for all substances.

Moseley *et al.*[310] have studied the developing (eluting) power of a series of pure solvents and of two- and three-component mixtures with silicic acid or calcium hydroxide as adsorbent and *o*-nitroaniline as adsorptive. No correlation of dipole moment of the solvent with adsorption affinity of the adsorptive was found. In the correlation of dielectric constant of the solvent with its developing power some exceptions were encountered; for example, the developing power of acetone was found greater than that of nitrobenzene,

TABLE XII

ELUTING POWER OF SOLVENT (in increasing order)

Trappe [308]	*Strain*[104]	*Jacques and Mathieu*[309]	ε
Light petroleum	Light petroleum 30–50°	Hexane	1.88
Cyclohexane	Light petroleum 50–70°	Benzene	2.29
CCl_4	Light petroleum 70–100°	Ether	4.47
Trichloroethylene	CCl_4	Chloroform	5.2
Toluene	Cyclohexane	Ethyl acetate	6.11
Benzene	CS_2	Dichloroethane	10.4
Dichloromethane	Anhydrous ether	Butanol-2	15.5
Chloroform	Anhydrous acetone	Acetone	21.5
Ether	Benzene	Ethanol	26
Ethyl acetate	Toluene	Methanol	31.2
Acetone	Esters of organic acids		
n-Propanol	1,2-Dichloroethane		
Ethanol	Alcohols		
Methanol	Water		
	Pyridine		
	Organic acids		
	Mixtures of acids or bases, water, alcohols or pyridine		

whereas acetone and nitrobenzene have dielectric constants of 20.7 and 34.8 respectively. This discrepancy is explained by Moseley *et al.*[310] as the effect of hydrogen bonding: acetone being capable of hydrogen bonding with the

$$—Si\overset{\displaystyle O}{\underset{\displaystyle OH}{\lessgtr}}$$

group of silicic acid or the hydroxyls of calcium hydroxide and thus exerting a displacement effect on the adsorptive, whereas nitrobenzene is much less capable of hydrogen bonding.

Knight and Groennings[311] have determined the following eluotropic series on silica gel (increasing order of adsorbability of the solvent):

Heptane	Diisopropyl ether	*sec.*-Butyl alcohol	Acetone
Diisobutylene	Ethyl ether	Ethyl alcohol	Methanol
Benzene	Ethyl acetate	Water	Pyruvic acid
Isopropyl chloride			

Bickoff[179] has classified a series of solvents based on their eluting power in 3% solution in light petroleum for β-carotene adsorbed on chalk (Table XIII). It is astonishing to see that methyl alcohol is classified as a weak eluant ($R_L = 25$) whereas ethyl alcohol is described as a strong eluant ($R_L = 93$). This fact has been repeatedly verified.

TABLE XIII

THE ELUTING POWER OF VARIOUS SOLVENTS IN 3% SOLUTION IN LIGHT PETROLEUM FOR β-CAROTENE ADSORBED ON CHALK (Bickoff[179])

Eluant	$R_L \times 100$	*Eluant*	$R_L \times 100$
CCl_4	20	Ethyl butyrate	56
n-Amyl ether	22	Butyl acetate	63
Tetrachloroethylene	23	Dioxane	64
Methanol	25	Anethole	65
Toluene	29	Ethyl acetate	67
Benzene	32	Acetone	68
Ethyl ether	33	Pyridine	72
Chloroform	35	Diacetone alcohol	74
Methylene chloride	38	Cetyl alcohol	77
Ethylene chloride	40	Acetophenone	79
Phenyl ether	42	Octanol	90
p-Cresyl methyl ether	44	Ethanol	93
sym.-Tetrachloroethane	45	Phenyl cellosolve*	95
Ethyl laurate	55	Butyl cellosolve**	95
		Methylcarbitol***	100

* $C_6H_5OCH_2CH_2OH$.
** $CH_3CH_2CH_2CH_2OCH_2CH_2OH$.
*** Diethylene glycol monomethyl ether.

It is clear that the classification of solvents on the basis of their eluting power has meaning only for a given system under the most precise conditions. The elution of organic acids adsorbed on alumina often necessitates the use of alcohol or ether containing 5 to 10% acetic acid or 5% potassium ethoxide. Appreciable amounts of aluminium acetate or other mineral salts are often found in the filtrates; these may be removed by taking up the residue in ether and washing the solution with water. The volume of each eluant should be at least double the weight of the adsorbent. In *liquid* or *flowing* chromatography elution should be continued with successive portions of solvent until only traces of substance are eluted.

(c) *Gradient elution*

In discussing column chromatography, Tiselius has said that "one of the most important practical problems of chromatography is to eliminate tailing as far as possible". One solution to the problem is *gradient elution*, which reduces tailing and thus improves the separation achieved. Tailing of bands is caused by the fact that under usual experimental conditions the adsorption isotherms are not linear, *i.e.* that the percentage of the substance which is adsorbed depends upon its concentration in solution. Most frequently adsorption increases strongly with dilution of the substance. With the usual form of

References p. 97

flowing chromatogram, where elution is obtained by a succession of different eluants with increasing eluting power, substances which trail on the column can be eluted partially with one solvent and then with the next one (Fig. 15).

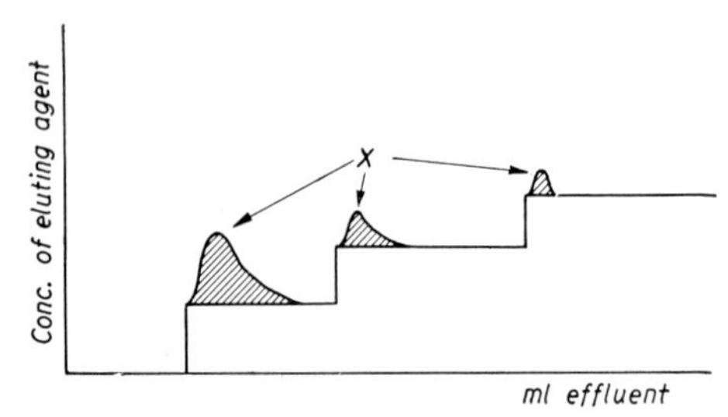

Fig. 15. Schematic representation of a stepwise elution experiment in which one substance occurs three times (Alm, Williams and Tiselius[312]).

If, however, during elution the composition of the eluting solvent is changed gradually in such a manner that the trailing end of the band comes in contact with a more strongly eluting solvent, trailing can be diminished.

When the equilibrium isotherm is linear, gradient elution may also be advantageous since an increase of the adsorbability at the front of a band and a corresponding decrease at the rear will sharpen the elution curves and change their shape from the Gauss type of curve to one with clear cut ends. Again the *right* gradient must be used, otherwise a band may either be cut in two or two components not resolved.

Fig. 16 shows the effect of the steepness of the eluting gradient; resolution of the two substances (dehydroisoandrosterone and androsterone) is improved by slowing down the gradient. With too slow a gradient, however, elution of the substances takes an unduly long time and they are eluted at very low concentrations, the elution curves being broadened out. Lakshmanan and Lieberman[313] point out that "a suitable concentration curve would be one in which the rate of increase of concentration was initially small and increased with time, a requirement satisfied by a concentration curve concave upward".

Fig. 17 shows the importance of using the proper gradient with the proper adsorbent; too weak an adsorbent gives no resolution. In certain cases, too steep a gradient may produce two peaks of one substance.

Devices for producing gradients are described by Alm *et al.*[312], Donaldson *et al.*[314], Mader[315], Bannister *et al.*[316], Bock and Ling[317], Lakshmanan and Lieberman[313], Boman[318] and Pontis and Blumson[319]. See Figs. 18a and b, also Cherkin *et al.*[320].

Busch *et al.*[321] have applied gradient elution for the separation of organic acids on Dowex-I columns and Donaldson *et al.*[314] separated organic acids on silica with a gradient. Tiselius *et al.*[291,312,322] have described the theory

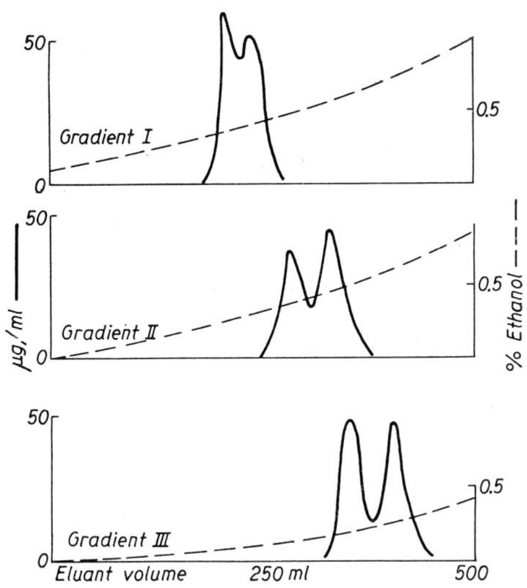

Fig. 16. Effect of variation in gradient on resolution (Lakshmanan and Lieberman[313]).

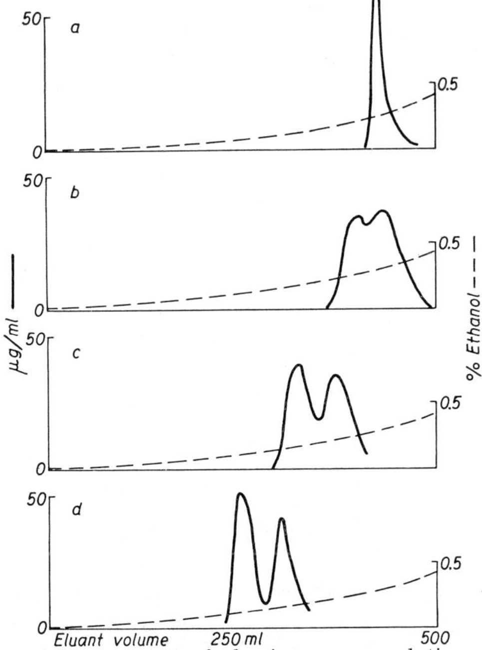

Fig. 17. Effect of moisture content of alumina upon resolution: (a) alumina dried *in vacuo* at 100°; (b) alumina dried *in vacuo* at 45°; (c) untreated alumina, moisture content about 3%; (d) alumina equilibrated over a saturated solution of $NaBr \cdot 2H_2O$, moisture content about 7.5%. Gradient same as III in Fig. 16 (Lakshmanan and Lieberman[313]).

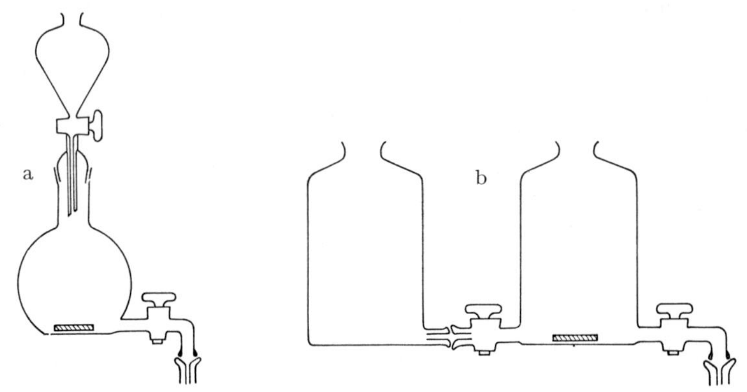

Fig. 18. (a) Apparatus for gradient elution, allowing an exponential increase of the eluting force. A flask fitted on a magnetic stirrer and containing the first solvent is surmounted by a separation funnel containing the second solvent. (b) Apparatus for gradient elution, allowing a linear increase of the eluting force. Two jars are connected at the bottom by a tube with a stopcock, the first one is mounted on a magnetic stirrer.

of the method in detail and its application to the separation of mixtures of amino acids, sugars and peptides. Alm[323] has described the gradient elution of oligosaccharides and Lakshmanan and Lieberman[313] the gradient elution of urinary ketosteroids. For gradient elution with ion exchange resins see also Freiling[324], Stein *et al.*[325] and Moore and Stein[326].

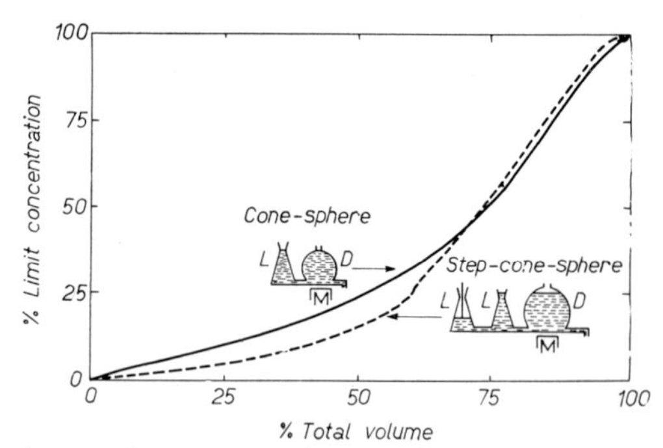

Fig. 19. Cone-sphere and step-cone-sphere gradients. L, represents the limit buffer; D, the dilute or starting buffer; M, a stirring device.

In their work on chromatography of proteins on cellulose ion exchangers, Sober and Peterson[327] first used a *cone-sphere* arrangement, "providing a gradient rising fairly rapidly for an initial period, then more slowly for a considerable distance and, finally, swinging upward towards the end, to sharpen the tail" (Fig. 19). Later this was modified, a *step-cone-sphere* being used, which gives a more gradual increase in concentration during the first half of the chromatogram, followed by a more rapid increase towards the end (Fig. 19). Later, Peterson and Sober[328] have used a mixing device called "Varigrad", which makes it possible to effect any desired adjustment in the gradient.

An apparatus used by Hirsch and Ahrens[329] for separation of complex lipid mixtures is shown in Fig. 20.

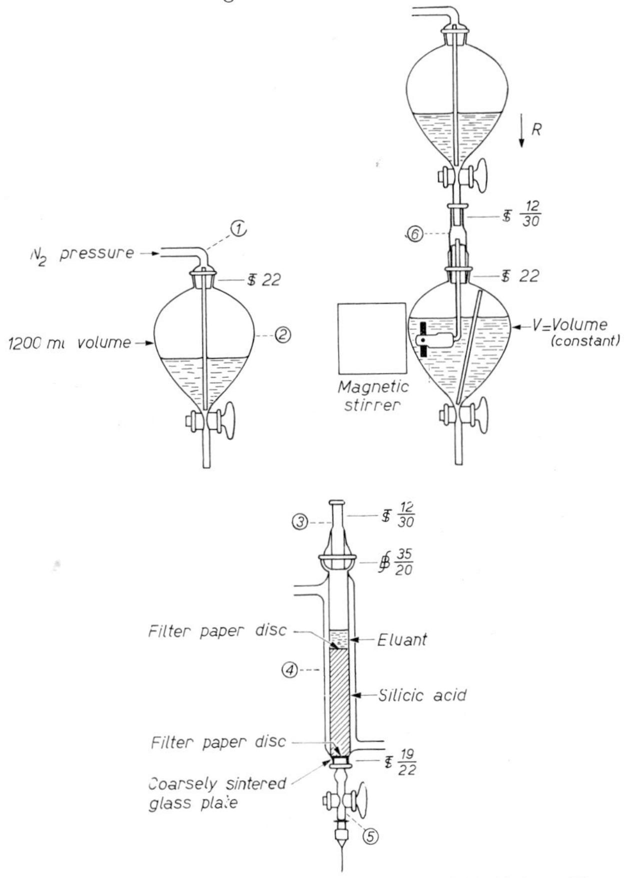

Fig. 20. Apparatus used for column chromatography with silicic acid consisting of a lower assembly and two types of upper assembly. Lower assembly: This shows the jacketed column and surrounding Pyrex parts. The top of this assembly fits into either type of upper assembly. Upper assemblies: The two arrangements shown here are for step-wise elution with a single flask (left) or for gradient elution with two flasks in tandem (right). All parts labeled by circled numbers are commercially available.

(d) *Elution curves*

Moore and Stein[330] have shown that it is often useful to analyse separate small fractions of the filtrate; in this way changes in the compo-

References p. 97

sition of the filtrate may be followed more easily and elution curves may be drawn (quantity of substance eluted as a function of the volume of eluant). These curves enable one to follow the behaviour of the substances to be separated and to judge the degree of separation obtained (see Figs. 16, 17). Quantitative results are obtained by measuring the area enclosed by the curves.

(e) *The description of chromatograms*

In the case of chromatography of pigments, it is useful to represent the appearance of a column after development by a drawing indicating the width of the bands and their colour (see Fig. 21). Bickoff[179] utilizes an excellent method of representing the separation of pigments as a function of the nature and quantity of the developing solvent (see Fig. 22).

Elution curves, tables or graphs[331] are also very useful.

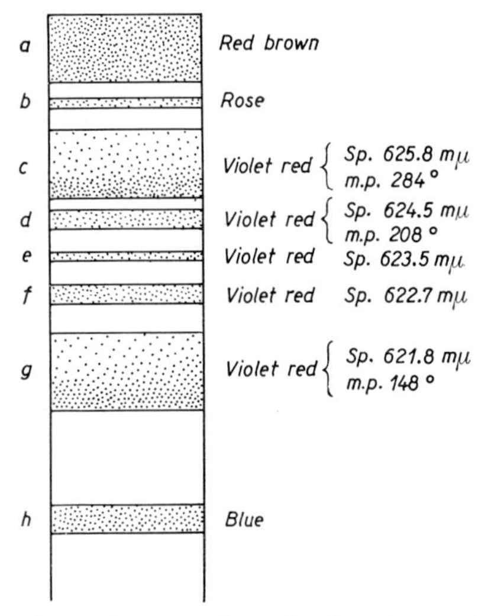

Fig. 21. Diagram of a chromatogram of porphyrin esters and other urine pigments (Grinstein *et al.*[331]).

5. Chemical constitution and chromatographic behaviour

(a) *General considerations*

The relationship between the chemical constitution of a substance and its behaviour on a chromatographic column depends on whether or not adsorption, partition or ion exchange are operating. It is more convenient to study each of these cases separately. It must be emphasized that it is not always easy in any given case to decide which of these phenomena is the most

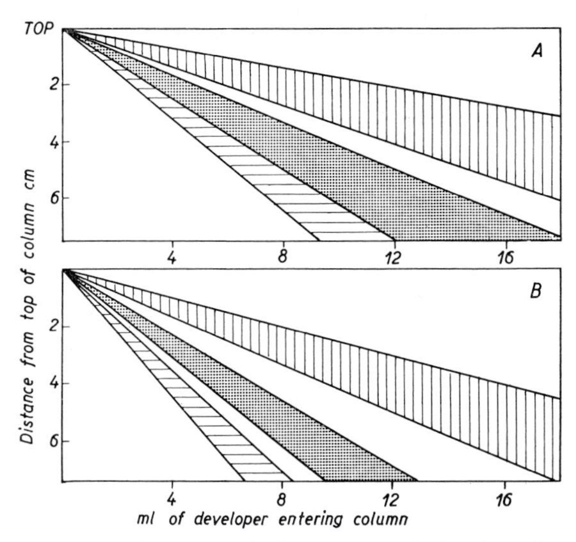

Fig. 22. Chromatogram (diagrammatically represented) showing effect of concentration of developer on resulting chromatogram. Developer: *p*-cresyl methyl ether dissolved in petroleum ether. Concentration of developers: A, 0%; B, 0.5%. Vertical hatching represents neo-β-carotene U; solid area, all *trans*; horizontal hatching, neo-β-carotene B zone (Bickoff[179]).

important. A great many cases of partition chromatography probably also involve adsorption; ion exchangers can function equally as adsorbents and this makes it more difficult to understand the mechanism of such separations.

The great majority of chromatographic separations carried out in organic media on carbon, alumina, calcium hydroxide, calcium carbonate, magnesia, silica gel, etc., as well as on charcoal in aqueous media, are due to true adsorption. It is necessary to distinguish between non-polar adsorbents (*e.g.* charcoal) where it is the undissociated molecule which is adsorbed (Kipling[332]) and adsorbents such as oxides and salts, where polar forces are acting between the solute and the adsorbent.

Many general rules concerning the position of organic substances on adsorption columns have been produced since the rebirth of Tswett's method in 1931. These were summarized in 1939 by one of the authors[103]. They concerned principally the role of double bonds and hydroxyl groups: the more double bonds and hydroxyl groups a molecule contains, the more strongly it is adsorbed. The carotenes arrange themselves on columns of alumina, calcium hydroxide, and magnesia following the number of double bonds; the xanthophylls (carotenols) follow the number of hydroxyl groups. Colour and adsorption are here functions of the same chemical structures, and run side by side. An aldehyde or a ketone is less adsorbed than the corresponding alcohol, esters are in general more adsorbed than hydrocarbons and less than ketones or aldehydes.

A rough classification is shown in the following list, the first members of which are the most strongly adsorbed, the latter members are the least strongly adsorbed:

acids and bases > alcohols, thiols > aldehydes, ketones > halogen containing substances, esters > unsaturated hydrocarbons > saturated hydrocarbons

A more detailed classification is possible for substances belonging to the same group or possessing the same carbon skeleton.

The effect of functional groups on adsorption affinity has been studied by Brockmann and Volpers[333] with a series of *p-substituted stilbenes* and *azobenzenes*. The compounds were adsorbed on alumina from benzene or carbon tetrachloride. These experiments lead to the sequence of functional groups (in order of decreasing adsorption affinity) shown in Table XIV. Compounds separated by a horizontal line could be separated, the others were not fully separable. It can be seen that the same order was found in both series.

Stewart[334] has found the following order of increasing adsorption, for *monosubstituted anthraquinones*: halogeno, nitro, arylamino, alkylamino, amino, acylamino, hydroxy group in the side chain, and hydroxy group attached to the nucleus. Adsorption generally increases with increasing number of substituent groups of the same type. The introduction of further groups of a different type may either increase or decrease the adsorption; thus methyl, halogeno and arylamino groups tend to decrease and amino, methoxy and hydroxy groups to increase the adsorption.

Hydrogen bonding diminishes adsorbability; thus Hoyer[335] has stated that 2-hydroxyanthraquinone is more strongly adsorbed on silica than 1,4,5-trihydroxy- or even 1,4,5,8-tetrahydroxyanthraquinone, the latter substances having their hydroxyl groups in positions where hydrogen bonding occurs.

Of the hydroxymethylanthraquinones shown in Fig. 23, the substances shown at the left side are less adsorbed on silica gel than the isomers at the right side (Hoyer[336]). Similar differences were also found for hydroxynitroanthraquinones, aminoanthraquinones and mercaptoanthraquinones (Hoyer[337–339]). Apparent exceptions observed with 1-nitro-2-amino- and 1-nitro-2-hydroxy-anthraquinones could be explained as the result of steric hindrance of the 1-nitro group (see also Franc[340]). Hydrogen bonding explains also, why 2-nitroresorcinol is less adsorbed (on silica) than *m*- or *p*-nitrophenol, and *o,o'*-dihydroxybenzophenone less adsorbed than *p*-hydroxybenzophenone. Ongley[341] has made similar observations with the hydroxybenzoic acids.

Hydrogen bonding can also have an influence on the eluting power of solvents (see p. 68).

TABLE XIV

FUNCTIONAL GROUPS IN ORDER OF DECREASING ADSORPTION AFFINITY

(Brockmann[231])

$R = C_6H_5$—CH=CH—C_6H_4—		$R = C_6H_5$—N=N—C_6H_4—	
R—COOH		R—COOH	
R—$CONH_2$			
R—OH		R—OH	
			R—NH—Ac
			R—O—Ac
R—NH_2		R—NH_2	
	R—NH—Ac		R—O—Bz
	R—O—Ac		
R—$COOCH_3$		R—$COOCH_3$	
R—$N(CH_3)_2$	R—O—Bz	R—$N(CH_3)_2$	
R—NO_2		R—NO_2	
R—OCH_3		R—OCH_3	
R—H		R—H	
(Ac = CH_3—CO—		Bz = C_6H_5—CO—)	

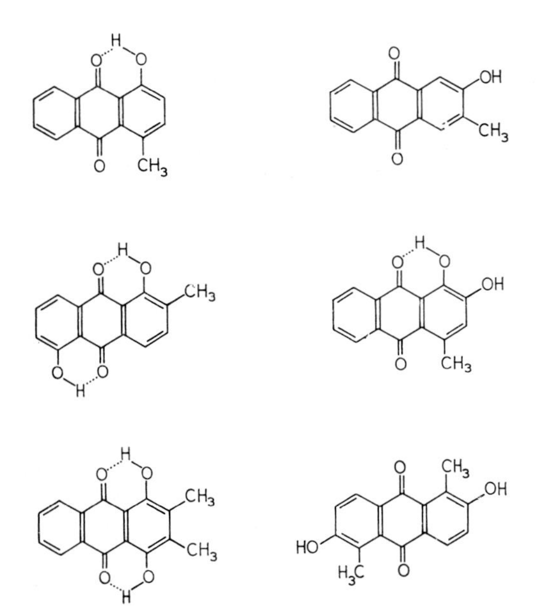

Fig. 23. Hydroxymethylanthraquinones: those on the left are less adsorbed on silica gel than those on the right (Hoyer[336]).

References p. 97

Strain[256] has made an interesting contribution to the problem of the relationship between the nature of the adsorbent and the chemical structure of the substance adsorbed. By studying the relative positions of seven carotenoids on *sucrose* columns he showed that sucrose has a much higher affinity for hydroxylgroups than for conjugated double bonds. Cryptoxanthin, with its unique hydroxyl group, is much more strongly adsorbed than lycopene which contains two more double bonds, or than rhodoxanthine which has two more carbonyl groups and one more double bond. Zeaxanthin and lutein, on the other hand, which differ only in the position of one double bond are almost inseparable on a column of sugar. *Magnesia,* on the contrary, exerts an attraction particularly for conjugated double bonds and less so for hydroxyl groups. A difference in position of one double bond allows an excellent separation of α- and β-carotenes and of zeaxanthin and lutein. Lycopene with 13 double bonds (of which 11 are conjugated) is more strongly adsorbed than zeaxanthin with 11 conjugated double bonds and two hydroxyl groups. Here the two isolated double bonds of lycopene exert a greater effect on adsorbability than the two hydroxyl groups of zeaxanthin (It is true that a rigorous comparison is not possible as lycopene is aliphatic and zeaxanthin is bicyclic.) The properties of Celite are intermediate between those of sugar and magnesia (Table XV).

The differences in adsorption observed by Strain[256] with different solvents, which affect particularly the relative position of rhodoxanthin, are explicable by the influence of polar solvents on the equilibrium between the ketonic and enolic forms of this pigment. These variations are paralleled by changes in the spectra of solutions of the pigments.

It is thus understandable that solvents which increase the proportion of groups for which the adsorbent has strong affinity increase also the adsorbability and *vice verca* (see also the section on *Elution,* p. 67).

In the steroid series detailed observations on the relation between chemical structure and adsorption affinity have been made by Lieberman *et al.*[172,174]. Table XVI (Lieberman *et al.*[172]) shows the elution order of sterols after chromatography on alumina. Lieberman *et al.*[174] have continued their study of the separation of urinary steroids and have indicated the following correlations between chemical constitution and relative order of elution during chromatography on alumina:

(1) "C_{21} pregnane derivatives are eluted before the corresponding C_{19} androstane derivatives."

(2) "Compounds with ring A–B having a *trans* juncture (androstane and allopregnane) are eluted before their corresponding isomers with rings A–B *cis* (etiocholane and pregnane). One exception to this rule has been noted: etiocholanol-3β-one-17 is eluted from alumina before androstanol-3α-one-17. This inversion in the expected sequence of elution may be a special case

TABLE XV

POSITION OF SEVEN CAROTENOIDS ON COLUMNS OF SUGAR, CELITE AND MAGNESIA (after Strain[256])

Sugar	*Celite*	*Magnesia*
{ Zeaxanthin	{ Zeaxanthin	Rhodoxanthin
{ Lutein	{ Lutein	Lycopene
Cryptoxanthin	Rhodoxanthin	Zeaxanthin
Rhodoxanthin	Cryptoxanthin	Lutein
{ Lycopene	{ Lycopene	Cryptoxanthin
{ β-Carotene	{ β-Carotene	β-Carotene
{ α-Carotene	{ α-Carotene	α-Carotene

Solvent: light petroleum with 4% to 25% of acetone; the most strongly adsorbed pigments are indicated at the top of the columns, the less adsorbed at the bottom. The brackets indicate pigments whose separation is not complete.

because these substances also differ in their configuration at C_3. The configuration of the 3-hydroxyl group seems to be more important in determining the chromatographic sequence than does the steric juncture of rings A and B."

(3) "Saturated compounds are eluted before their unsaturated analogues except in the case of etiocholanolone, which is eluted after $\Delta^{9,11}$-etiocholenolone. Δ^1-Androstenedione-3,17, as expected, is eluted after its saturated analogue androstanedione-3,17. The unsaturated Δ^1-compound (XI) precedes its Δ^4-isomer (XII) in the sequence of elution."

(4) "The diketomonohydroxy compounds are eluted before their corresponding dihydroxymonoketo compounds with the important exception that the dihydroxymonoketones having one hydroxyl group on C_{11} are eluted before those diketomonohydroxy compounds with one ketonic group on C_{11}."

"Thus, 11-hydroxyandrosterone and 11-hydroxy-etiocholanolone are eluted before their corresponding C_{11} carbonyl derivatives 11-keto-androsterone and 11-keto-etiocholanolone."

The reviews of Strain[104], Zechmeister and von Cholnoky[106], Saenz *et al.*[342–344] should be consulted for information on the influence of different substituents (—OH, NH_2, halogens, —SO_3H, etc.) on the adsorbability of organic dyestuffs.

Steric effects

Steric effects often play an important role in determining the degree of adsorption of a compound. Thus, for instance, the presence of a bulky substituent in *ortho* position to a phenolic hydroxyl may considerably diminish the adsorbability of a compound by blocking the approach of the —OH group to the surface of the adsorbent. The two following examples illustrate this effect:

TABLE XVI

ELUTION ORDER OF KETOSTEROIDS AFTER CHROMATOGRAPHY ON ALUMINA

(Lieberman *et al.*[172])

	Example
(1) Monoketones	I
(2) Monoketones containing one acetoxy group	II
(3) Diketones (*a*) of the allopregnane series	III
(*b*) of the pregnane series	IV
(*c*) of the androstane series	V
(*d*) of the etiocholane series	VI
(4) Mono-hydroxy-monoketones:	
(*a*) of the allopregnane series	VII
(*b*) of the pregnane series	VIII
(*c*) of the androstane series	IX
(*d*) of the etiocholane series	X

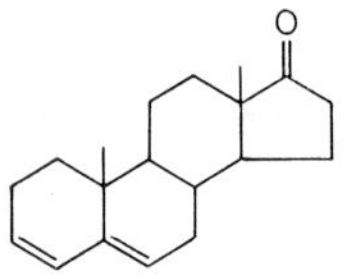

(I) 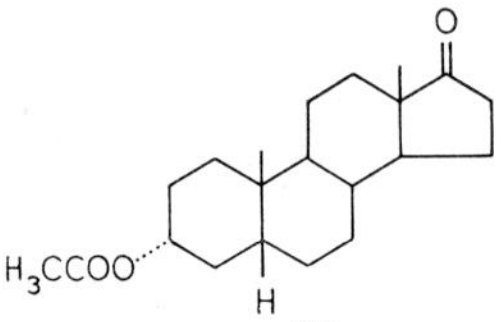 (II) 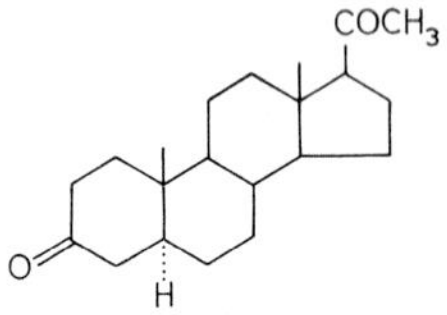 (III)

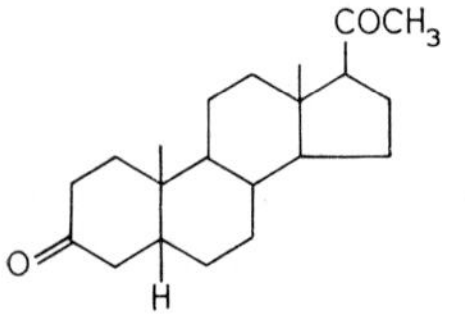

(IV) 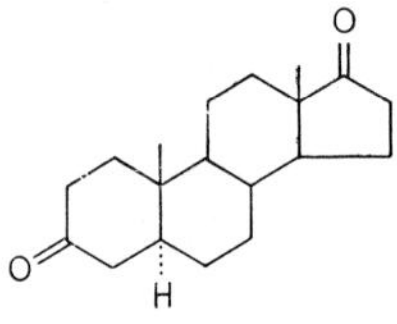 (V) 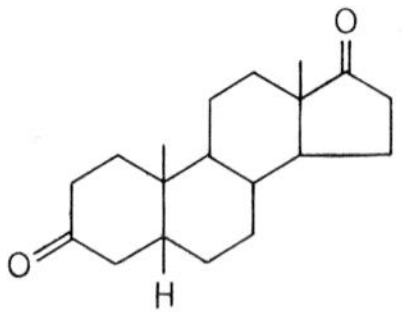 (VI)

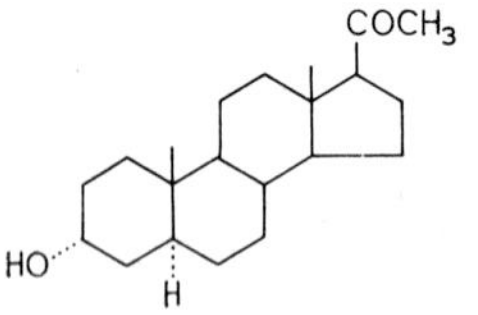

(VII) 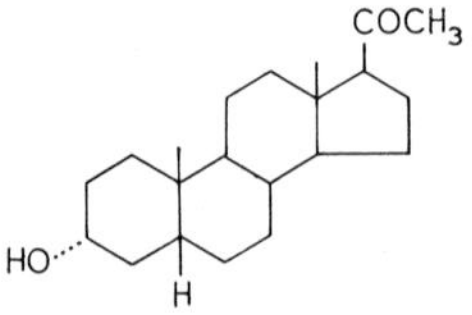 (VIII) 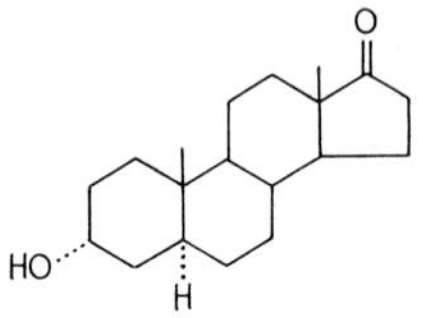 (IX)

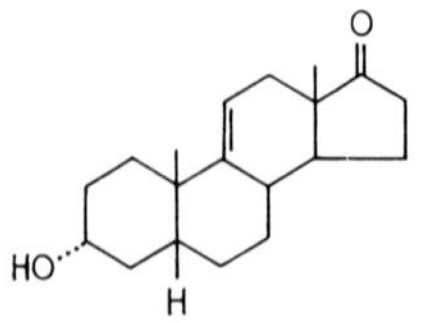

(X) 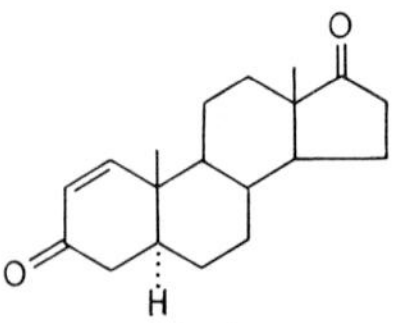 (XI) 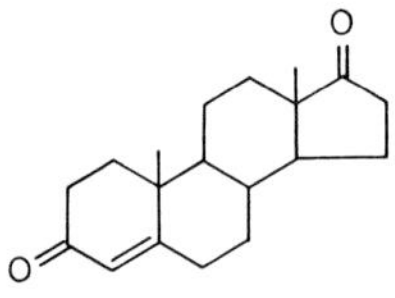 (XII)

(1) Kofler[160] has found that the adsorbability of the tocopherols on alumina increases in the series α-tocopherol (5,7,8-trimethyltocol) 5,7-dimethyltocol, β-tocopherol (5,8-dimethyltocol), γ-tocopherol (7,8-dimethyltocol) and δ-tocopherol, (8-methyltocol). It can be seen that, as expected, the mono-methyltocol is the most strongly adsorbed, the trimethyltocol, the least.

HO, 5, 6, 7, 8, O, CH_2, CH_2, C—$C_{16}H_{33}$, CH_3

Tocol

(2) Carlton and Bradbury[345] have measured the *R* values of the *ortho* and *para* isomers of methylphenol, ethyl phenol, isopropylphenol and *tert.*-butylphenol on silicic acid, with benzene as developer. It is seen that the adsorption affinity of the *ortho* isomer decreases with increasing size of the alkyl group, the effect of the *tert.*-butyl group being very pronounced. Thus the alkyl group in *ortho*-position gives rise to *R* values which are markedly greater than those observed for the *para*-isomer.

In certain cases the *form of the surface of the adsorbent* can explain differences in the behaviour of the substances to be adsorbed. Nederbragt and

TABLE XVII

R-VALUES OF ALKYL SUBSTITUTED PHENOLS (Carlton and Bradbury[345])

Type formula / *R*	OH, R (ortho)	OH, R (para)	OH, R, R (2,6)	OH, R, R (3,5)
Hydrogen	0.26	0.26	0.26	0.26
Methyl	0.37	0.28	0.55	0.28
Ethyl	0.43	0.30		
Isopropyl	0.52	0.30	0.95	
t-Butyl	0.74	0.31	1.00	
Cyclohexyl	0.49			

De Jong[346] have separated paraffins and alkyl-decahydronaphthalenes on floridin, the long chain paraffins being held back more than the saturated naphthalenes. The difference in adsorption can be explained by the existence of pores of diameter 4 × 6.5 Å in the surface of the adsorbant which allow entry only of the paraffins and not of the alkyl-decahydronaphthalenes.

Charcoal retains specifically those substances possessing an aromatic nucleus (Cassidy[347], Tiselius[16,59], Schramm and Primosigh[233], Fromageot *et al.*[211]). This is probably due to the already mentioned fact that the —C—C— spacings in graphite are of the same order as those in benzene.

In the purification of the *cord factor*, a glycolipide of molecular weight 3000 on silica gel Davison, it was observed that only about 20% of the compound was adsorbed, the greater part traversing the column rapidly. On rechromatography of this latter fraction, again about 20% was retained on the silica gel. This has been thought to be due to the large molecular weight of the lipid which can be adsorbed only by the largest pores of the adsorbent (Polonsky *et al.*[348]).

Coplanarity factors may play an important part in chromatographic adsorbabilities of conjugated isomeric biaryls and arylalkenes. Thus Orchin and Reggel[349-351], found that 2,2′-binaphthyl (effectively coplanar) was held more tenaciously than the more twisted 1,2′-binaphthyl. For mixtures of the geometric isomers of stilbene, 4,4′-dimethylstilbene, and 4,4′-dimethoxystilbene the coplanar *trans* form was adsorbed more strongly in every case. A mixture of the three possible 1,4-diphenylbutadienes, moreover, showed the order of adsorbability *trans-trans* (coplanar) > *trans-cis* > *cis-cis* (non-coplanar). Also indicative of such an effect are the findings of Orchin and coworkers that "adsorbabilities of certain conjugated iso-π-electronic (though not isomeric) aromatic hydrocarbons fall in the orders: fluoranthene > mixed 1- and 2-phenyl-naphthalenes > 1-phenylnaphthalene; benzofluoranthene > 1,2′-binaphthyl; and perylene > 1,1′-binaphthyl".

Klemm *et al.*[282] have studied the behaviour of isomeric α- and β-substituted naphthalenes bearing cyclohexenyl and cyclopentenyl groups. The more nearly coplanar β-substituted naphthalenes were adsorbed more tenaciously.

In the case of strongly polar substances like fatty acids the presence of one or more double bonds does not necessarily increase the adsorption, in fact the contrary is often true. We have already mentioned the important relation between boiling point and retention volume of members of homologous series found by Claesson[52] and extended by Hall and Tiselius[69] to isomeric members of series with the same functional group (see p. 37 and Table II). An example of the quantitative treatment of the relation between functional groups and adsorption has been given by LeRosen *et al.* (see p. 59).

The *separation of stereoisomers* is reviewed in detail by Lederer and Lederer (see ref. 1, Chapter 39) and by Jacques and Kogan (see ref. 2, Chapter 11).

(b) *The relative position of zones on a chromatographic column*

The adsorption of an organic substance is a function of its chemical structure, the nature of the adsorbent and of the solvent. Papers published in the years following 1931 allowed the determination of certain rules connecting adsorption and chemical constitution (the number of conjugated double bonds, the number of hydroxyl groups, etc.) and the classification of adsorbents and solvents in series on the basis of their adsorbing and eluting properties. It was supposed that in general the order of the zones of various substances was always the same.

Later on, however, a number of observations have accumulated to show that the order of zones can be varied with the adsorbent[178,352,353] or the solvent[342,344,354] used. Finally, Strain[355] gave a large number of examples of the change of zone order with small changes in the nature of the adsorbent, the composition of the solvent mixtures and also the temperature. The examples given by Strain[355] are as follows:

Solvent effects. In light petroleum or benzene, chlorophyll *b* forms a yellow-green band above the yellow band of neoxanthin (xanthophyll $C_{40}H_{56}O_4$) on Celite. After the addition of 25% of acetone to the light petroleum or benzene, chlorophyll *b* is adsorbed below neoxanthin. Fucoxanthin ($C_{40}H_{56}O_6$) is adsorbed above violaxanthin ($C_{40}H_{56}O_4$) on a sugar column with 1,2-dichloroethane as solvent. The order of the zones is inverted if light petroleum containing 0.5% of methanol or any other aliphatic alcohol is used.

Effect of impurities in the solvents. Traces of alcohol present in the solvents often change zone order. On sugar columns with light petroleum as solvent fucoxanthin is adsorbed below chlorophyll *a*; if 0.5% of amyl alcohol is added to the solvent, fucoxanthin is adsorbed above chlorophyll *a*. The same effect is observed if 0.1% cholesterol or ergosterol is dissolved in the light petroleum.

The use of different solvents in developing a chromatogram. On changing solvents in the course of development a change of zone is often observed. Lutein ($C_{40}H_{56}O_2$) with dichloroethane as solvent, forms a band below taraxanthin ($C_{40}H_{56}O_4$) on a column of magnesium oxide–Celite. On washing with light petroleum containing 25% of acetone, taraxanthin is displaced more rapidly than lutein and moves to a position below the lutein band.

pH effects. It is obvious that pH changes will exert a marked effect on the adsorption of polar substances in aqueous media. One example of inversion of zone order is given by Strain: bromothymol blue is adsorbed below fluorescein on cellulose columns in aqueous ammonia, but in neutral or acid solution bromothymol blue is adsorbed above fluorescein.

The effect of concentration changes. At very high concentrations most substances move more rapidly through the column than at low concentrations. For this reason, an increase in concentration of a strongly adsorbed substance (*e.g.* fluorescein) can accelerate the rate of movement of the zone to such an extent that it passes the zone of the second substance originally adsorbed further down the column (*e.g.* bromothymol blue).

Changes in the adsorbent. With dichloroethane as solvent and a mixture of magnesium oxide and Celite as adsorbent, zeaxanthin ($C_{40}H_{56}O_2$) is adsorbed above fucoxanthin ($C_{40}H_{56}O_6$); with sugar as the adsorbent zeaxanthin is

References p. 97

adsorbed below fucoxanthin. On Celite or magnesium silicate, bromothymol blue in ammoniacal solution is adsorbed above fluorescein; on Celite–magnesium oxide, cellulose or filter paper, bromothymol blue is less adsorbed than fluorescein.

The degree of hydration or the impurities present in the adsorbent can also cause changes in the relative positions of the zones.

Several differences in the order of elution concerning steroids[356] are shown in Table XVIII.

TABLE XVIII

Order of elution (→) *on*		
alumina		*magnesium silicate*
↓	3α-hydroxy-5α-androstan-11,17-dione	↑
	3α-hydroxy-5β-androstan-11,17-dione	
↓	3α-hydroxy-androst-5-en-17-one	↑
	3β-hydroxy-androst-5-en-17-one	
↓	3α,6α-dihydroxy-5α-pregnan-20-one	↑
	3α,6β-dihydroxy-5β-pregnan-20-one	

The relation between temperature and adsorption. On sugar columns, lutein is adsorbed below chlorophyll *a* at 95° in decalin containing 0.5% propanol, but at 20° under otherwise identical conditions, lutein is adsorbed above chlorophyll *a*.

The adsorption of mixtures. Table XIX (Strain[355]) shows six different results obtained by changing solvents and adsorbents with four substances (24 different results are theoretically possible with four components). Brockmann[231] has found different orders of adsorption of the azo-dyes he uses for standardization of alumina (see p. 85) on different adsorbents, such as SiO_2, MgO, $CaSO_4$ and $CuSO_4$. The adsorption sequence of acidic or basic dyes is influenced by the acidity or alkalinity of the adsorbent (Table XX). The order of these dyestuffs on alumina or $CaSO_4$ columns is also dependent on the solvent used (Brockmann[231]).

Double zoning. Usually, in chromatographic columns, each substance yields only one zone; Strain[357] has studied the conditions which may lead to the formation of two zones, by one single pigment, a phenomenon which is called "double zoning" and which has also been described by Schroeder[358]. Two zones were obtained by first adsorbing zeaxanthin on magnesia in presence of propylene glycol, a strongly adsorbed substance, and then washing the column with light petroleum containing 25% of acetone. Adsorption of an acetamide solution on a column of magnesia followed by adsorption of a solution of zeaxanthin also yielded two pigment zones. With

TABLE XIX

THE ZONE ORDER OF FOUR PIGMENTS AS A FUNCTION OF THE ADSORBENT AND THE SOLVENT

(Strain[355])

Adsorbent	*Sucrose*		*Magnesia + Celite (1:1)*		*Sucrose + Celite*	
Solvent	Light petroleum +		Light petroleum +		Light petroleum +	
	1% ethanol	5% acetone + 0.75% ethanol	3% ethanol	25% acetone	5% acetone + 0.5% ethanol	
Zone order	fucoxanthin	fucoxanthin	chlorophyll *b*		chlorophyll *b*	
	chlorophyll *b*	chlorophyll *b*	chlorophyll *a*		fucoxanthin	
	zeaxanthin	chlorophyll *a*	fucoxanthin	zeaxanthin	chlorophyll *a*	zeaxanthin
	chlorophyll *a*	zeaxanthin	zeaxanthin	fucoxanthin	zeaxanthin	chlorophyll *a*

weakly adsorbed contaminants, similar phenomena were observed.

When adsorbing xanthophylls from light petroleum on powdered sugar, very narrow bands of pigments of high concentration are formed; if one adds a small concentration of an eluant (0.5% *n*-propanol) then the pigment is eluted, but as it is only sparingly soluble in the surrounding solvent, the greater part precipitates, forming an upper dark band from which the descending solvent carries away continuously small fractions which will form a lower lighter band; on continuing the development, the upper band of precipitated pigment will dissolve entirely.

By adsorption of two xanthophylls from light petroleum containing a strongly adsorbed impurity, followed by adsorption of more of the pigment solution without impurity, Strain[357] obtained as many as three or four

TABLE XX

ADSORPTION SEQUENCE OF DYES AS INFLUENCED BY THE ADSORBENT

(Brockmann[231])

Alkaline Al_2O_3	*HCl treated Al_2O_3*
Hydroxyazobenzene	Hydroxyazobenzene
Aminoazobenzene	Sudan Red
Sudan Red	Aminoazobenzene
Sudan Yellow	Sudan Yellow
Methoxyazobenzene	Methoxyazobenzene
NaOH treated SiO_2	*HCl treated SiO_2*
Sudan Red	Sudan Red
Aminoazobenzene	Hydroxyazobenzene
Hydroxyazobenzene	Aminoazobenzene
Sudan Yellow	Sudan Yellow
Methoxyazobenzene	Methoxyazobenzene

Solvent: benzene–light petroleum 1:4

References p. 97

coloured zones. These experiments of Strain show the necessity of working under well-defined conditions and of using solutions of uniform composition.

See also the review of Keller and Giddings[357a] on "Multiple Zones and Spots in Chromatography".

(c) *The identification of substances by chromatography*

Strain[355] has emphasised the importance of his results for the chromatographic identification of chemical substances. Chromatographic homogeneity can only be proved when a number of adsorbents and solvents have been tried. It is clear that mixtures declared to be inseparable by chromatography could be dealt with by a judicious choice of solvent, adsorbent, concentration and temperature.

This applies equally to the identification of compounds by mixed chromatograms. It is often preferable to carry out this proof of identity with three columns run simultaneously (two columns for each of the separate substances and the third for the mixture)[359]. This is necessary because two different pigments are sometimes adsorbed in one apparently homogeneous zone at slightly different heights and with slightly different colours.

6. The chromatography of colourless substances

With colourless substances a number of possibilities present themselves:

(*1*) The column can be cut arbitrarily into a number of sections after development and each can be separately eluted.

(*2*) The column can be washed successively with a series of solvents of increasing eluting power. This is the most frequently adopted technique since its introduction by Reichstein[14,47,48]; it is usually described as a *liquid chromatogram* although this term is not very appropriate; *flowing chromatogram* is a better term. The series of solvents usually adopted for the chromatography of colourless substances of a lipid nature is given on p. 68.

(*3*) Various methods can be used to render the zones visible (see below).

Sometimes colourless substances give rise to visible zones. Waldschmidt-Leitz and Turba[360,361] obtained clear zones of peptides on acidic earths and Trappe[362] observed that lipids give rise to almost transparent zones on columns of silica gel. Bendall *et al.*[363] obtained visible brownish zones of glycine and creatinine on the synthetic resin Zeo Karb which is almost black.

(a) *Conversion into coloured derivatives*

(*i*) *Derivatives of alcohols*

In sugar chemistry, *p*-phenylazobenzoyl chloride, $C_6H_5N{=}NC_6H_4COCl$ has been used to obtain coloured esters. The same reagent transforms sterols into coloured esters which form coloured zones on chromatographic columns[364,365]. Bielenberg *et al.*[366,367] coupled phenols with diazotised *p*-nitroanilin, in order to separate chromatographically the derived coloured azo-compounds.

(ii) Derivatives of aldehydes and ketones

The chromatography of the 2,4-dinitrophenylhydrazones of aldehydes and ketones recommended by Strain[104] has been used by many workers and is reviewed in detail in the chapter on aldehydes and ketones[1].

(iii) Derivatives of acids

Silberman and Silberman-Martyncewa[368] describe the chromatographic separation of the bile acids after reaction of their salts with *p*-(ω-bromomethyl)-azobenzene $C_6H_5—N=N—C_6H_4—CH_2Br$. The esters form orange zones on magnesium carbonate.

(iv) Derivatives of nitrogenous substances

Karrer *et al.*[183] used *p*-phenyl-azobenzoyl chloride in order to prepare coloured N-acyl derivatives of amino acids. Their methyl esters are adsorbed on basic zinc carbonate, the coloured zones given by the derivatives of glycine, alanine, leucine, and valine were well separated. The N-(*p*-phenylazobenzene)-sulphonyl derivatives of amino acids, $R—CH(COOH)—NH—SO_2—C_6H_4—N=N—C_6H_5$, have been separated on alumina by Reich. Lemberg *et al.*[369,370] separate the aminobenzoic acids after diazotisation and coupling with dimethyl-α-naphthylamine.

Wieland *et al.*[371] and Karrer and Schmid[372] have separated the reineckates of the curare alkaloids.

(b) *The addition of coloured indicators*

Graff and Skau[168] coloured a column of heavy magnesia with phenol red as a means of following the separation of mixtures of long-chain fatty acids.

Criddle and LeTourneau[373] have described a fluorescent-indicator method for the determination of hydrocarbon types in petroleum; a sample containing traces of fluorescent dyes is chromatographed on silica gel, with alcohol as displacing agent. The components of the sample are aligned in the column on the basis of adsorbability: paraffins first, followed by olefins, aromatics and alcohol last. The boundaries between the zones are made visible in ultraviolet light by the fluorescent dyes, and the composition of the sample can be determined by measuring the zones, the lengths of which are proportional to the concentrations of the components of the sample. Ellis and LeTourneau[374] have employed a mixture of ordinary and fluorescent dyes as indicators for the determination of hydrocarbon types and

References p. 97

total oxygenated solvent content in lacquer thinners. The indicator chromatographic analysis of mixtures of simple organic compounds has also been studied by Knight and Groennings[311].

Trautner and Roberts[375] use dimethylaminoazobenzene as a coloured indicator in the separation of alkaloids on silica gel. The adsorbent is coloured red except in the positions in which the alkaloids are adsorbed.

Organic compounds which react with $FeCl_3$ to give coloured compounds can be made visible by first saturating the alumina with an ether solution of $FeCl_3$ (Valentin and Kirchübel[262]). See also Knight and Groennings[311].

(c) *Streaking techniques*

This method, proposed by Zechmeister *et al.*[376], consists in applying a thin streak of a convenient reagent, with a brush, down the length of the column after it has been extruded from the tube. Zechmeister and McNeely[377] used a solution of 1% $KMnO_4$ in the separation of *cis* and *trans* stilbenes; Wolfrom *et al.*[378,379] used the same solution in the separation of sugar acetates on magnesol; Lew *et al.*[380] used permanganate, pH indicators, and 2,6-dichlorophenol–indophenol with a series of derivatives of sugars. Bell[381] showed up the position of methylated sugars on a silica gel column by applying an alcoholic solution of α-naphthol followed by concentrated sulphuric acid (Molisch reaction).

As it is often difficult to extrude the column intact from its tube, Turkevich[382] has suggested carrying out the extrusion by applying air pressure to the bottom of the column. Lew *et al.*[383] have found that the use of aluminium tubes allows an easier extrusion of the columns. Georges *et al.*[108] use tapered glass tubes. LeRosen *et al.*[273,384] have tabulated a series of streak reagents which can be used for the detection of a wide variety of substances. Olefins are detected with permanganate, amines with a diazonium reagent or with bromine in carbon tetrachloride, ketones with 2,4-dinitrophenylhydrazine in HCl, etc. Further streak reagents are listed by LeRosen *et al.*[385].

(d) *Fluorescence*

Examination of the column with ultra-violet radiation suggested by Karrer and also by Winterstein (see [103,104,106]) allows the localisation of colourless substances. This technique has been used in the separation of methylglucoses[386], *p*-phenyl-phenacylates of fatty acids[387], alkaloids[388,389], the isolation of natural polyenes[390], vitamins A and D[264,391] and the estimation of vitamin E[392] and vitamin K[393]. See also Brumberg[394].

The preparation of fluorescent derivatives has not been studied systematically from the point of view of chromatography. The fluorescent hydrazine (9-hydrazino-acridine) prepared by Boxer and Jelinek[395] offers certain possibilities for the separation of colourless substances containing carbonyl groups.

Brockmann and Volpers[396] have separated colourless substances on alumina columns impregnated with a fluorescent material. The adsorption zones show up in monochromatic ultraviolet light as non-fluorescent bands against a brilliant background. The pentahydroxyflavone morin has been used to make alumina columns fluoresce (300 mg to 500 g of alumina), berberine for silica columns, and morin or diphenylfluorindene sulphonic acid for calcium carbonate or magnesia columns. As examples of separations carried out on alumina impregnated with morin, the following will suffice: the separation of the three synthetic musks (I, II, III) where, contrary to

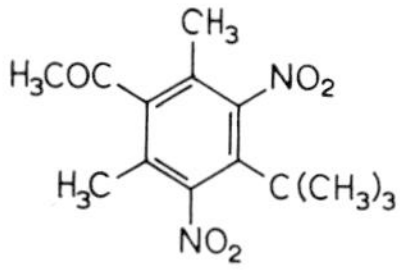

(I) 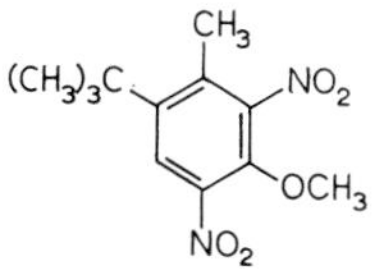 (II) 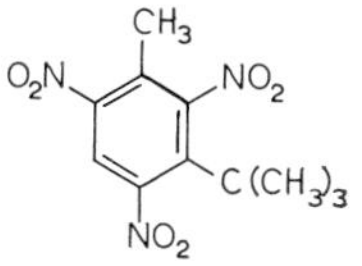 (III)

expectation, the trinitro compound is the least adsorbed; the purification of aromatic aldehydes (separation of vanillin and piperonal); the separation of β-ionone and pseudoionone, and also of phorone and mesityl oxide.

This method is only applicable to those unsaturated compounds which absorb ultraviolet light in the region causing fluorescence; it has been used by White and Dryden[397] for the separation of 3,5-dinitrobenzoates of aliphatic alcohols. Anet *et al.*[398] have used morine-coated alumina for the separation of two natural acetylene derivatives.

Sease[399] has described the use of silica gel mixed with 2.5% of fluorescent zinc sulphide. The wavelengths causing fluorescence lie between 330 and 390 mμ. Sease[400] has carried out the separation of many binary mixtures, *e.g.* azoxybenzene and nitrobenzene, *p*-nitrobenzoyl bromide and nitrobenzene, cinnamic and salicylic aldehydes, and nitrobenzene and iodoform. The zone order varies with different silica gels.

Brockmann and Volpers[333] later used alumina mixed with fluorescent zinc sulphide and have discussed in detail the mechanism of formation of dark zones. Quenching of fluorescence by the adsorbed substance seems to play an important part. For numerous examples of the use of this fluorescent alumina, see the original paper and [401].

Miller and Kirchner have separated terpenes on fluorescent *chromatobars* (see p. 37) obtained by incorporating 0.075% zinc cadmium sulphide and 0.075% zinc silicate in the adsorbent. The same authors have prepared fluorescent *chromatostrips* (see p. 43) for the separation of terpenes.

Fluorescent indicators are also used for the separation of hydrocarbon groups (paraffins, olefins, aromatics) (Criddle and LeTourneau[373]).

(e) *Other methods*

Claesson[56] has suggested a new method of revealing the position of colourless zones on a column by observation of the changes in refractive index of the solution along the length of the column.

The technique used by Tiselius in observing changes in refractive index of the column eluate has already been described (p. 36).

Sease[402] has described the location of colourless chromatographic zones with an ultraviolet sensitive multiplier phototube. Harvalik[403] has studied the illumination of columns with infrared radiation and has developed an electronic image converter to convert infrared radiation into visible light so that colourless zones can be detected by a process analogous to the use of ultraviolet fluorescence.

High frequency oscillations were used by Moseley *et al.*[404] to detect zones on a chromatogram.

7. Secondary reactions caused by the adsorbent

(a) *Alumina*

Alumina containing free alkali often gives rise to secondary reactions during the course of adsorption; for example the saponification of glycerides and the autoxidation of fatty acids[308], the deacetylation of acetylated sugars[405,406], the destruction of vitamin A[263], its transformation into an ether[407], the destruction of vitamin K[408], the decomposition of insecticides of the rotenone group[409,410], the hydration of porphyrins with a vinyl side chain[411] and the addition of CH_3OH to the same vinyl group in methanolic solution[411]. The alkali sensitive alkaloids of *Veratrum viride* are easily inactivated by alkaline alumina (Fried *et al.*[412]).

Prelog and Osgan[413] have observed the transformation of a monocyclic diketone to a bicylic hydroxyketone on contact with alumina. Pinckard *et al.*[414] have found that anthrone is oxidized to anthraquinone on some alumina columns. Schönberg *et al.*[415] explain the deep orange colour formed by addition of activated alumina to a colourless solution of 10-nitroanthrone by isomerisation to 10-nitroanthranol. Migrations of benzoyl groups have been observed in carbohydrate benzoates after chromatography on weakly alkaline alumina (Schmid and Bolliger[416]).

$$\begin{array}{rl} & CH{<}^{SC_2H_5}_{SC_2H_5} \\ & | \\ & |{-}OCOC_6H_5 \\ C_6H_5COO{-} & |{-}OCOC_6H_5 \\ & |{-}OCOC_6H_5 \\ & CH_2OH \end{array} \longrightarrow \begin{array}{rl} & CH{<}^{SC_2H_5}_{SC_2H_5} \\ & | \\ & |{-}OH \\ C_6H_5COO{-} & |{-}OCOC_6H_5 \\ & |{-}OCOC_6H_5 \\ & CH_2OCOC_6H_5 \end{array}$$

Mycobactin, a mycobacterial growth factor is converted to its crystalline aluminium complex by filtration on alumina columns and elution with alcohol (Francis *et al.*[417]).

Halogen derivatives of terpenes, especially tertiary halides are easily dehydrohalogenated on alkaline activated alumina; high yields of the original unsaturated hydrocarbons are obtained from the hydrohalides (Zaoral[418]). Oroshnik *et al.*[419] have observed a prototropic rearrangement of the acetylene $-C{\equiv}C-CH_2-\overset{|}{C}=$ to the allene $-C{=}C{=}C-\overset{|}{C}=$ through action of alcoholic alkali, alumina columns or florisil. Geissman *et al.*[420] have observed the elimination of one molecule of acetic acid from xanthinin

$$(-\overset{|}{C}{=}\overset{|}{C}-\underset{OCOCH_3}{\overset{|}{\underset{|}{C}}}-\overset{|}{C}H-\overset{|}{C}O)$$

to form xanthatin $(-\overset{|}{C}{=}\overset{|}{C}-\overset{|}{C}{=}\overset{|}{C}-\overset{|}{C}O)$, on columns of alumina. An analogous reaction caused by activated alumina has been reported by Hein[421].

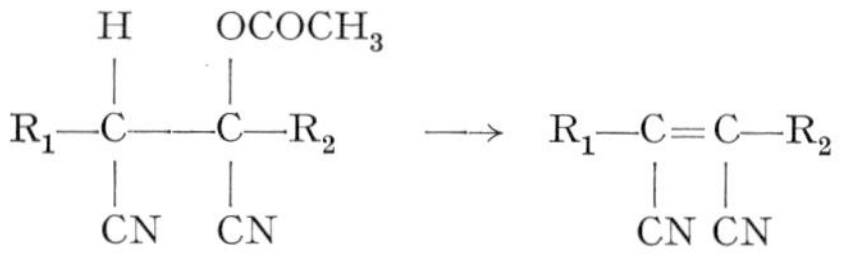

$$R_1-\underset{CN}{\underset{|}{\overset{H}{\overset{|}{C}}}}-\underset{CN}{\underset{|}{\overset{OCOCH_3}{\overset{|}{C}}}}-R_2 \longrightarrow R_1-\underset{CN}{\underset{|}{C}}{=}\underset{CN}{\underset{|}{C}}-R_2$$

The use of acetone as solvent with alumina columns should be avoided as it undergoes condensation reactions with the formation of oily products[422].

Stoll *et al.*[423] have observed the cyclisation of (A) to (B) by neutral alumina.

(A) (B)

Many interesting reactions produced by alumina have been reported in the *steroid* field, such as the saponification of steroid benzoates[424], the splitting out of a molecule of acetic acid from a sterol acetate with the formation of a double bond[425] (I → II), the debromination of steroids[426] (III → IV) and of lactones[427], the instability of an $\alpha\beta$-unsaturated ketosteroid[422]. Reichstein and Shoppee[107] report that Δ^5-3-ketones (V) undergo isomerisation to Δ^4-3-ketones (VI) by alumina containing alkali, but not when neutralised Al_2O_3 is employed (*cf.* Shoppee and Summers[428]).

References p. 97

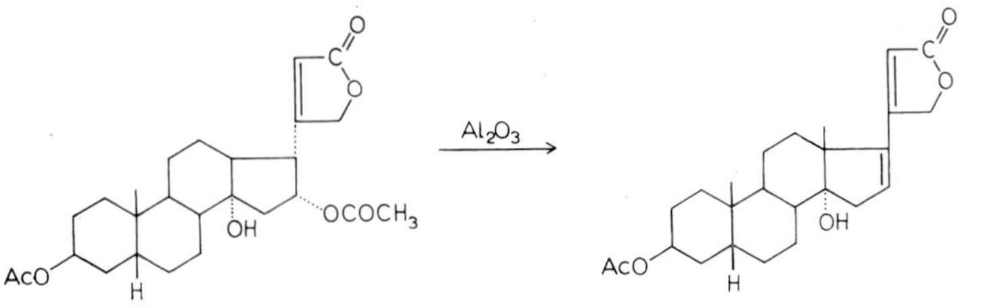

Al_2O_3

(I) (II)

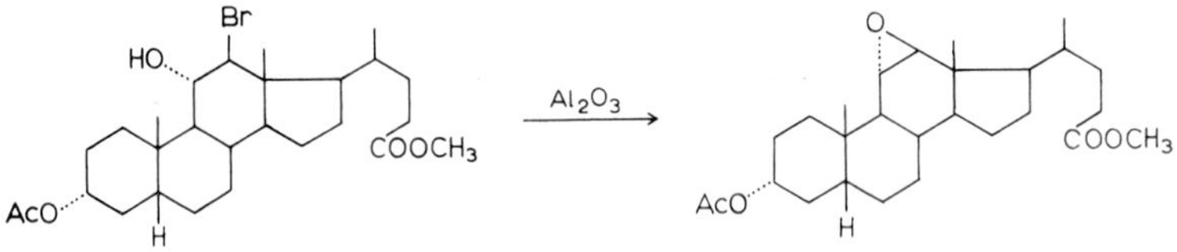

Al_2O_3

(III) (IV)

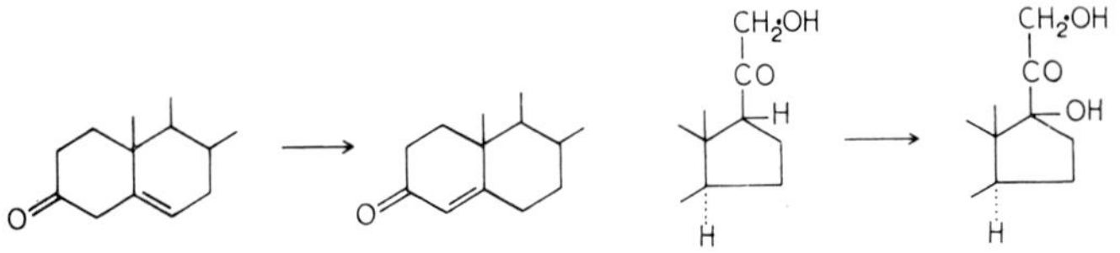

(V) (VI) (VII) (VIII)

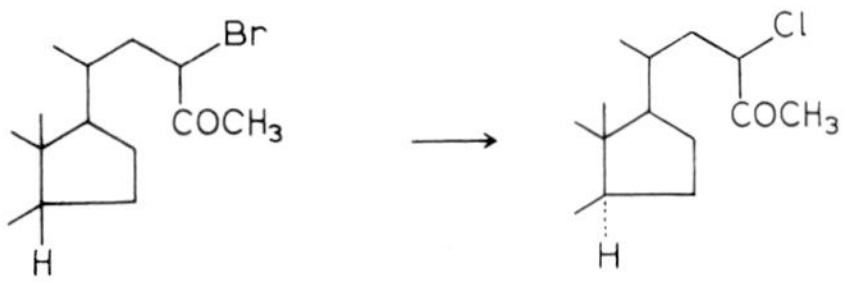

(IX) (X)

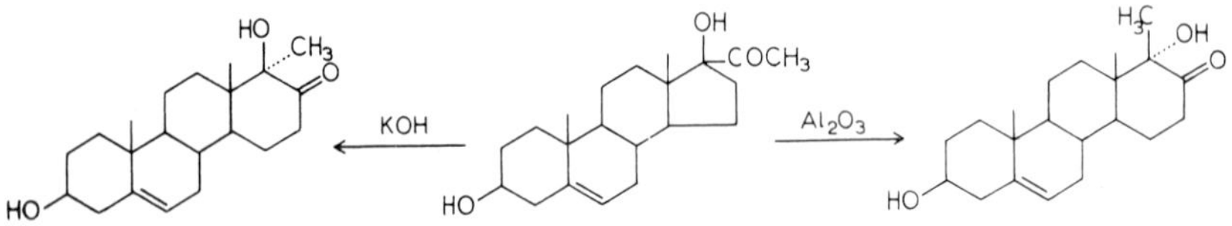

KOH Al_2O_3

(XIII) (XI) (XII)

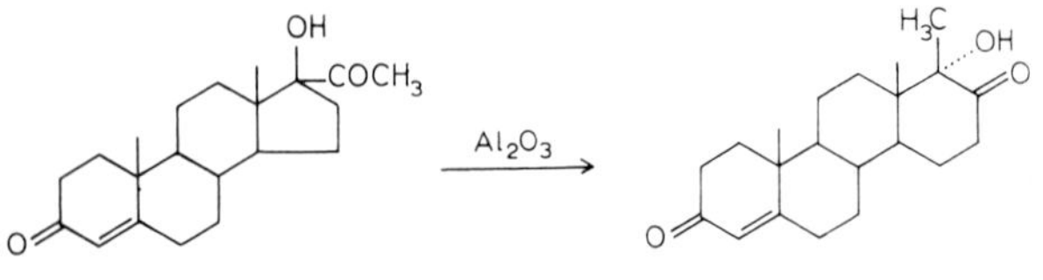

Al_2O_3

(XIV) (XV)

References p. 97

Fieser[429] observed a similar migration of the double bond with acid washed alumina. Elks *et al.*[430] found that the migration of the double bond of Δ^9-7-keto steroids to Δ^8-7-keto steroids can be avoided by treatment of the alumina with acetic acid and reactivation by heating.

There is often considerable loss with free hydroxy-ketones of the types (VII, VIII) which cannot be avoided completely by the use of neutralised alumina; it is best to chromatograph the 21-acetates (Reichstein and Shoppee[107]). The same authors report the substitution of Br by Cl on chromatographing the compound (IX) on alumina which had been neutralised by treatment with dilute HCl, then extensively washed with water.

Stavely[431] has described an interesting isomerisation caused by an alumina column: Δ^5-pregnenediol-3,17-one-20 (XI) gives the isomer (XII) having a hexacyclic D ring; an analogous compound (XIII) is produced by the action of KOH on (XI). 17(α)-Hydroxyprogesterone (XIV) undergoes the same isomerisation (to XV). Shoppee and Prins[432] confirmed these observations and noticed that the amount of isomerisation depended on the time of contact with the alumina.

Sarett[433] has observed two interesting reactions of the steroid cyanohydrin (XVI); when passed through an acid-washed alumina column the steroid was dehydrated to give an unsaturated nitrile (XVII) whereas a column of alkaline alumina caused the elimination of a molecule of HCN to regenerate the original ketone (XVIII) in 90% yield.

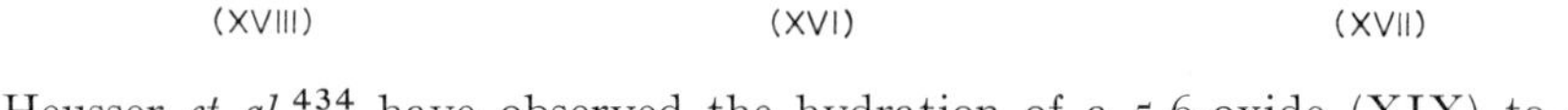

(XVIII) (XVI) (XVII)

Heusser *et al.*[434] have observed the hydration of a 5,6-oxide (XIX) to a 5,6-diol (XX) on alumina, Lieberman and Fukushima[173] report acyl migrations on chromatographing monoacetates of 3,4-diols on alumina (XXI → XXII) and the replacement of Br by OH in the allylic bromide (XXIII) (Fukushima *et al.*[435]). See also Keverling-Buisman *et al.*[436]. Sutton and Dutta[437] observed a similar instability of allylic bromides in the aliphatic series (a bromo-oleate being transformed into the corresponding ricinoleate). The same authors state that allyl bromide itself does not react with activated alumina at room temperature, but when they filtered a light petroleum solution of 3-bromocyclohexene through a column of alumina, the adsorbent became warm and turned blue.

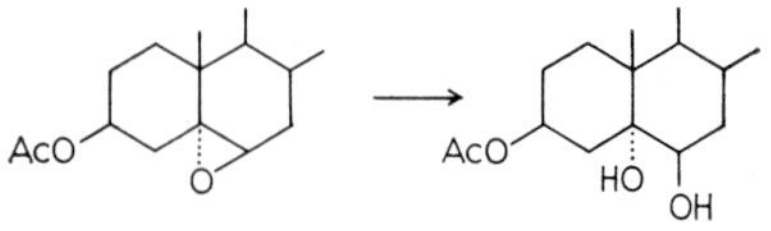

(XIX) (XX)

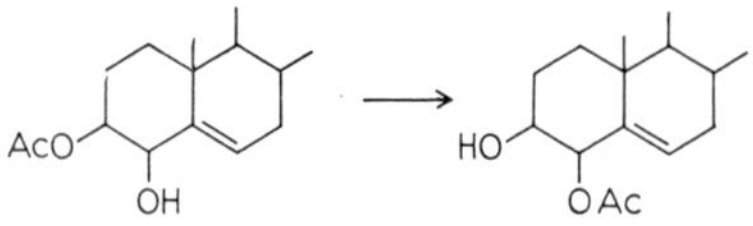

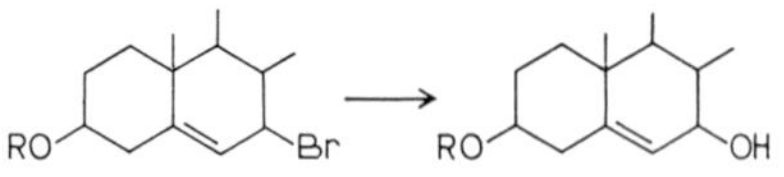

(XXI) (XXII) (XXIII) (XXIV)

Cremlyn and Shoppee[438] have reported that 7β-toluene-*p*-sulphonyloxy-cholestane (XXV) is partly decomposed by neutralised alumina in pentane to give cholest-7-ene (XXVI) whilst use of alkaline aluminium oxide in pentane furnished cholest-7-ene accompanied by cholesten-7α-ol (XXVII), the formation of which is due to a Walden inversion.

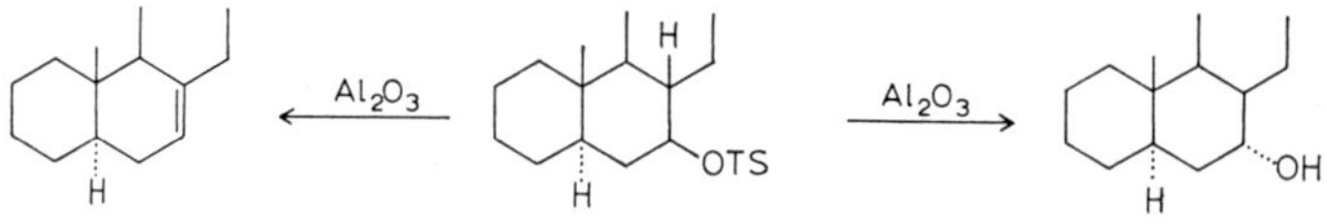

(XXVI) (XXV) (XXVII)

Fieser and Stevenson[439] have described an isomerisation of a 3-keto-4-acetate (XXVIII) to a 3-acetyl-4-keto steroid (XXIX)

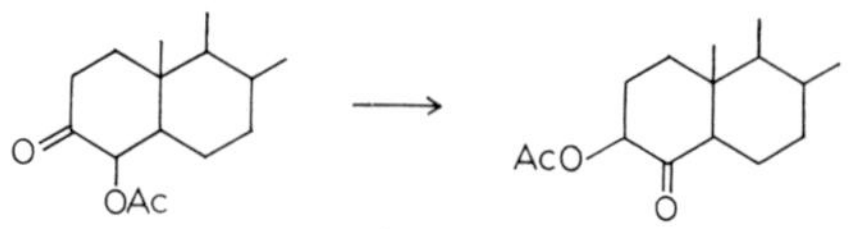

(XXVIII) (XXIX)

on alumina; a cyclic acetal is considered to be formed as intermediate compound.

Tosylates (toluene-*p*-sulphonates) of equatorial alcohols can be chromatographed on alumina to give a mixture of the epimeric axial alcohols and an olefin (Douglas *et al.*[440]). The proportion of axial alcohol to olefin varies with the type of alumina used. Acetylated cardiotonic glycosides are best chromatographed not on alumina, but on magnesium silicate to prevent loss of acetyl groups (Aebi, Schindler and Reichstein[175,176]). Cholesterol ozonide cannot be eluted from an alumina column[441].

Many of these secondary reactions on alumina can be prevented by removing the free alkali by washing first with acid and then with water, or simply by washing with water[150] (see also the section on alumina, p. 49).

Plattner and Pfau[442] have shown that *picrates* of aromatic hydrocarbons are dissociated when passed over alumina, the picric acid being retained at the top of the column while the hydrocarbons pass out in the eluate. This is a practical method for the decomposition of these picrates and is equally applicable to styphnates and trinitrobenzolates[443,444]. Picrates of alkaloids, however, are transformed into hydrochlorides if HCl activated alumina or Wofatit M/HCl are used (Karrer and Schmid[372]). In the same way Wieland *et al.*[371] transformed a β-anthraquinone sulphonate of a curare alkaloid into the hydrochloride by the use of HCl-activated alumina.

(*b*) *Silica and silicates*

Arbuzov and Isaeva[445] have reported isomerisation of terpene hydrocarbons by chromatography on silica gel.

Borgström[446] has observed the isomerisation of 2-monoglycerides to 1-monoglycerides during chromatography on silicic acid.

Sterols can undergo isomerisation on activated silica in the presence of halogenated solvents[362].

Mattox and Mason[447] reported that cortisone and hydrocortisone were unstable in presence of silica gel, adrenosterone and 11β-hydroxy Δ^4-androsterone-3,17-dione being, respectively, the major products formed. Other authors do not seem to have observed these side reactions (Neher[356]).

Soloway *et al.*[448] have observed the isomerisation of the steroid epoxide (XXX) to the methyl ketone (XXXI) by heat or chromatography on silica gel; Leeds *et al.*[449] have reported the analogous conversion of (XXXII) to (XXXIII) by heat or silica gel.

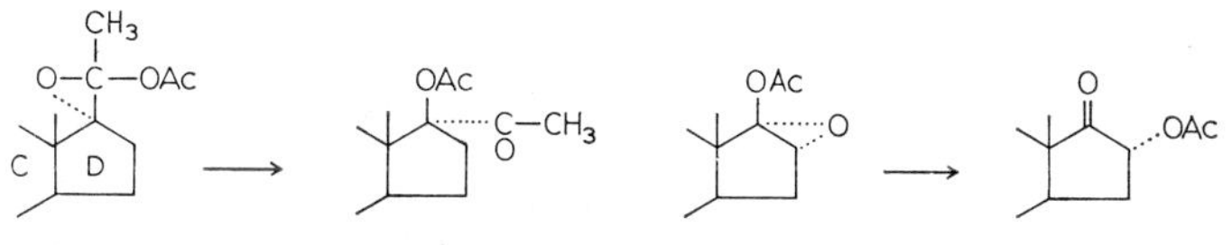

(XXX) → (XXXI)   (XXXII) → (XXXIII)

The acid earth adsorbents (Fuller's earth, Jagolite, Superfiltrol) with an incomplete electronic octet adsorb carotenoids and vitamin A to give a green or blue coloration. Meunier[450] has discussed the analogy between this phenomenon and the Carr-Price-reaction (see also Zechmeister and

Sandoval[451]). Meunier and Vinet[251] have treated in detail the theoretical aspects of the adsorption of mesomeric forms of vitamin A, β-carotene and vitamin D.

Talc can cause acetal formation of aldehydes of the porphyrin series in the presence of methanol (Fischer and Conrad[411]).

(*c*) *Manganous dioxide*

Wald[452] has described the "chromatographic oxidation" of vitamin A to retinene (—$CH_2OH \rightarrow$ —CHO) on a column of MnO_2. Meunier *et al.*[453] have described the oxidative fission of β-carotene and lycopene on MnO_2.

(*d*) *Charcoal*

Charcoal can cause aminolysis of amino acids and also complete oxidation to CO_2, H_2O and NH_3 (Wachtel and Cassidy[347]). These oxidations can be prevented by the use of small quantities of KCN or water saturated with H_2S (Tiselius[19]; Schramm and Primosigh[233]). Some losses are often inevitable in the course of elution of substances adsorbed on charcoal (Tiselius *et al.*[110]). See also the chapter on *modified adsorbents.*

Charcoal can lead to partial decomposition of steroids, especially those with a dioxyacetone side chain, thus, for example, cortisone yields adrenosterone (Levy and Kushinsky[454]).

Picrates of amino acids can be decomposed by adsorption on charcoal; the hydrochlorides are eluted by dilute HCl (Robson and Selim[455]). Picrates of bases, for instance indoles, can also be decomposed by chromatography on $CaSO_4$; Henbest *et al.*[456].

(*e*) *Polarisation by adsorbents*

Polarisation caused by adsorbents has been reported by Weitz *et al.*[457,458]; non-polar colourless substances such as triarylmethanes can be polarised on alumina or silica gel with the formation of coloured zones. By elution with polar solvents the colourless compounds can be recovered unchanged. This phenomenon has been also examined by Buu-Hoi and Cagniant[459], concerning triphenylmethane derivatives and by Cruse and Mittag[460,461] for di- and trinitrobenzene. Schönberg *et al.*[415] have described a series of anthrones, nitrotoluenes, spiropyranes and xanthydrols giving deeply coloured adsorbates with activated alumina or silica gel. In the case of the *adsorptiochromism* of hydroxynaphthoquinones described by Green and Dam[462] formation of an alkali salt could be a possible explanation.

REFERENCES

[1] E. LEDERER AND M. LEDERER, *Chromatography, a Review of Principles and Applications*, Elsevier, Amsterdam, 2nd ed., 1957, 711 pp.
[2] E. LEDERER (Ed.), *La chromatographie en chimie organique et biologique*, 2 Vol., Masson & Cie, Paris, 1959/1960, 671 and 900 pp.
[3] H. H. STRAIN, *Anal. Chem.*, 31 (1959) 818.
[4] M. LEDERER (Ed.), *Chromatographic Reviews*, Vols. I–IV, Elsevier, Amsterdam, 1959–1962.
[5] H. WEIL AND T. I. WILLIAMS, *Nature*, 166 (1950) 1000.
[6] H. WEIL AND T. I. WILLIAMS, *Nature*, 167 (1951) 906.
[7] J. FARRADANE, *Nature*, 167 (1951) 120.
[8] L. ZECHMEISTER, *Nature*, 167 (1951) 405.
[9] M. TSWETT, *Trav. soc. natl. Varsovie*, 14 (1903); *Ber. deut. botan. Ges.*, 24 (1906) 316–384; *Biochem. Z.*, 5 (1907) 6; *Chromofilli wrastitelnom i schivotnom mirje*, Warsaw (1910)
[10] M. S. TSWETT, *Chromatographic Adsorption Analysis*. Selected papers edited by A. A. RICHTER AND T. A. KRASNOSSELSKAJA, Academy of Sciences of the URSS. Press, 1946; see also *Michael Tswett's erste chromatographische Schrift* by G. HESSE AND H. WEIL, M. Woelm, Eschwege, Germany, 1954, 37 pp.
[11] C. DHÉRÉ, *Candollea, Genève*, 10 (1943) 23–73.
[12] L. ZECHMEISTER, *Isis*, 36 (1946) No. 104, 108; *C.A.*, 40 (1946) 2703–4.
[13] R. KUHN AND E. LEDERER, *Naturwiss.*, 19 (1931) 306; *Ber.*, 64 (1931) 1349.
[14] M. STEIGER AND T. REICHSTEIN, *Helv. Chim. Acta*, 21 (1938) 546.
[15] A. TISELIUS, *Arkiv Kemi, Mineral. Geol.*, 14B (1940) No. 22.
[16] A. TISELIUS, *Arkiv Kemi, Mineral. Geol.*, 14B (1941) No. 32; 15B (1942) No. 6: *C.A.*, 35 (1941) 5407-1; 36 (1942) 369-2.
[17] A. TISELIUS, *Science*, 94 (1941) 145.
[18] A. TISELIUS, *Advances in Colloid Sci.*, I (1941) 81; *C.A.*, 36 (1942) 3413–8.
[19] A. TISELIUS, *Kolloid-Z.*, 105 (1943) 101.
[20] A. TISELIUS, *Arkiv Kemi, Mineral. Geol.*, 16A (1943) No. 18; *C.A.*, 88 (1944) 2895–7.
[21] A. J. F. MARTIN AND R. L. M. SYNGE, *Biochem. J.*, 35 (1941) 1358.
[22] R. CONSDEN, A. H. GORDON AND A. J. P. MARTIN, *Biochem. J.*, 38 (1944) 224.
[23] A. T. JAMES AND A. J. P. MARTIN, *Biochem. J.*, 50 (1952) 679.
[24] J. N. WILSON, *J. Am. Chem. Soc.*, 62 (1940) 1583.
[25] D. DE VAULT, *J. Am. Chem. Soc.*, 65 (1943) 532.
[26] J. I. COATES AND E. GLUECKAUF, *J. Chem. Soc.*, (1947) 1302.
[27] E. GLUECKAUF, *Nature*, 155 (1945) 205; 156 (1945) 571.
[28] E. GLUECKAUF, *Nature*, 156 (1945) 748.
[29] E. GLUECKAUF, *Nature*, 160 (1947) 301.
[30] E. GLUECKAUF, *J. Chem. Soc.*, (1947) 1321.
[31] E. GLUECKAUF, *J. Chem. Soc.*, (1949) 3280.
[32] E. GLUECKAUF, *Discussions Faraday Soc.*, 7 (1949) 12.
[33] E. GLUECKAUF, *J. Am. Chem. Soc.*, 73 (1951) 849.
[34] A. C. OFFORD AND J. WEISS, *Discussions Faraday Soc.*, 7 (1949) 26.
[35] J. WEISS, *J. Chem. Soc.*, (1943) 297.
[36] G. E. BOYD, A. W. ADAMSON AND L. S. MYERS JR., *J. Am. Chem. Soc.*, 69 (1947) 2836.
[37] G. E. BOYD, L. S. MYERS JR. AND A. W. ADAMSON, *J. Am. Chem. Soc.*, 69 (1947) 2849.
[38] G. E. BOYD, J. SCHUBERT AND A. W. ADAMSON, *J. Am. Chem. Soc.*, 69 (1947) 2818.
[39] F. H. SPEDDING, E. I. FULMER, T. A. BUTLER, E. M. GLADROW, M. GOBUSH, P. E. PORTER, J. E. POWELL AND J. M. WRIGHT, *J. Am. Chem. Soc.*, 69 (1947) 2812.
[40] F. H. SPEDDING, A. F. VOIGT, E. M. GLADROW AND N. R. SLEIGHT, *J. Am. Chem. Soc.*, 69 (1947) 2777.
[41] F. H. SPEDDING, A. F. VOIGT, E. M. GLADROW N. R. SLEIGHT, J. E. POWELL, J. M. WRIGHT, T. A. BUTLER AND P. FIGARD, *J. Am. Chem. Soc.*, 69 (1947) 2786.
[42] E. R. TOMPKINS, *Anal. Chem.*, 22 (1950) 1352.
[43] E. R. TOMPKINS, J. X. KHYM AND W. E. COHN, *J. Am. Chem. Soc.*, 69 (1947) 2769.
[44] E. R. TOMPKINS AND S. W. MAYER, *J. Am. Chem. Soc.*, 69 (1947) 2859.

[45] M. Lederer, *Anal. Chim. Acta*, 2 (1948) 261.
[46] T. V. Arden, F. H. Burstall, G. R. Davies, J. A. Lewis and R. P. Linstead, *Nature*, 162 (1948) 691.
[47] T. Reichstein and J. van Euw, *Helv. Chim. Acta*, 21 (1938) 1197.
[48] T. Reichstein and C. Montigel, *Helv. Chim. Acta*, 22 (1939) 1212.
[49] S. Claesson, *Arkiv Kemi, Mineral. Geol.*, 15A (1941) No. 9.
[50] S. Claesson, *The Svedberg Memorial Volume*, (1944) 82: *C.A.*, 39 (1945) 842-g.
[51] S. Claesson, *Arkiv Kemi, Mineral. Geol.*, 20A (1945) No. 3.
[52] S. Claesson, *Arkiv Kemi, Mineral. Geol.*, 23A (1946) No. 1.
[53] S. Claesson, *Arkiv Kemi, Mineral. Geol.*, 24A (1946) No. 7.
[54] S. Claesson, *Rec. trav. chim.*, 65 (1946) 571.
[55] S. Claesson, *Arkiv Kemi, Mineral. Geol.*, 24A (1947) No. 16.
[56] S. Claesson, *Nature*, 159 (1947) 708.
[57] S. Claesson, *Ann. N.Y. Acad. Sci.*, 49 (1948) 183.
[58] S. Claesson, *Discussions Faraday Soc.*, 7 (1949) 34.
[59] A. Tiselius, *The Svedberg Memorial Volume*, (1945) 370: *C.A.*, 39 (1945) 1117–7.
[60] A. Tiselius, *Advances in Protein Chem.*, 3 (1947) 67.
[61] A. Tiselius, *Arkiv Kemi, Mineral. Geol.*, 26B (1948) No. 1: *C.A.*, 43 (1949) 1624-e.
[62] A. Tiselius and S. Claesson, *Arkiv. Kemi, Mineral. Geol.*, 15B (1942) No. 18: *C.A.*, 38 (1944) 35-b.
[63] H. Svensson, *Acta Chem. Scand.*, 4 (1950) 99; 1329.
[64] H. Svensson, *Acta Chem. Scand.*, 5 (1951) 72; 1301; 1410.
[65] H. Svensson and I. Brattsten, *Arkiv Kemi*, 1 (1949) 401.
[66] R. T. Holman, *Anal. Chem.*, 22 (1950) 832.
[67] N. Hellström and H. Borgiel, *Acta. Chem. Scand.*, 3 (1949) 403.
[68] A. Tiselius, *Advances in Protein Chem.*, 3 (1947) 67.
[69] D. A. Hall and A. Tiselius, *Acta Chem. Scand.*, 5 (1951) 854.
[70] A. J. P. Martin and R. L. M. Synge, *Advances in Protein Chem.*, 2 (1945) 1–83.
[71] R. T. Holman and L. Hagdahl, *Arch. Biochem.*, 17 (1948) 301.
[72] A. Tiselius, *Naturwiss.*, 37 (1950) 25.
[73] B. Drake, *Anal. Chim. Acta*, 3 (1949) 452.
[74] L. Hagdahl, *Acta Chem. Scand.*, 2 (1948) 574.
[75] L. Hagdahl, *Sci. Tools*, 1 (1954) 21: *C.A.*, 49 (1955) 5896-b.
[76] A. Wetterholm, *Harald Nordenson Anniv. Volume*, (1946) 460: *C.A.*, 43 (1949) 5325-d.
[77] R. T. Holman, *J. Am. Chem. Soc.*, 73 (1951) 3337.
[78] R. T. Holman and W. T. Williams, *J. Am. Chem. Soc.*, 73 (1951) 5285.
[79] C. H. Li, A. Tiselius, K. O. Pedersen, L. Hagdahl and H. Carstensen, *J. Biol. Chem.*, 190 (1951) 317.
[80] J. Porath and C. H. Li, *Biochim. Biophys. Acta*, 13 (1954) 268.
[81] A. Tiselius and L. Hagdahl, *Acta Chem. Scand.*, 4 (1950) 394.
[82] R. T. Holman, *J. Am. Chem. Soc.*, 73 (1951) 1261.
[83] F. E. Kurtz, *J. Am. Chem. Soc.*, 74 (1952) 1902.
[84] J. Porath, *Acta Chem. Scand.*, 6 (1952) 1237.
[85] C. H. Li, L. Ash and H. Papkoff, *J. Am. Chem. Soc.*, 74 (1952) 1923.
[86] H. Svensson, *Swed. Pat.*, 133,951: *C.A.*, 46 (1952) 4863-g.
[87] H. Svensson, C.-E. Agrell, S.-O. Dehlén and L. Hagdahl, *Sci. Tools*, 2 (1955) 17: *C.A.*, 49 (1955) 14389-e.
[88] J. Solms, *Helv. Chim. Acta*, 38 (1955) 1127.
[89] J. L. Olsen, *U.S. Pat.*, 2,564,717: *C.A.*, 45 (1951) 9312-g.
[90] L. F. Fieser, W.-Y. Huang and B. K. Bhattacharyya, *J. Org. Chem.*, 22 (1957) 1380.
[91] J. G. Kirchner, J. M. Miller and G. J. Keller, *Anal. Chem.*, 23 (1951) 420.
[92] J. M. Miller and J. G. Kirchner, *Anal. Chem.*, 26 (1954) 2002.
[93] R. H. Reitsema, *Anal. Chem.*, 26 (1954) 960.
[94] E. Demole and E. Lederer, *Bull. soc. chim. France*, (1958) 1128.
[95] E. Lederer, *Scand. J. Clin. & Lab. Invest.*, 10 (1957) Suppl. 31, 89.
[96] M. Barbier, *J. Chromatog.*, 2 (1959) 649.

[97] E. Demole, *J. Chromatog.*, 1 (1958) 24; 6 (1961) 2.
[98] E. Stahl, *Chemiker-Ztg.*, 82 (1958) 323: *C.A.*, (1959) 27-c.
[99] E. Stahl, *Die Pharmazie*, II (1956) 633; *Chemiker-Ztg.*, (1958) 323; *Angew. Chem.*, 73 (1961) 646.
[99a] E. G. Wollish, M. Schmall and M. Hawrylyshyn, *Anal. Chem.*, 33 (1961) 1138.
[100] J. W. Dieckert and R. Reiser, *J. Am. Oil Chemists' Soc.*, 33 (1956) 123.
[101] J. W. Dieckert and R. Reiser, *J. Am. Oil Chemists' Soc.*, 33 (1956) 535.
[102] J. W. Dieckert and N. J. Morris, *Anal. Chem.*, 29 (1957) 31.
[103] E. Lederer, *Bull. soc. chim. France*, [5] 6 (1939) 897.
[104] H. H. Strain, *Chromatographic Adsorption Analysis*, Interscience, New York, 1942.
[105] T. I. Williams, *An Introduction to Chromatography*, Blackie and Son, London, 1946, 100 pp.
[106] L. Zechmeister and L. von Cholnoky, *Principles and Practice of Chromatography*, 2nd Ed., Chapman and Hall, London; J. Wiley and Sons, New York, 1943.
[107] T. Reichstein and C. W. Shoppee, *Discussions Faraday Soc.*, 7 (1949) 305.
[108] L. W. Georges, R. S. Bower and M. L. Wolfrom, *J. Am. Chem. Soc.*, 68 (1946) 2169.
[109] H. Gault and C. Ronez, *Bull. soc. chim. France*, (1950) 597.
[110] A. Tiselius, B. Drake and L. Hagdahl, *Experientia*, 3 (1947) 21.
[111] T. H. S. Huisman and H. K. Prins, *Clin. Chim. Acta*, 2 (1957) 307.
[112] H. K. Prins, *J. Chromatog.*, 2 (1959) 445.
[113] J. M. Miller and J. G. Kirchner, *Anal. Chem.*, 23 (1951) 428.
[114] V. H. Booth, *Analyst*, 75 (1950) 109.
[115] D. F. Mowery Jr., *J. Am. Chem. Soc.*, 73 (1951) 5047.
[116] B. J. Mair, A. L. Gaboriault and F. D. Rossini, *Ind. Eng. Chem.*, 39 (1947) 1072.
[117] K. H. Meng, *Brit. Pat.*, (1949) 621,620: *C.A.*, 43 (1949) 6013-c.
[118] C. G. Lynam and H. Weil, *Ind. Chemist*, 26 (1950) 109: *C.A.*, 44 (1950) 5158-i.
[119] P. P. Hopf, *Ind. Eng. Chem.*, 39 (1947) 983.
[120] P. P. Hopf, C. G. Lynam and H. Weil, *Brit. Pat.*, (1947) 585,224: *C.A.*, 44 (1950) 3750-c.
[121] C. G. Lynam and H. Weil, *Mfg. Chemist*, 21 (1950) 195-9, 205: *C.A.*, 44 (1950) 7594-c.
[122] C. G. Lynam and H. Weil, *Mfg. Chemist*, 21 (1950) 228: *C.A.*, 44 (1950) 9590-e.
[123] R. Williams Jr. and J. V. Hightower, *Chem. Eng.*, 55 (1948) 133.
[124] W. H. Shearon and O. F. Gee, *Ind. Eng. Chem.*, 41 (1949) 218.
[125] T. I. Williams, *Mfg. Chemist*, 20 (1949) 16.
[126] H. Weil, *Chim. & ind. (Paris)*, 64 (1950) 432.
[127] E. A. Swinton and D. E. Weiss, *Australian J. Appl. Sci.*, 4 (1953) 316.
[128] D. E. Weiss, *Australian J. Appl. Sci.*, 4 (1953) 510.
[129] D. W. Minty, M. Ross and D. E. Weiss, *Australian J. Appl. Sci.*, 4 (1953) 519.
[130] D. W. Minty, R. McNeil, M. Ross, E. A. Swinton and D. E. Weiss, *Australian J. Appl. Sci.*, 4 (1953) 530.
[131] G. Moir, M. Ross and D. E. Weiss, *Australian J. Appl. Sci.*, 4 (1953) 543.
[132] S. G. Mokrushin, *Soobshcheniya Nauch. Rabot Vsesoyuz. Khim. Obshchestva im. Mendeleeva*, No. 2 (1953) 26: *C.A.*, 49 (1955) 2149-h.
[133] R. T. Holman and L. Hagdahl, *Anal. Chem.*, 23 (1951) 794.
[134] G. Kegeles and H. A. Sober, *Anal. Chem.*, 24 (1952) 654.
[135] R. A. Glenn, J. S. Wolfarth and C. W. DeWalt Jr., *Anal. Chem.*, 24 (1952) 1138.
[136] N. R. Trenner, C. V. Warren and S. L. Jones, *Anal. Chem.*, 25 (1953) 1685.
[137] H. McCormick, *Analyst*, 78 (1953) 562.
[138] N. Hellström, *Acta Chem. Scand.*, 7 (1953) 329.
[139] R. N. Jeffrey, *Anal. Chem.*, 23 (1951) 936.
[140] A. T. James, A. J. P. Martin and S. S. Randall, *Biochem. J.*, 49 (1951) 293.
[141] S. M. Partridge and R. G. Westall, *Biochem. J.*, 44 (1949) 418.
[142] C.-H. De Verdier and C. I. Sjöberg, *Acta Chem. Scand.*, 8 (1954) 1161.
[143] F. Turba and N. Heimburger, *Biochem. Z.*, 330 (1958) 359.
[144] M. Verzele, *Nature*, 183 (1959) 604.
[145] W. L. Porter, *Anal. Chem.*, 26 (1954) 439.
[146] G. Johansson, K. J. Karrman and A. Norman, *Anal. Chem.*, 30 (1958) 1397.
[147] J. E. S. Bradley, *Biochem. J.*, 56 (1954) xlviii.

[148] G. HESSE, I. DANIEL AND G. WOHLLEBEN, *Angew. Chem.*, 64 (1952) 103.
[149] G. SIEWERT AND H. JUNGNICKEL, *Ber.*, 76 (1943) 210.
[150] J. VON EULER, A. LARDON AND T. REICHSTEIN, *Helv. Chim. Acta*, 27 (1944) 1287.
[151] K. A. KRIEGER, *J. Am. Chem. Soc.*, 63 (1941) 2712.
[152] A. S. RUSSELL AND C. N. COCHRAN, *Ind. Eng. Chem.*, 42 (1950) 1336.
[153] M. JUTISZ AND S. TEICHNER, *Bull. soc. chim. France*, (1947) 389.
[154] G. DUPONT, R. DULOU AND M. VILKAS, *Bull. soc. chim. France*, (1948) 785.
[155] N. A. FUKS, *Zavodskaya Lab.*, 16 (1950) 878: *C.A.*, 45 (1951) 971-c.
[156] H. WISLICENUS, *Kolloid-Z.*, 100 (1942) 66.
[157] A. STEWART and Imp. Chem. Ind., *Brit. Pat.*, (1944) 565,405: *C.A.*, 40 (1946) 4490-2.
[158] F. KRCZIL, *Aktive Tonerde, ihre Herstellung und Anwendung*, Stuttgart, 1938.
[159] B. IMELIK, M. V. MATHIEU, M. PRETTRE AND S. TEICHNER, *J. chim. phys.*, 51 (1954) 651: *C.A.*, 49 (1955) 7324-f.
[160] M. KOFLER, *Helv. Chim. Acta*, 30 (1947) 1053.
[161] M. STOLL, *Helv. Chim. Acta*, 30 (1947) 991.
[162] R. KUHN AND T. WIELAND, *Ber.*, 73 (1940) 962.
[163] T. WIELAND, *Z. physiol. Chem.*, 273 (1942) 24.
[164] L. ZECHMEISTER, G. TÓTH AND E. VAJDA, *Enzymologia*, 7 (1939) 170: *C.A.*, 34 (1940) 1340-8.
[165] W. A. LALANDE Jr., *Ind. Eng. Chem.*, 33 (1941) 108.
[166] H. R. KRAYBILL, M. H. THORNTON AND K. E. ELDRIDGE, *Ind. Eng. Chem.*, 32 (1940) 1138.
[167] M. H. THORNTON, H. R. KRAYBILL AND F. K. BROOME, *J. Am. Chem. Soc.*, 63 (1941) 2079.
[168] M. M. GRAFF AND E. L. SKAU, *Ind. Eng. Chem., Anal. Ed.*, 15 (1943) 340.
[169] H. H. STRAIN AND W. M. MANNING, *J. Biol. Chem.*, 146 (1942) 275.
[170] G. S. FRAPS, A. R. KEMMERER AND S. M. GREENBERG, *Ind. Eng. Chem., Anal. Ed.*, 12 (1940) 16.
[171] G. H. COLEMAN, A. G. FARNHAM AND A. MILLER, *J. Am. Chem. Soc.*, 64 (1942) 1501.
[172] S. LIEBERMAN, K. DOBRINER, B. R. HILL, L. F. FIESER AND C. P. RHOADS, *J. Biol. Chem.*, 172 (1948) 263.
[173] S. LIEBERMAN AND D. K. FUKUSHIMA, *J. Am. Chem. Soc.*, 72 (1950) 5211.
[174] S. LIEBERMAN, D. K. FUKUSHIMA AND K. DOBRINER, *J. Biol. Chem.*, 182 (1950) 299.
[175] A. AEBI AND T. REICHSTEIN, *Helv. Chim. Acta*, 33 (1950) 1013.
[176] O. SCHINDLER AND T. REICHSTEIN, *Helv. Chim. Acta*, 34 (1951) 18.
[177] M. L. WOLFROM, A. THOMPSON, T. T. GALKOWSKI AND E. J. QUINN, *Anal. Chem.*, 24 (1952) 1670.
[178] A. L. LEROSEN, *J. Am. Chem. Soc.*, 64 (1942) 1905.
[179] E. M. BICKOFF, *Anal. Chem.*, 20 (1948) 51.
[180] P. KARRER AND E. JUCKER, *Helv. Chim. Acta*, 28 (1945) 300; 471.
[181] P. KARRER AND E. JUCKER, *Helv. Chim. Acta*, 28 (1945) 717.
[182] P. KARRER AND E. JUCKER, *Carotenoids*, Elsevier, Amsterdam, 1950.
[183] P. KARRER, R. KELLER AND G. SZÖNYI, *Helv. Chim. Acta*, 26 (1943) 38.
[184] N. HALFTER, *Z. ges. Schiess. u. Sprengstoffw.*, 38 (1943) 173: *C.A.*, 39 (1945) 3671-i.
[185] L. ZECHMEISTER, *Progress in Chromatography, 1938–1947*, Chapman and Hall, London, 1950, 368 pp.
[186] R. KUHN AND K. WALLENFELS, *Ber.*, 72 (1939) 1407.
[187] E. LEDERER, *Biochim. Biophys. Acta*, 9 (1952) 92.
[188] E. LEDERER AND R. GLASER, *Compt. rend.*, 207 (1938) 454.
[189] E. LEDERER, *Compt. rend.*, 209 (1939) 528.
[190] J. STOLKOWSKI, *Compt. rend.*, 225 (1947) 312.
[191] M. MATHIEU, *Bull. soc. chim. France*, (1947) 14.
[192] L. A. MOORE, *Ind. Eng. Chem., Anal. Ed.*, 14 (1942) 707.
[193] J. B. SUMMER, A. L. DOUNCE AND V. L. FRAMPTON, *J. Biol. Chem.*, 136 (1940) 343.
[194] S. M. SWINGLE AND A. TISELIUS, *Biochem. J.*, 48 (1951) 171.
[195] O. GLEMSER AND G. RIECK, *Naturwiss.*, 45 (1958) 569.
[196] O. GLEMSER, G. RIECK AND H. L. ACKNER, *Chem. Ber.*, 92 (1959) 662.
[197] A. TISELIUS, *Gazz. chim. ital.*, 84 (1954) 1177: *C.A.*, 49 (1955) 9052-f.

[198] A. TISELIUS, *Angew. Chem.*, 67 (1955) 245.
[199] A. TISELIUS, *Ann. Acad. Sci. Fennicae*, Ser. A.II, 60 (1955) 257.
[200] H. BROCKMANN AND K. MÜLLER, *Ann.*, 540 (1939) 51.
[201] H. BROCKMANN, F. POHL, K. MAIER AND M. N. HASCHAD, *Ann.*, 553 (1942) 1.
[202] P. KARRER AND C. H. EUGSTER, *Helv. Chim. Acta*, 33 (1950) 1172.
[203] P. KARRER, E. JUCKER, J. RUTSCHMANN AND K. STEINLIN, *Helv. Chim. Acta*, 28 (1945) 1146.
[204] R. BRETSCHNEIDER, *Monatsh. Chem.*, 74 (1941) 53.
[205] H. P. KAUFMANN, *Fette u. Seifen*, 46 (1939) 268; 47 (1940) 460.
[206] H. P. KAUFMANN, *Angew. Chem.*, 53 (1940) 98.
[207] H. P. KAUFMANN AND P. KIRSCH, *Fette u. Seifen*, 49 (1942) 841.
[208] H. NOLL, H. BLOCH, J. ASSELINEAU AND E. LEDERER, *Biochim. Biophys. Acta*, 20 (1956) 299.
[209] J. K. MERTZWEILLER, D. M. CARNEY AND F. F. FARLEY, *J. Am. Chem. Soc.*, 65 (1943) 2367.
[210] W. S. REICH, *Biochem. J.*, 33 (1939) 1000.
[211] C. FROMAGEOT, M. JUTISZ AND E. LEDERER, *Biochim. Biophys. Acta*, 2 (1948) 487.
[212] G. SCHRAMM AND J. PRIMOSIGH, *Ber.*, 77 (1944) 417.
[213] L. KH. FREĬDLIN, L. F. VERESHCHAGIN, I. E. NEĬMARK, I. U. NUMANOV AND R. YU. SHEĬNFAĬN, *Izvest. Akad. Nauk. S.S.S.R, Otdel Khim. Nauk*, (1953) 945: *C.A.*, 48 (1954) 4929-f.
[214] I. E. NEĬMARK, I. B. SLINYAKOVA AND F. I. KHATSET, *Akad. Nauk S.S.S.R., Otdel Khim. Nauk*, (1950) 98: *C.A.*, 46 (1954) 2442-g.
[215] W. STÖBER, G. BAUER AND K. THOMAS, *Ann. Chem., Liebigs*, 604 (1957) 104.
[216] A. V. KISELEV, *Doklady Akad. Nauk S.S.S.R.*, 106 (1956) 1046.
[217] A. H. GORDON, A. J. P. MARTIN AND R. L. M. SYNGE, *Biochem. J.*, 37 (1943) 79.
[218] R. HARRIS AND A. N. WICK, *Ind. Eng. Chem., Anal. Ed.*, 18 (1946) 276.
[219] F. A. ISHERWOOD, *Biochem. J.*, 40 (1946) 688.
[220] G. R. TRISTRAM, *Biochem. J.*, 40 (1946) 721.
[221] Y. CARTERET, *J. chim. phys.*, 51 (1954) 625: *C.A.*, (1955) 7324-e.
[222] K. N. TRUEBLOOD AND E. W. MALMBERG, *J. Am. Chem. Soc.*, 72 (1950) 4112.
[223] L. M. KAY AND K. N. TRUEBLOOD, *Anal. Chem.*, 26 (1954) 1566.
[224] E. W. MALMBERG, *Anal. Chem.*, 27 (1955) 840.
[225] C. L. MANTELL, *Adsorption*, McGraw-Hill, New York, 1945.
[226] M. S. BERGDOLL AND D. M. DOTY, *Ind. Eng. Chem., Anal. Ed.*, 18 (1946) 600.
[227] F. TURBA, *Ber.*, 74 (1941) 1829.
[228] H. S. FORREST AND H. K. MITCHELL, *J. Am. Chem. Soc.*, 76 (1954) 5656.
[229] D. T. EWING, T. D. SCHLABACH, M. J. POWELL, J. W. VAITKUS AND O. D. BIRD, *Anal. Chem.*, 26 (1954) 1406.
[230] J. W. WHITE JR., *Anal. Chem.*, 20 (1948) 726.
[231] H. BROCKMANN, *Discussions Faraday Soc.*, 7 (1949) 58.
[232] E. R. COOK, S. R. STITCH, A. E. HALL AND M. P. FELDMAN, *Analyst*, 79 (1954) 24.
[233] G. SCHRAMM AND J. PRIMOSIGH, *Ber.*, 76 (1943) 373.
[234] H. G. CASSIDY, *J. Am. Chem. Soc.*, 62 (1940) 3073; 3076.
[235] H. G. CASSIDY AND S. E. WOOD, *J. Am. Chem. Soc.*, 63 (1941) 2628.
[236] J. ENGLISH JR., *J. Am. Chem. Soc.*, 63 (1941) 941.
[237] H. G. CASSIDY, *J. Am. Chem. Soc.*, 63 (1941) 2735.
[238] J. CASON AND G. A. GILLIES, *J. Org. Chem.*, 20 (1955) 419.
[239] D. E. WEISS, *Nature*, 162 (1948) 372.
[240] D. E. WEISS, *Discussions Faraday Soc.*, 7 (1949) 142.
[241] D. E. WEISS, *Nature*, 166 (1950) 66.
[242] P. H. EMMETT, *Chem. Revs.*, 43 (1948) 69.
[243] W. M. MANNING AND H. H. STRAIN, *J. Biol. Chem.*, 151 (1943) 1.
[244] H. H. STRAIN AND W. M. MANNING, *J. Biol. Chem.*, 144 (1942) 625.
[245] H. H. STRAIN, W. M. MANNING AND G. HARDIN, *J. Biol. Chem.*, 148 (1943) 655.
[246] V. CARELLI, A. M. LIQUORI AND A. MELE, *Nature*, 176 (1955) 70.
[247] R. NEU, *Nature*, 182 (1958) 660.

[248] H. Hörmann and H. von Portatius, *Z. physiol. Chem., Hoppe-Seyler's*, 315 (1959) 141.
[249] J. K. Carlton and W. C. Bradbury, *Anal. Chem.*, 27 (1955) 67.
[250] V. R. Deitz, *Ann. N.Y. Acad. Sci.*, 49 (1948) 315.
[251] P. Meunier and A. Vinet, *Chromatographie et Mésomérie*, Masson & Cie, Paris, 1947, 126 pp.
[252] J. D. Roberts and C. Green, *Ind. Eng. Chem., Anal. Ed.*, 18 (1946) 335.
[253] J. B. Wilkes, *Ind. Eng. Chem., Anal. Ed.*, 18 (1946) 329.
[254] H. Clauser and C. H. Li, *J. Am. Chem. Soc.*, 76 (1954) 4337.
[255] V. T. Riley, *Science*, 107 (1948) 573.
[256] H. H. Strain, *J. Am. Chem. Soc.*, 70 (1948) 588.
[257] J. B. Wilkes, *Ind. Eng. Chem., Anal. Ed.*, 18 (1946) 702.
[258] A. J. P. Martin, *Biochem. Soc. Symposia (Cambridge, Engl.)*, No. 3 (1949) 4.
[259] H. Brockmann and H. Schodder, *Ber.*, 74 (1941) 73.
[260] R. A. Boissonnas, *Helv. Chim. Acta*, 30 (1947) 1689.
[261] G. Boutillon and M. Prettre, *Compt. rend.*, 240 (1955) 1216.
[262] J. Valentin and G. Kirchübel, *Arch. Pharm.*, 284 (1951) 114: *C.A.*, 45 (1951) 10488-e.
[263] P. B. Müller, *Helv. Chim. Acta*, 26 (1943) 1945.
[264] P. B. Müller, *Helv. Chim. Acta*, 27 (1944) 443.
[265] P. B. Müller, *Helv. Chim. Acta*, 30 (1947) 1172.
[266] M. Kofler, *Helv. Chim. Acta*, 28 (1945) 702.
[267] J. B. Wilkie and S. W. Jones, *Anal. Chem.*, 24 (1952) 1409.
[268] N. C. Sen Gupta and A. Gupta, *Sci. and Culture (Calcutta)*, 17 (1951) 265: *C.A.*, 46 (1952) 10049-f.
[269] K. J. Keuning, G. J. van Dijk and M. J. Wiggers de Vries, *Rec. trav. chim.*, 76 (1957) 747: *C.A.*, (1958) 11158-b.
[270] A. L. LeRosen, J. K. Carlton and P. B. Moseley, *Anal. Chem.*, 25 (1953) 666.
[271] A. L. LeRosen, *J. Am. Chem. Soc.*, 67 (1945) 1683.
[272] A. L. LeRosen, *J. Am. Chem. Soc.*, 69 (1947) 87.
[273] A. L. LeRosen and G. A. Rivet, *Anal. Chem.*, 20 (1948) 1093.
[274] A. L. LeRosen, P. H. Monaghan, C. A. Rivet and E. D. Smith, *Proc. Louisiana Acad. Sci.*, 12 (1951) 99.
[275] A. L. LeRosen, P. H. Monaghan, C. A. Rivet and E. D. Smith, *Anal. Chem.*, 23 (1951) 730.
[276] A. H. Sporer and K. N. Trueblood, *J. Chromatog.*, 2 (1959) 499.
[277] F. H. Dickey, *Proc. Natl. Acad. Sci. U.S.*, 35 (1949) 229.
[278] S. A. Bernhard, *J. Am. Chem. Soc.*, 74 (1952) 4946.
[279] F. H. Dickey, *J. Phys. Chem.*, 59 (1955) 695.
[280] R. Curti and U. Colombo, *J. Am. Chem. Soc.*, 74 (1952) 3961.
[281] M. Godlewicz, *Nature*, 164 (1949) 1132.
[282] L. H. Klemm, D. Reed and C. D. Lind, *J. Org. Chem.*, 22 (1957) 739.
[283] J. Cason, G. Sumrell, C. F. Allen, G. A. Gillies and S. Elberg, *J. Biol. Chem.*, 205 (1953) 435.
[284] G. L. Brown and M. Watson, *Nature*, 172 (1953) 339.
[285] D. J. D. Hockenhull and D. Herbert, *Biochem. J.*, 39 (1945) 102.
[286] D. French and D. W. Knapp, *J. Biol. Chem.*, 187 (1950) 463.
[287] L. S. Lerman, *Nature*, 172 (1953) 635.
[288] J. M. Ghuysen, *Compt. rend. soc. biol.*, 146 (1952) 1812.
[289] L. S. Lerman, *Proc. Natl. Acad. Sci. U.S.*, 39 (1953) 232: *C.A.*, 47 (1953) 8167-h.
[290] R. L. M. Synge and A. Tiselius, *Acta Chem. Scand.*, 3 (1949) 231.
[291] L. Hagdahl, R. J. P. Williams and A. Tiselius, *Arkiv Kemi*, 4 (1952) 193.
[292] R. J. P. Williams, L. Hagdahl and A. Tiselius, *Arkiv Kemi*, 7 (1954) 1.
[293] J. Porath, *Arkiv Kemi*, 7 (1954) 535.
[294] A. Asatoor and C. E. Dalgliesh, *J. Chem. Soc.*, (1956) 2291.
[295] C. C. Shepard and A. Tiselius, *Discussions Faraday Soc.*, 7 (1949) 275.
[296] H. K. Mitchell, M. Gordon and F. A. Haskins, *J. Biol. Chem.*, 180 (1949) 1071.

[297] M. G. Kritsman and M. B. Lebedeva, *Ukrain. Biokhim. Zhur.*, 22 (1950) 430: *C.A.* 48 (1954) 2159-g.
[298] H. Brandenberger, *Helv. Chim. Acta*, 37 (1954) 97.
[299] S. Schwimmer, *Nature*, 171 (1953) 442.
[300] V. T. Riley, *J. Natl. Cancer Inst.*, II (1950) 199: *C.A.*, 45 (1951) 3019-i.
[301] V. T. Riley, *J. Natl. Cancer Inst.*, II (1950) 215: *C.A.*, 45 (1951) 3019-d.
[302] V. T. Riley and M. W. Woods, *Proc. Soc. Exptl. Biol. Med.*, 73 (1950) 92.
[303] V. T. Riley, M. L. Hesselbach, S. Fiala, M. W. Woods and D. Burk, *Science*, 109 (1949) 361.
[304] H. Leyon, *Arkiv Kemi*, 1 (1949) 313.
[305] C. C. Shepard, *J. Immunol.*, 68 (1952) 179.
[306] P. Å. Albertsson, *Nature*, 177 (1956) 771.
[307] W. Dasler and C. D. Bauer, *Ind. Eng. Chem., Anal. Ed.*, 18 (1946) 52.
[308] W. Trappe, *Biochem. Z.*, 305 (1940) 150.
[309] J. Jacques and J. P. Mathieu, *Bull. soc. chim. France*, (1946) 94.
[310] P. B. Moseley, A. L. LeRosen and J. K. Carlton, *Anal. Chem.*, 26 (1954) 1563.
[311] H. S. Knight and S. Groennings, *Anal. Chem.*, 26 (1954) 1549.
[312] R. S. Alm, R. J. P. Williams and A. Tiselius, *Acta Chem. Scand.*, 6 (1952) 1826.
[313] T. K. Lakshmanan and S. Lieberman, *Arch. Biochem. Biophys.*, 53 (1954) 258.
[314] K. O. Donaldson, V. J Tulane and L. M. Marshall, *Anal. Chem.*, 24 (1952) 185.
[315] C. Mader, *Anal. Chem.*, 26 (1954) 566.
[316] D. W. Bannister, C. S. G. Philips and R. J. P. Williams, *Anal. Chem.*, 26 (1954) 1451.
[317] R. M. Bock and N.-S. Ling, *Anal. Chem.*, 26 (1954) 1543.
[318] H. G. Boman, *Biochim. Biophys. Acta*, 16 (1955) 245.
[319] H. C. Pontis and N. L. Blumson, *Biochim. Biophys. Acta*, 27 (1958) 3618.
[320] A. Cherkin, F. E. Martinez and M. S. Dunn, *J. Am. Chem. Soc.*, 75 (1953) 1244.
[321] H. Busch, R. B. Hurlbert and V. R. Potter, *J. Biol. Chem.*, 196 (1952) 717.
[322] A. Tiselius, *Endeavour*, II (1952) 5.
[323] R. S. Alm, *Acta Chem. Scand.*, 6 (1952) 1186.
[324] E. C. Freiling, *J. Am. Chem. Soc.*, 77 (1955) 2067.
[325] W. H. Stein, A. C. Paladini, C. H. W. Hirs and S. Moore, *J. Am. Chem. Soc.*, 76 (1954) 2848.
[326] S. Moore and W. H. Stein, *J. Biol. Chem.*, 211 (1954) 893.
[327] H. A. Sober and E. A. Peterson, *Chromatography of Protein and Nucleic Acids* in C. Calmon and T. R. E. Kressman, *Ion-exchangers in Organic Chemistry and Biochemistry*, Interscience, New York, 1957, 761 pp.
[328] H. A. Sober and E. A. Peterson, *Federation Proc.*, 17 (1958) 1116.
[329] J. Hirsch and E. H. Ahrens, *J. Biol. Chem.*, 233 (1958) 311.
[330] S. Moore and W. H. Stein, *Ann. N.Y. Acad. Sci.*, 49 (1948) 265.
[331] M. Grinstein, S. Schwartz and C. J. Watson, *J. Biol. Chem.*, 157 (1945) 323.
[321] D. H. R. Barton and E. Miller, *J. Chem. Soc.*, (1949) 337.
[332] J. J. Kipling, *J. Chem. Soc.*, (1948) 1487.
[333] H. Brockmann and F. Volpers, *Chem. Ber.*, 82 (1949) 95.
[334] A. Stewart, *Discussions Faraday Soc.*, 7 (1949) 65.
[335] H. Hoyer, *Kolloid-Z.*, 116 (1950) 121.
[336] H. Hoyer, *Chem. Ber.*, 86 (1953) 1016.
[337] H. Hoyer, *Kolloid-Z.*, 121 (1951) 121: *C.A.*, 45 (1951) 6528-e.
[338] H. Hoyer, *Kolloid-Z.*, 122 (1951) 142: *C.A.*, 45 (1951) 8848-b.
[339] H. Hoyer, *Z. Elektrochem.*, 54 (1950) 413.
[340] J. Franc, *Collection Czechoslov. Chem. Communs.*, 24 (1959) 250.
[341] P. A. Ongley, *J. Chem. Soc.*, (1954) 3634.
[342] I. Saenz-Lascaño-Ruiz, *Ind. parfum.*, 1 (1946) 187: *C.A.*, 42 (1948) 5675-c.
[343] I. Saenz-Lascaño-Ruiz, P. Chovin and H. Moureu, *Bull. soc. chim. France*, (1946) 592.
[344] I. Saenz-Lascaño-Ruiz, P. Chovin and H. Moureu, *La séparation chromatographique des colorants alimentaires et son application à la détection des fraudes*, Actualités scientifiques et industrielles, No. 1046, Hermann et Cie, Paris, 1948, 59 pp.

[345] J. K. Carlton and W. C. Bradbury, *J. Am. Chem. Soc.*, 78 (1956) 1069.
[346] G. W. Nederbragt and J. J. De Jong, *Rec. trav. chim.*, 65 (1946) 831.
[347] J. L. Wachtel and H. G. Cassidy, *J. Am. Chem. Soc.*, 65 (1943) 665.
[348] J. Polonsky, G. Ferréol, R. Toubiana and E. Lederer, *Bull. soc. chim. France*, (1956) 1471.
[349] M. Orchin and L. Reggel, *J. Am. Chem. Soc.*, 69 (1947) 505.
[350] M. Orchin and L. Reggel, *J. Am. Chem. Soc.*, 68 (1946) 573.
[351] M. Orchin and L. Reggel, *J. Am. Chem. Soc.*, 73 (1951) 436.
[352] R. Duschinsky and E. Lederer, *Bull. soc. chim. biol.*, 17 (1935) 1534.
[353] H. H. Strain, *J. Phys. Chem.*, 46 (1942) 1151.
[354] K. A. Williams, *Analyst*, 71 (1946) 259.
[355] H. H. Strain, *Ind. Eng. Chem., Anal. Ed.*, 18 (1946) 605.
[356] R. Neher, in M. Lederer (Ed)., *Chromatog. Revs.*, 1 (1959) 99–192.
[357] H. H. Strain, *Ind. Eng. Chem.*, 42 (1950) 1307.
[357a] R. A. Keller and J. C. Giddings, *Chromatog. Revs.*, 3 (1961) 1.
[358] W. A. Schroeder, *Ann. N.Y. Acad. Sci.*, 49 (1948) 204.
[359] E. Lederer, *Bull. soc. chim. biol.*, 20 (1938) 554.
[360] E. Waldschmidt-Leitz, J. Ratzer and F. Turba, *J. prakt. Chem.*, 158 (1941) 72.
[361] E. Waldschmidt-Leitz and F. Turba, *J. prakt. Chem.*, 156 (1940) 55.
[362] W. Trappe, *Biochem. Z.*, 306 (1940) 316.
[363] J. R. Bendall, S. M. Partridge and R. G. Westall, *Nature*, 160 (1947) 374.
[364] J. R. Coffmann, *J. Biol. Chem.*, 140 (1941) xxviii.
[365] D. R. Idler and C. A. Baumann, *J. Biol. Chem.*, 195 (1952) 623.
[366] W. Bielenberg and L. Fischer, *Brennstoff-Chem.*, 22 (1941) 278; 23 (1942) 283.
[367] W. Bielenberg and H. Goldhahn, *Brennstoff-Chem.*, 21 (1940) 236.
[368] H. Silberman and S. Silberman-Martyncewa, *J. Biol. Chem.*, 165 (1946) 359.
[369] R. Lemberg, J. P. Callaghan, D. E. Tandy and N. E. Goldsworthy, *Australian J. Exptl. Biol. Med. Sci.*, 26 (1948) 9: *C.A.*, 44 (1950) 3079-b.
[370] R. Lemberg, D. E. Tandy and N. E. Goldsworthy, *Nature*, 157 (1946) 103.
[371] H. Wieland, K. Bähr and B. Witkop, *Ann.*, 547 (1941) 156.
[372] P. Karrer and H. Schmid, *Helv. Chim. Acta*, 29 (1946) 1853.
[373] D. W. Criddle and R. L. LeTourneau, *Anal. Chem.*, 26 (1954) 1620.
[374] W. H. Ellis and R. L. LeTourneau, *Anal. Chem.*, 25 (1953) 1269.
[375] E. M. Trautner and M. Roberts, *Analyst*, 73 (1948) 140.
[376] L. Zechmeister, L. von Cholnoky and E. Ujhelyi, *Bull. soc. chim. biol.*, 18 (1936) 1885.
[377] L. Zechmeister and W. H. McNeely, *J. Am. Chem. Soc.*, 64 (1942) 1919.
[378] W. W. Binkley, M. G. Blair and M. L. Wolfrom, *J. Am. Chem. Soc.*, 67 (1945) 1789.
[379] W. W. Binkley and M. L. Wolfrom, *J. Am. Chem. Soc.*, 68 (1946) 1720.
[380] B. W. Lew, M. L. Wolfrom and R. M. Goepp Jr., *J. Am. Chem. Soc.*, 67 (1945) 1865.
[381] D. J. Bell, *J. Chem. Soc.*, (1944) 473.
[382] J. Turkevich, *Ind. Eng. Chem., Anal. Ed.*, 14 (1942) 792.
[383] B. W. Lew, M. L. Wolfrom and R. M. Groepp Jr., *J. Am. Chem. Soc.*, 68 (1946) 1449.
[384] A. L. LeRosen, P. H. Monaghan, C. A. Rivet, E. D. Smith and H. A. Suter, *Anal. Chem.*, 22 (1950) 809.
[385] A. L. LeRosen, R. T. Moravek and J. K. Carlton, *Anal. Chem.*, 24 (1952) 1335.
[386] E. J. Norberg, I. Auerbach and R. M. Hixon, *J. Am. Chem. Soc.*, 67 (1945) 342.
[387] J. G. Kirchner, A. N. Prater and A. J. Haagen-Smit, *Ind. Eng. Chem., Anal. Ed.*, 18 (1946) 31.
[388] K. Folkers and J. Shavel Jr., *J. Am. Chem. Soc.*, 64 (1942) 1892.
[389] V. S. Krasnova, *Zhur. Priklad. Khim.*, 18 (1945) 86: *C.A.*, 39 (1945) 5399-6.
[390] L. Zechmeister and A. Polgár, *Science*, 100 (1944) 317.
[391] J. B. DeWitt and M. X. Sullivan, *Ind. Eng. Chem., Anal. Ed.*, 18 (1946) 117.
[392] M. Kofler, *Helv. Chim. Acta*, 25 (1942) 1469; 26 (1943) 2166; 28 (1945) 26.
[393] M. Kofler, *Helv. Chim. Acta*, 28 (1945) 702.
[394] E. M. Brumberg, *Uspekhi Fiz. Nauk*, 43 (1951) 600.

[395] G. E. Boxer and V. C. Jelinek, *J. Biol. Chem.*, 170 (1947) 491.
[396] H. Brockmann and F. Volpers, *Chem. Ber.*, 80 (1947) 77.
[397] J. W. White Jr. and E. C. Dryden, *Anal. Chem.*, 20 (1948) 853.
[398] E. F. L. J. Anet, B. Lythgoe, M. H. Silk and S. Trippet, *J. Chem. Soc.*, (1953) 309.
[399] J. W. Sease, *J. Am. Chem. Soc.*, 69 (1947) 2242.
[400] J. W. Sease, *J. Am. Chem. Soc.*, 70 (1948) 3630.
[401] H. R. Bentley and J. K. Whitehead, *Biochem. J.*, 46 (1950) 341.
[402] J. W. Sease, *Anal. Chem.*, 21 (1949) 1430.
[403] Z. V. Harvalik, *Anal. Chem.*, 22 (1950) 1149.
[404] P. H. Monaghan, P. B. Moseley, T. S. Burkhalter and O. A. Nance, *Anal. Chem.*, 24 (1952) 193.
[405] H. Bredereck, H. Dürr and K. Ruck, *Chem. Ber.*, 87 (1954) 526.
[406] E. A. Talley, D. R. Reynolds and W. L. Evans, *J. Am. Chem. Soc.*, 65 (1943) 575.
[407] P. Meunier and A. Vinet, *Bull. soc. chim. biol.*, 27 (1945) 186.
[408] H. Dam and L. Lewis, *Biochem. J.*, 31 (1937) 17.
[409] R. S. Cahn, R. F. Phipers and J. Boam, *J. Soc. Chem. Ind. (London)*, 57 (1938) T200.
[410] L. B. Norton and R. Hansberry, *J. Am. Chem. Soc.*, 67 (1945) 1609.
[411] H. Fischer and M. Conrad, *Ann.*, 538 (1939) 143.
[412] J. Fried, H. L. White and O. Wintersteiner, *J. Am. Chem. Soc.*, 72 (1950) 4621.
[413] V. Prelog and M. Osgan, *Helv. Chim. Acta*, 35 (1952) 981.
[414] J. H. Pinckard, A. Chatterjee and L. Zechmeister, *J. Am. Chem. Soc.*, 74 (1952) 1603.
[415] A. Schönberg, A. Mustafa and W. Asker, *J. Am. Chem. Soc.*, 74 (1952) 5640.
[416] M. D. Schmid and H. R. Bolliger, *Helv. Chim. Acta*, 37 (1954) 884.
[417] J. Francis, H. M. Macturk, J. Madinaveitia and G. S. Snow, *Biochem. J.*, 55 (1953) 596.
[418] M. Zaoral, *Chem. listy*, 47 (1953) 1872: *C.A.*, 49 (1955) 966-i.
[419] W. Oroshnik, A. D. Mebane and G. Karmas, *J. Am. Chem. Soc.*, 75 (1953) 1050.
[420] T. A. Geissman, P. Deuel, E. K. Bonde and F. A. Addicott, *J. Am. Chem. Soc.*, 76 (1954) 685.
[421] D. W. Hein, *J. Am. Chem. Soc.*, 77 (1955) 2797.
[422] K. Dobriner, S. Lieberman and C. P. Rhoads, *J. Biol. Chem.*, 172 (1948) 241.
[423] M. Stoll, M. Hinder and B. Willhalm, *Helv. Chim. Acta*, 39 (1956) 200.
[424] A. Butenandt and L. Poschmann, *Ber.*, 77 (1944) 392.
[425] K. Meyer, *Helv. Chim. Acta*, 29 (1946) 718.
[426] G. H. Ott and T. Reichstein, *Helv. Chim. Acta*, 26 (1943) 1799.
[427] L. Ruzicka, P. A. Plattner and J. Pataki, *Helv. Chim. Acta*, 28 (1945) 1360.
[428] C. W. Shoppee and G. H. R. Summers, *J. Chem. Soc.*, (1950) 687.
[429] L. F. Fieser, *J. Am. Chem. Soc.*, 75 (1953) 4377.
[430] J. Elks, R. M. Evans, A. G. Long and G. H. Thomas, *J. Chem. Soc.*, (1954) 451.
[431] H. E. Stavely, *J. Am. Chem. Soc.*, 63 (1941) 3127.
[432] C. W. Shoppee and D. A. Prins, *Helv. Chim. Acta*, 26 (1943) 201.
[433] L. H. Sarett, *J. Am. Chem. Soc.*, 70 (1948) 1454.
[434] H. Heusser, E. V. Jensen, N. Frick and P. A. Plattner, *Helv. Chim. Acta*, 32 (1949) 1326.
[435] D. K. Fukushima, S. Lieberman and B. Praetz, *J. Am. Chem. Soc.*, 72 (1950) 5205.
[436] J. A. Keverling-Buisman, W. Stevens and J. Van der Vliet, *Rec. trav. chim.*, 66 (1947) 83.
[437] D. A. Sutton and J. Dutta, *J. Chem. Soc.*, (1949) 939.
[438] R. J. W. Cremlyn and C. W. Shoppee, *J. Chem. Soc.*, (1954) 3515.
[439] L. F. Fieser and R. Stevenson, *J. Am. Chem. Soc.*, 76 (1954) 1728.
[440] G. H. Douglas and P. S. Ellington, *J. Chem. Soc.*, (1959) 1720.
[441] M. Berenstein, A. Georg and E. Briner, *Helv. Chim. Acta*, 29 (1946) 258.
[442] P. A. Plattner and A. S. Pfau, *Helv. Chim. Acta*, 20 (1937) 224.
[443] E. Lederer, F. Marx, D. Mercier and G. Pérot, *Helv. Chim. Acta*, 29 (1946) 1354.
[444] E. Lederer, D. Mercier and G. Pérot, *Bull. soc. chim. France*, (1947) 345.
[445] B. A. Arbuzov and Z. G. Isaeva, *Izvest. Akad. Nauk S.S.S.R., Otdel Khim. Nauk*, (1953) 843.

[446] B. Borgström, *Acta Physiol. Scand.*, 30 (1954) 231.
[447] V. R. Mattox and H. L. Mason, *J. Biol. Chem.*, 223 (1956) 215.
[448] A. H. Soloway, W. J. Considine, D. K. Fukushima and T. F. Gallagher, *J. Am. Chem. Soc.*, 76 (1954) 2941.
[449] N. S. Leeds, D. K. Fukushima and T. F. Gallagher, *J. Am. Chem. Soc.*, 76 (1954) 2943.
[450] P. Meunier, *Bull. soc. chim. France*, 73 (1946) 77.
[451] L. Zechmeister and A. Sandoval, *Science*, 101 (1945) 585.
[452] G. Wald, *J. Gen. Physiol.*, 31 (1948) 489: *C.A.*, 43 (1949) 157-i.
[453] P. Meunier, J. Jouanneteau and G. Zwingelstein, *Compt. rend.*, 231 (1950) 1170; 1570.
[454] H. Levy and S. Kushinsky, *Recent Progr. in Hormone Research*, 9 (1954) 357.
[455] W. Robson and A. S. M. Selim, *Biochem. J.*, 53 (1953) 431.
[456] H. B. Henbest, E. R. H. Jones and G. F. Smith, *J. Chem. Soc.*, (1953) 3796.
[457] E. Weitz and F. Schmidt, *Ber.*, 72 (1939) 1740; 2099.
[458] E. Weitz, F. Schmidt and J. Singer, *Z. Elektrochem.*, 46 (1940) 222.
[459] Ng. Ph. Buu-Hoï and P. Cagniant, *Bull. soc. chim. France*, (5) 11 (1944) 410.
[460] K. Cruse and R. Mittag, *Z. anal. Chem.*, 131 (1950) 273.
[461] K. Cruse and R. Mittag, *Z. Elektrochem.*, 54 (1950) 418.
[462] J. P. Green and H. Dam, *Acta Chem. Scand.*, 8 (1954) 1093.

Chapter II

PART B

Ion Exchange Chromatography

Introduction

In this section we propose to review the methods of ion exchange chromatography, *i.e.* the separation of substances using an ion exchange mechanism, as well as chromatography on ion exchangers where the separation process takes place on the surface of ion exchange resins, without participation of the actual ion exchange mechanism.

Ion exchangers are employed in numerous industrial processes such as water softening, sugar refining, metal concentration and catalysis of reactions in a batch process manner and not in combination with chromatographic elution. These applications will not be discussed here. However, the rather extensive literature on ion exchangers deals mainly with these topics and only refers briefly to chromatographic separations.

Literature

The treatise by Nachod[1] has been revised in a newer edition by Nachod and Schubert[2]. The book by Samuelson[3] will shortly appear in German in a revised form[4]. Kunin and Myers[5] hardly mention chromatography. Other general monographs of ion exchange or adsorption and ion exchange were written by Cassidy[6], Osborn[7], Austerweil[8] and Helfferich[9]. Of specialised books we shall mention: Martin[10] medical applications; Calmon and Kressman[11] organic and biochemistry; Blasius[12] inorganic separations; and Jones[13] one chapter on analytical applications. A translation of Russian research in ion exchange chromatography (a collection of papers) has been prepared[14].

The early cation exchangers were silicates, either natural products such as montmorillonite clay or fuller's earth, or synthetic alumino silicates prepared from aluminium compounds and sodium silicate.

The application of these inorganic exchangers is limited to a narrow pH range as they peptize in alkaline solutions and dissolve in acid. Jagolite, a montmorillonite earth, has been used for adsorption of vitamin E[15], also

References p. 146

for carotenoids[15], fuller's earth for vitamin K[16] and for sugars[17]. Decalso (a synthetic alumino silicate) for vitamin K[18], vitamin B_1[19] and urinary pigments[20], permutit (another synthetic alumino silicate) for antibiotics[21,22], also for the gonadotropic hormone[23].

Acid-washed alumina has been shown to act as an anion exchanger[24], and alumina containing Na ions as a cation exchanger.

Recently Kraus *et al.*[25] have used *insoluble zirconium salts* such as tungstates or phosphates for ion exchange separations of the alkali metals.

1. Synthetic ion exchange resins

(a) *Properties*

The first synthesis of an ion exchange resin was carried out by Adams and Holmes in 1935[26], who prepared a condensation product of phenol sulphonic acid with formaldehyde. Similar substances were prepared by Liebknecht[27] and Smit[28] by sulphonation of coal. All these resins possessed reactive OH and COOH in addition to the more important SO_3H exchange groups.

In order to prepare a resin with only one type of reactive group, D'Alelio[29] sulphonated a hydrocarbon polymer containing benzene rings (styrene with 10% divinylbenzene). An analogous resin with basic groups was prepared by reacting the polymer with chloromethyl ether,

$$-CH(C_6H_5)-CH_2- + CH_3OCH_2Cl \longrightarrow -CH(C_6H_4CH_2Cl)-CH_2- + CH_3OH$$

then reacting the chloro groups in the network with *tertiary* amines,

$$-CH(C_6H_4CH_2Cl)-CH_2- + R_3N \longrightarrow -CH(C_6H_4CH_2\overset{+}{N}R_3)-CH_2- + Cl^-$$

For a review of ion exchange resin synthesis see Craig[30]. The functional acidic (or basic) groups of an exchanger will always be occupied by ions of the opposite charge. When holding hydrogen ions a resin is said to be in the *hydrogen form,* similarly when holding sodium ions in the *sodium form* etc.

When a polymer containing active groups (*e.g.* SO_3H) is formed, the ionisation of the respective groups is not changed, thus a *vast sponge-like network* is produced with properties identical with those of the monomer[31,32]. Resins with sulphonic groups or quaternary amine groups are thus highly ionised though very insoluble and react throughout their entirety. Resins with highly ionised groups such as SO_3H and NR_3 are called strong exchange resins and resins with only partially ionised groups such as COOH, OH, NH_2 are called weak exchange resins. The degree of ionisation as well as the similarity to the monomer can be best illustrated by titrating, for example, the hydrogen form of a strong acid resin such as Dowex-50. A titration curve identical to that of a strong acid with a strong base is produced (Fig. 1).

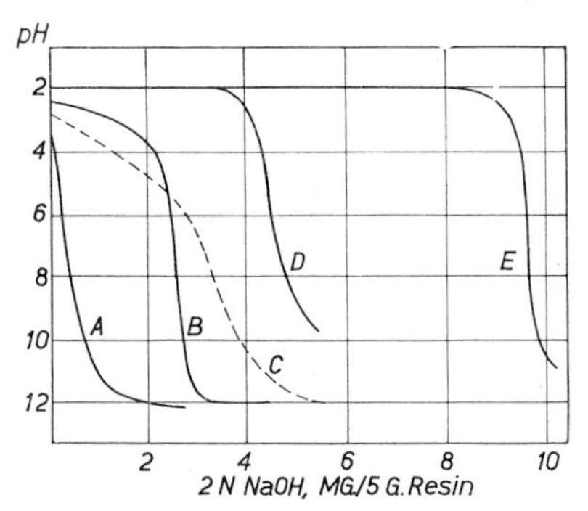

Fig. 1. Titration curves of several cation exchanger functional groups; (A) phenolic O H (B) methylene sulphonic CH_2SO_3H: (C) carboxyl COOH: (D) and (E) nuclear SO_3H (Tompkins[33]).

A similar analogy exists with weak exchange resins, these giving titration curves typical of weak acids and weak bases. For titration curves see also Topp and Pepper[34].

(b) *Crosslinkage*

Crosslinkage of various degrees may be obtained by copolymerising various quantities of divinylbenzene with the polystyrene. In Dowex resins the amount of crosslinkage is expressed by the percentage of divinylbenzene as no known analytical method for its determination is available. For example

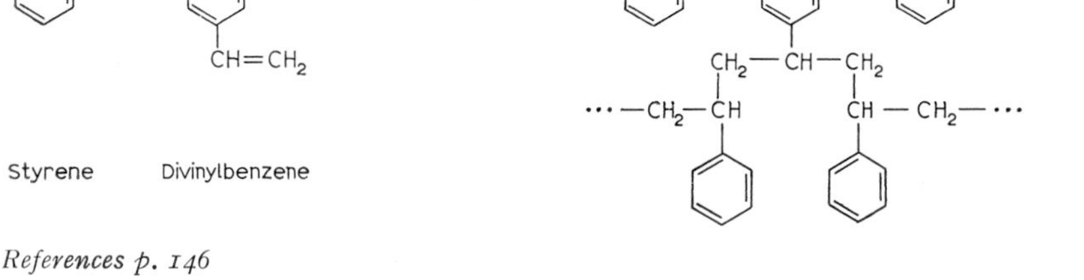

Styrene Divinylbenzene

Dowex-50-X4 is prepared from a mixture of styrene and divinylbenzene containing 4% divinylbenzene.

A commercial pamphlet of the Dow Chemical Co.[35] lists the following cross-linkage effects. Copolymers of styrene containing *low* amounts of divinylbenzene (1–4%) are characterised as follows:

(*1*) High degree of permeability.
(*2*) Contain a large amount of moisture.
(*3*) Capacities are lower on a wet volume basis.
(*4*) Equilibrium rates are high.
(*5*) Physical stability is reduced.
(*6*) Selectivity for various ions is decreased, but ability to accommodate larger ions is increased.

Copolymers of styrene containing *high* amounts of divinylbenzene (12–16%) would exhibit characteristics in the opposite direction. An average divinylbenzene content for the Dowex Fine Mesh Resins series is 8% divinylbenzene and the terms high and low or decreased and increased are all relative to an 8% crosslinked resin.

TABLE I

CONVERSION OF MESH RANGES TO PARTICLE DIAMETERS[35]

Mesh range	*Diameter of particles*		
	inches	*mm*	*microns*
20–50	0.0331–0.0117	0.84 –0.297	840–297
50–100	0.0117–0.0059	0.297–0.149	297–149
100–200	0.0059–0.0029	0.149–0.074	149– 74
200–400	0.0029–0.0015	0.074–0.038	74– 38
> 400	< 0.0015	< 0.038	< 38

As the particle of an ion exchange resin is decreased to the fine mesh range (50–100 mesh or finer) the following effects are observed[35]:

(*1*) The time required to reach equilibrium is decreased.
(*2*) The flow rate decreases.
(*3*) The pressure drop across the ion exchange column increases.
(*4*) The bed expansion during a backwash cycle is greater.
(*5*) The efficiency of a given volume of resin increases or the volume of resin required to perform a specific operation is decreased.

(c) *Characteristics of some ion exchange resins*

(i) *Properties of resins*

For the selection of a resin for analytical purposes several important features must be known as is evident from theoretical considerations. This information is available in most cases in pamphlets published by the manufacturers of the resins. In Tables II–V a number of the resins which are often referred to in the text are tabulated.

TABLE II

DUOLITE ION EXCHANGERS (Tompkins[36])

	C_1	C_2	A_2	A_3
Chemical composition	Phenol-formaldehyde type			
Active groups	sulphonic acid		aliphatic amine	
Density (wet)	1.07	1.13	1.07	1.08
Colour	white to pink red		light yellow	—
Capacity in mequiv./g dried at 80°	2.75	3.44	9.35	6.65
Capacity in equiv./l of wet tamped vol.	0.5	1.2	2.25	2.0
Stability, chemical	unstable to oxidising agents			
Stability, physical	stable at reasonable periods from 77–100° but not absolutely stable at these temperatures			

TABLE III

PERMUTIT ION EXCHANGERS (Tompkins[36])

	Zeo Karb	*Zeo Rex*	*Permutit Q*	*De Acidite*
Colour	black	amber	yellow	orange
Form	granular	granular	spherical	granular
Density dry g/l	735	925	900	610
General chemical composition	sulphonated coal	sulphonated phenolic	sulphonated hydrocarbon	aliphatic amine resin
Exchange groups	COOH and SO_3H	SO_3H	SO_3H	R_3N
Analyses	S = 6%	S = 8.5%	S = 16%	—
Capacity in mequiv./g	1.8	3.0	5.0	6.7

References p. 146

TABLE IV

AMBERLITE ION EXCHANGE RESINS

Summary of properties (Information supplied by the manufacturer)

Resin	*Amberlite IR-120*	*Amberlite IRC-50*	*Amberlite IRA-400*	*Amberlite IRA-401*	*Amberlite IRA-410*	*Amberlite IRA-411*	*Amberlite IR-4B*	*Amberlite IR-45*	*Monobed MB-1*	*Monobed MB-2*	*Monobed MB-3*
Type	Strongly acidic cation exchanger	Weakly acidic cation exchanger	Strongly basic anion exchanger	More porous analog of Amberlite IRA-400	Strongly basic anion exchanger	More porous analog of Amberlite IRA-410	Weakly basic anion exchanger	Weakly basic anion exchanger	Mixture of Amberlite IR-120 and Amberlite IRA-400	Mixture of Amberlite IR-120 and Amberlite IRA-410	Mixture of Amberlite IR-120 and Amberlite IRA-410 with indicator
Active group	nuclear sulfonic acid	carboxylic acid	quaternary amine	quaternary amine	quaternary amine	quaternary amine	polyamine	polyamine	Same as components		
Form supplied	Bead Na	Bead H	Bead Cl	Bead Cl	Bead Cl	Bead Cl	Granular OH	Bead OH	Bead H OH	Bead H OH	Bead with indicator H OH
Density (lbs/ft³)	53	43	42	42	44	42	35	42	44	44	44
Moisture content	44–48	45–55	40–50	55–60	35–45	53–63	40–45	37–45	Same as components		
Effective size (mm)*	0.45–0.6	0.33–0.5	0.35–0.45	0.40–0.55	0.35–0.45	0.35–0.50	0.4–0.55	0.35–0.50	Same as components		
Total exchange capacity											
kg as $CaCO_3$, per ft³	41.5	71.0	22.0	17.5	26.0	15.0	65.0	43.0	9.0	11.0	11.0
meq./ml wet resin	1.9	3.5	1.0	0.8	1.2	0.7	3.0	2.0	0.4	0.5	0.5
meq./g dry resin	4.25	10.0	2.5	3.0	3.0	3.0	5.23	5.0	—	—	—
Maximum operating temperature (°F)	250	250	140 (OH form)	140 (OH form)	105 (OH form)	105 (OH form)	105	212	140	105	105
Effective operating pH range	1–14	7–14	0–12	0–12	0–12	0–12	0–7	0–7	0–14	0–14	0–14
Maximum swelling (%)**	5 Na → H	100 H → Na	5 Cl → OH	10 Cl → OH	5 Cl → OH	10 Cl → OH	25 OH → HCl	15 OH → HCl	Same as components		

* Sieve opening that will retain 90% of the sample. ** % increase in volume of exchangers when form is changed.

(ii) Complexing resins

The preparation of resins containing complexing groups instead of ion exchange groups has been attempted by Skogseid[37] who attached dipierylamine groups (see formula) for the fixation of potassium; the same ideas were advanced and tried by Mellor[38] and Dwyer *et al.*[39].

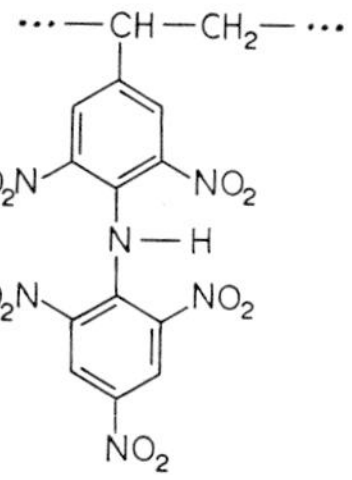

A complexing resin with amino-diacetic acid groups on a styrol–divinylbenzene network is marketed by the Dow Chemical Co. under the name of *Dowex Chelating Resin A*-1. It may be obtained in the sodium form with a grain size of 30–70 mesh.

(iii) Electron exchange resins

Electron exchange resins prepared by polymerising vinylhydroquinone alone or mixed with styrene were described by Cassidy[40,41]. In a later paper by Ezrin and Cassidy[42] some of the properties of this electron exchange resin are reviewed. Its titration curve (volt against % oxidised) is almost a straight line from 0.24 V to 0.4 V. Hence it may be considered as an insoluble redox system with an $E_0 = 0.32$ V. No chromatographic applications of this electron exchanger have so far been reported. Several reactions have, however, been carried out by passing a solution through a column, such as the quantitative reduction of dichromate or the oxidation or reduction of iodide–iodine. For such reactions it was also employed in other forms such as dispersed on filter paper or precipitated on diatomaceous earth.

2. Preparation of the resin column

(a) Washing and conversion to the required form

Most commercial resins, especially cation exchangers, contain appreciable quantities of iron and heavy metals. Washing on a Büchner funnel with 6–8 *N* HCl until the washings are free of iron was found adequate in the author's laboratory. Kressman[11] recommends washing with NaCl solution containing sodium citrate or EDTA.

It is also recommended, even for analytical grade resins of a given mesh

References p. 146

TABLE V

DOWEX ION EXCHANGE RESINS

(Information supplied by the manufacturer)

Name	*Dowex 50*	*Dowex 1*	*Dowex 2*	*Dowex 3*
Type	Strongly acidic cation exchanger	Strongly basic anion exchanger	Strongly basic anion exchanger	Weakly basic anion exchanger
Crosslinkage – Standard % DVB	8%	7.5%	7.5%	Not defined
Approximate density (lbs/ft.^{3}) standard material	53	45	45	45
Active group	Nuclear sulfonic acid	Trimethyl benzyl ammonium	Dimethyl ethanol benzyl ammonium	Polyamine
Resin form as shipped	Na (20–50 mesh) H (All other mesh)	Cl	Cl	OH
Form	Spheres	Spheres	Spheres	Spheres
Standard mesh size	20–50	20–50	20–50	20–50
Total dry weight capacity– H^+ or Cl^- form	5 mequiv./g	approximately 3 mequiv./g	approximately 3 mequiv./g	approximately 6 mequiv./g
Total wet volume capacity– H^+ or Cl^- form	1.8 mequiv./ml	approximately 1.1 mequiv./ml	approximately 1.1 mequiv./ml	approximately 3 mequiv./ml
Moisture content– H^+ or Cl^- form	55% (H^+ form)	45% (Cl^- form)	40% (Cl^- form)	30% (Base form)

Volume change	$\Delta V_{H}^{Na} = -8\%$	$\Delta V_{Cl}^{OH} = +24\%$	$\Delta V_{Cl}^{OH} = +14\%$	$\Delta V_{Cl}^{OH} = -20$ to -30%
Selectivity – *e.g.* K_{H}^{Na}	$K_{H}^{Na} = 1.2$	K_{Cl}^{OH} = approximately 15	K_{Cl}^{OH} = approximately 1.5	
Order of selectivity for ions	Ag > Rb > Cs > K > NH_4 > Na > H > Li	I > NO_3 > Br > Cl > Acetate > OH > F	I > NO_3 > Br > Cl > OH > Acetate > F	
Breakage	< 15%	< 25%	< 25%	< 25%
Bed expansion	< 40% at upflow velocity of 4 gpm/ft.²	< 35% at upflow velocity of 2 gpm/ft.²	< 35% at upflow velocity 2 gpm/ft.²	< 35% at upflow velocity of 2 gpm/ft.²
Pressure drop	approximately 0.5 lb/ft. at 5 gpm/ft.²	approximately 0.5 lb/ft at 5 gpm/ft.²	approximately 0.5 lb/ft. at 5 gpm/ft.²	approximately 0.5 lb/ft. at 5 gpm/ft.²
Special mesh sizes (dry)	50–100, 100–200, 200–400, –400, colloidal	50–100, 100–200, 200–400, –400	50–100, 100–200, 200–400, –400	Not stocked
Special crosslinkages	1%–16% DVB	1%–10%	1%–10%	Not defined
Stability – thermal	Good up to 150°	OH^- form – Fair up to 50° Cl^- form – Good up to 150°	OH^- form – Fair up to 30° Cl^- form – Good up to 150°	Tentatively limited to 65°. Upward revision may result with additional factual data
Stability – solvent	Very good	Very good	Very good	Very good
Stability – oxidation	Slow solution in hot 15% HNO_3	Slow solution in hot 15% HNO_3	Slow solution in hot 15% HNO_3	Good
Stability – reduction	Very good	Break down in presence of sulfur containing reducing agents		Unknown

References p. 146

range, to stir the resin to be used with water, allow to settle and then to decant the "fines".

Conversion of a cation exchanger to the hydrogen form is readily carried out by washing with HCl (which one does already to remove the iron) and then washing with distilled water until the washings are neutral. Spedding *et al.*[43] recommend for Amberlite IR-1, washing on the column with 5% HCl (leaving the acid in contact for 30 min) then with 2% NaCl and repeating the washing with HCl and NaCl at least two times, leaving it finally in the acid form.

The sodium form of a strong cation exchanger can of course be prepared by reacting the hydrogen form with either a sodium salt (which will liberate HCl) or even with NaOH and washing the column until it reaches neutrality. With carboxylic resins hydrolysis occurs (as with weak acids), hence if the sodium form is required the reaction must be carried out with the necessary amount of NaOH, noting that if the column is washed with water some of the Na^+ is lost due to hydrolysis and the washing will react alkaline even without excess NaOH.

Strongly basic anion exchangers are only converted to the OH^- form with an excess of NaOH (in absence of carbonate which, being divalent, adsorbs more strongly than OH^-). Weak anion exchangers can be converted to the free amine form by washing with NaOH or even with ammonia.

(*b*) *Preparation of columns*

A dry resin cannot be filled into columns as it swells on addition of water and will burst the tube or at least give an uneven column. Hence a suspension of the resin is always poured into the column, which also may be filled with water.

Kraus[44] recommends short columns for most work with anion exchange resins, for which graduated 10-ml or 1-ml pipettes (with the top cut off) are very suitable, as they also permit a rapid estimation of the resin volume and the speed of elution, amount of eluant passed, etc. For much of the work usual chromatography tubes may be employed, but in the case of large particle size resins a stop-cock or other device (see Fig. 2) to regulate the flow rate must be used.

Prins[46] employed perspex cuvettes with flat sides instead of round tubes in the separation of haemoglobins.

When elevated temperatures are employed during elution, jacketed columns are usually used. However, before passing the eluant into the resin, it must be preboiled to expel dissolved gases, which otherwise form air-bubbles on contact with the large surface of the resin.

An apparatus permitting work up to temperatures above 100° was constructed by Kraus *et al.*[47].

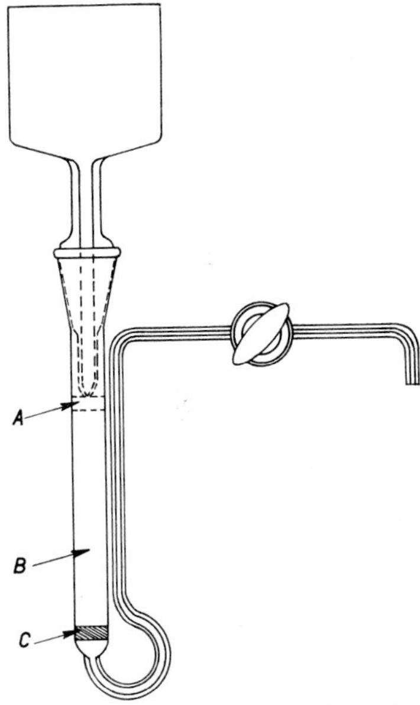

Fig. 2. Experimental column. The funnel is removable to facilitate resin addition and removal. The resin bed, B, in this column is 1 $cm^2 \times 10$ cm and rests on the porous glass disc, C. A stopcock in the outlet tube allows regulation of the flow rate. The opening in the outlet tube is above the top of the resin bed, thus maintaining a liquid layer, A, above the resin at all times (Tompkins *et al.*[45]).

Except in the case of coloured substances, a fraction collector is usually employed with ion exchange columns. With many micro-scale techniques the eluate is collected in drops or in lots of several drops.

3. Ion exchange equilibria

When an ion exchange resin in the hydrogen form is immersed in a sodium chloride solution, the hydrogen ions on the resin are replaced by sodium and sodium chloride is converted to hydrochloric acid.

This ion exchange reaction can be considered either as an adsorption system obeying the Langmuir isotherm[48,49] or Freundlich isotherm, or as a reaction obeying the law of mass action[48,50]; or as a Donnan equilibrium between the inside of the resin particles and the outside solution[32,51,52]. All these theories agree in that the amount of an ion inside the resin particle increases with the concentration of that ion in the solution. However, only the Donnan theory adequately explains the volume changes (swelling) on replacing one ionic species by another. In his application of the Gibbs–Donnan equilibrium to ion exchange resins, Gregor[51,52] points out that an equilibrium is reached between the osmotic pressure of the hydrated ion

References p. 146

and the back pressure of the elastic net-work of the cross-linked polymer.

Thus the affinity of ions to the resin phase or the *free energy of the exchange reaction* is directly related to the volume change of the resin particles during the reaction. The amount of cross-linking influences the *elasticity* of the resin and hence the equilibrium between ions, as was shown by Reichenberg, Pepper and McCauley[53].

Duncan and Lister[54] suggest that secondary adsorption could account for the difficulties in evaluating the activities inside the resin phase.

(*a*) *Exchange equilibria between various ions*

(*i*) *Inorganic cations*

Walton[55] has reviewed the data on the affinity of cations for various exchangers and found that for the Group 1A and 2A metals the affinity increases with atomic weight.

Hydration of the ions decreases the affinity as shown by Jenny, and the experiments of Wiegner[57,58] indicated that in a range of alcohol–water mixtures the affinities of Cs and Na became more alike as the hydration differences fell.

Extensive investigations were carried out by Boyd *et al.*[48] on the relative affinities of various cations for cation exchange resins. This work has special importance in the identification of radio-active isotopes of otherwise unknown elements. Table VI gives the free energy of *salt formation* and the

TABLE VI

FREE ENERGY OF SALT FORMATION AND IONIC RADIUS OF SOME METALS

(Boyd *et al.*[48])

Ion	*Free energy* $\Delta F°$ *(298.1°) cal/mole*	*Crystal ionic radius*
H^+	0	
Li^+	—60	0.78
Na^+	320	0.98
NH_4^+	410	
K^+	530	1.33
Rb^+	615	1.49
Cs^+	860	1.65
Ba^{++}	1680	1.43
Y^{+++}	1830	1.06
La^{+++}	2110	1.22

ionic radius of a number of metals studied with Amberlite IR-1. It was thus shown that the adsorption affinities are determined chiefly by the magnitude of the charge and the radius of the hydrated ions in solution. Russell and

Pearce[59] found, contrary to the above, that the rare earth ions of a larger radius are less strongly held than smaller ions, and this observation was also confirmed by Kozak and Walton[60]. Ketelle and Boyd[61,62] also found that when eluting mixtures of rare earth metals with citrate solutions, the sequence of relative adsorbability is in the order of their ionic radii thus: La, Ce, Pr, Nd, Pm, Sm, Eu, Gd, Tb, Dy, Y, Ho, Er, Tm, Yb and Lu. Yttrium falls between dysprosium and holmium in this series. Using this rule, Marinsky *et al.*[63] were able to obtain evidence for the existence of element 61 in a mixture of rare earths.

(ii) Inorganic and organic anions

Kunin and Myers[64] examined the exchange equilibria of anions with Amberlite IR-4B. The relative exchange abilities of the anions studied are: hydroxide > sulphate > chromate > citrate > tartrate > nitrate > arsenate > phosphate > molybdate > acetate = iodide = bromide > chloride > fluoride. Reactions between the chloride form of the resin with sodium borate desorbed all the chloride without adsorption of borate, due to the extremely small ionisation of boric acid. Organic acids were found to be in the following order: benzoic < oxalic < formic < acetic = citric < salicylic.

(b) *Elution*

The *elution* of ions attached to the resin is possible either by displacement with a more strongly adsorbed ion or with highly concentrated solutions of other ions or again the concentration of the adsorbed ion in solution can be decreased by the addition of a complexing agent. For example in an equimolecular solution of lanthanum and hydrogen ions, the lanthanum is almost completely adsorbed on the resin; however, in presence of citrate ions a lanthanum citrate complex is formed and the concentration of free lanthanum ions so reduced as to have practically no lanthanum inside the resin.

Tompkins *et al.*[45] first used solutions of citric acid in this manner for the elution of rare earth ions. The pH of such solutions plays an important role as it influences the proportions of H_3Cit, and the ions H_2Cit^-, $HCit^{--}$ and Cit^{---}.

The equilibrium constant of the distribution of an ion between the solution and the resin is called K_d where

$$K_d = \frac{M_s/\text{mass of resin}}{M_e/\text{volume of solution}} = \frac{M_s}{M_e} \cdot \frac{\text{volume of solution}}{\text{mass of resin}}$$

where M_s and M_e are the fractions of the cation M in the resin and liquid phases.

References p. 146

The reaction between the ammonium resin and the citrate complex of the rare earth metals depends on the following chemical equilibria:

$$M^{3+} + 3NH_4R \rightleftarrows MR_3 + 3NH_4^+ \quad (1)$$

$$M^{3+} + nH_xCit^{x-3} \rightleftarrows M(H_xCit)_n^{3+n(x-3)} \quad (2)$$

where M^{3+} = rare earth ion
NH_4R = ammonium form of the resin
MR_3 = the rare earth resin compound
and $M(H_xCit)_n^{3+n(x-3)}$ = the rare earth citrate complex.

The distribution coefficient K_d varies interdependently with ammonium ion concentration, total rare earth concentration and pH.

(c) *The separation factor*

As a measure of the chromatographic separation possible between two ions, the ratio of the two equilibrium constants is employed and called the separation factor α.

$$\frac{K_{d_1}}{K_{d_2}} = \alpha$$

For an equilibrium between a rare earth citrate complex, the rare earth ion and its resin compound (for example $Ce^{+++} + H_2Cit^-$ etc.)

$$K_d = \frac{K_{\text{exchange}} \cdot K_{\text{complex}}}{K^3_{1\text{cit}}} \cdot \left(\frac{NH_4R}{NH_4^+}\right)^3 \left(\frac{H^+}{H_3Cit}\right)^3$$

(for derivation see [61]). In taking ratios between two K_d's the variation due to ammonium ion concentration, H^+ concentration, etc., cancel out. Thus

TABLE VII

EFFECT OF COMPLEXING ACIDS ON THE SEPARATION FACTOR

(Tompkins and Mayer[65])

Complexing compound	*pH at which Kd of Eu is 21.9*	*α Kd Pm/Kd Eu*
Citric acid	3.05	1.45
Tartaric acid	2.85	1.94
Lactic acid	3.40	1.71
Sulphosalicylic acid	5.4	1.49
Ethyl acetoacetate	7.4	1.33
Oxalic acid	1.7	1.32
Citric acid in 50% EtOH	3.0	1.31
Acetylacetone	7.2	1.91

the separation factor is only dependent on the exchange and complexing constants.

$$\alpha = \frac{K^1_{\text{exchange}}}{K^2_{\text{exchange}}} \cdot \frac{K^1_{\text{complex}}}{K^2_{\text{complex}}}$$

Improvement of a particular separation can be effected by varying either the resin or the complexing agent. Table VII gives the effect of various complexing acids on α; the efficiency of various ion exchange resins was compared as shown in Table VIII.

TABLE VIII

COMPARISON OF THE EFFICIENCIES OF SEVERAL RESINS FOR RARE EARTH SEPARATIONS (Eu and Pm) (Tompkins and Mayer[65])

Dowex-50			*Dowex-30*			*Duolite-C*			*Amberlite IR-1*		
pH	*Kd Eu*	*Kd Pm* / *Kd Eu*	*pH*	*Kd Eu*	*Kd Pm* / *Kd Eu*	*pH*	*Kd Eu*	*Kd Pm* / *Kd Eu*	*pH*	*Kd Eu*	*Kd Pm* / *Kd Eu*
2.9	92	1.45	2.61	118	1.56	2.40	230	1.65	2.42	39	1.32
3.08	18.8	1.44	2.82	13	1.57	2.55	85	1.60	2.58	19	1.24
3.25	5.2	1.41				2.80	27	1.62	2.83	8.3	1.30
						3.00	3.1	1.52			

(*d*) *Diffusion into and inside the ion exchange resin*

According to Boyd *et al.*[66] the kinetics of an ion exchange reaction may be divided into five steps:

(*1*) Diffusion of A^+ through the solution up to the resin particle.
(*2*) Diffusion of A^+ through the resin particle.
(*3*) Chemical exchange between A^+ and BR (BR being the resin R with the cation B) at the exchange position inside the particles.
(*4*) Diffusion of the displaced ion B^+ out of the interior of the exchanger.
(*5*) Diffusion of the displaced ion B^+ through the solution away from the resin particle.

By vigorous mixing (*1*) and (*5*) can be made negligible and (*3*), the chemical exchange, is either instantaneous or, according to Gregor[51,52], non-existent. Thus if by the use of radioactive tracers the rate of exchange in stirred solutions is measured, the diffusion rates inside the particles can be arrived at.

In solutions from 0.1 *M* up, the rate of diffusion through the particle determines the rate of the exchange reaction for any given grain size of resin particles. In very dilute solutions, 0.003 *M* and less, the limiting rate was the diffusion from the outside to the surface of the resin particle. Diffusion inside the resin particle will depend on the affinity of the ion to the resin; a strongly

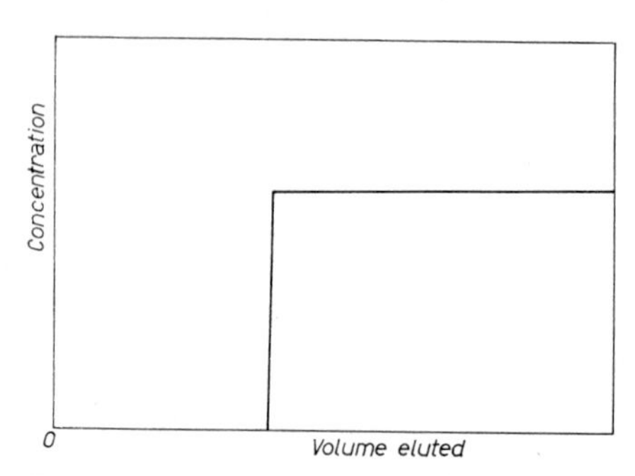

Fig. 3. Equilibrium elution (diagrammatic).

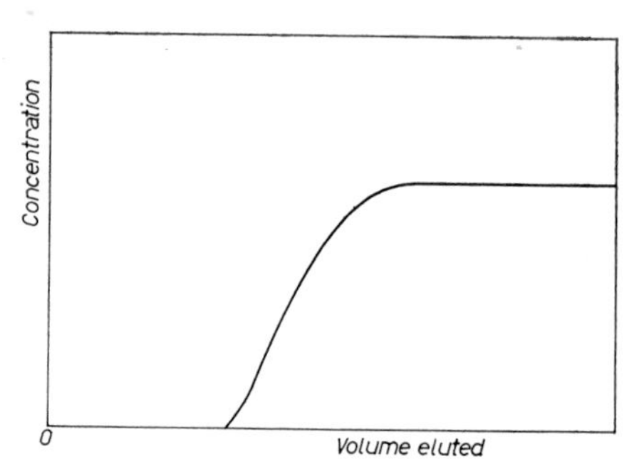

Fig. 4. Non-equilibrium elution (diagrammatic).

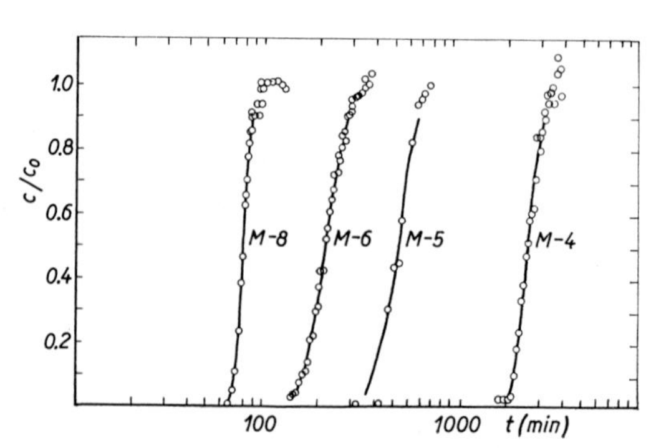

Fig. 5. Adsorption showing non-equilibrium conditions (Boyd *et al.*[71]).

bonded ion will diffuse much slower through a pore on whose surface active groups are situated, than a less strongly bonded. This retardation is counterbalanced by the faster diffusion of more strongly "adsorbed" ions in the water phase. The rate of absorption of an ion into the resin particle will still be dependent on the equilibrium constant as it will determine the concentration gradient inside the pores of the resin. This was also illustrated by Gapon and Gapon[67] by examination of the cross section of granules of exchange resin dipped into a solution containing two coloured ions. Usually diffusion rates through a resin are 5–10 times slower than in water. Hale and Reichenberg[68] examined the exchange kinetics of a sulphonated polystyrene resin in which the *chemical process of exchange* was found to be the rate controlling process, the rate of exchange being independent of particle size. Kressman and Kitchener[69] studied sulphonated phenol formaldehyde resins and their equilibria with NH_4^+ and quaternary substituted ammonium ions. Two mechanisms control the rate: diffusion in the particles and the bounding Nernst film, as was shown by Boyd *et al.*[66] above. Also see Baumann and Eichhorn[32].

Depending on the comparative size of the resin pores and cations, the energy of activation for diffusion varies from *ca.* 5 kcal/mole for small ions to 8 kcal/mole for large ones[69], for example

$$\left[C_6H_5-N(CH_3)_2-CH_2-C_6H_5 \right]^+$$

A mathematical treatment of the kinetics of ion exchange may be found in Thomas' chapter in *Ion Exchange*, edited by Nachod[1].

(e) *Non-equilibrium conditions*

Ion exchange can be carried out by pouring a solution of an ion over a column of the resin saturated with another ion, analogous to frontal analysis. If the rate of flow and the particle size is so as to establish a perfect equilibrium an elution curve as shown in Fig. 3 will be obtained. This has been achieved at very low speeds by Ekedahl *et al.*[70]. However, it is an ideal condition which is not usually approached in practice. Owing to the rate of flow and the particle size being too large, curves as shown in Fig. 4 are usually obtained.

Boyd *et al.*[71] have examined the non-equilibrium conditions from the point of view of incomplete equilibria and without considering vertical diffusion which has the same effect. Their experimental results with active tracers on a column saturated with the same but inactive ion are shown in

References p. 146

Figs. 5 and 6 for adsorption and desorption and in Fig. 7 for a band being chromatographically eluted.

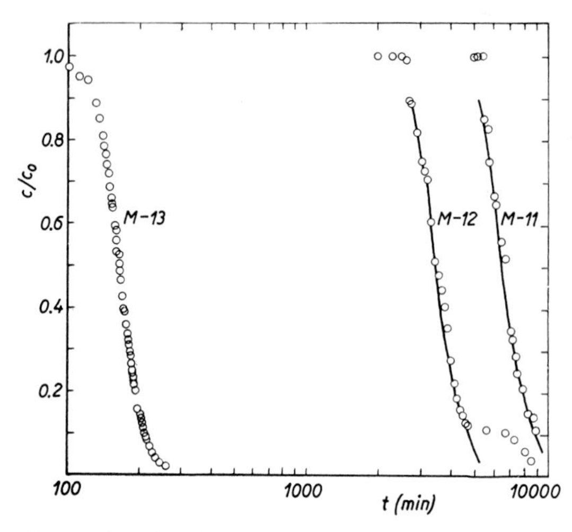

Fig. 6. Desorption showing non-equilibrium conditions (Boyd *et al.*[71]).

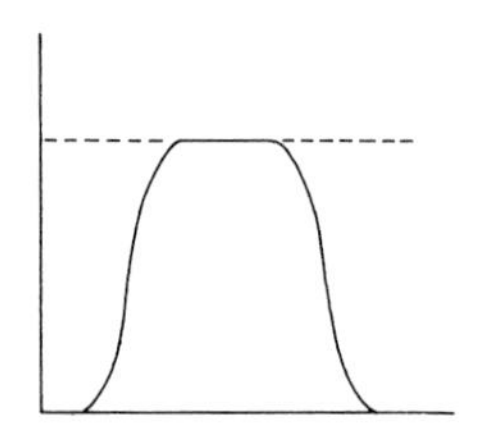

Fig. 7. A band eluted, showing at the front and end non-equilibrium conditions (after Boyd *et al.*[71]).

(*f*) *Ion exchange chromatography with organic solvents*

Carleson[72] developed methods of separation of Zn, Cu, Ni, Co, Mn and Fe on Dowex-50 with such solvents as methyl-*n*-propyl ketone containing water and HCl. In this work as in the work on resin impregnated filter paper[73] it seems that the resin plays mainly the part of an inert stationary phase holding HCl and water.

Kember *et al.*[74] studied the separation of Cu and Ni on Zeo Karb 225 and recommend acetone containing 4% of HCl and 10% of water as a suitable solvent. Here the ion exchange properties of the resin seem to interfere since in other mixtures of acetone–HCl (reported by the above) sharp separation could not be obtained. See also d'Ans *et al.*[75].

Carroll[76] who examined the elution sequence of *organic acids* from Dowex-1 with alcohol also concluded that the elution sequence seems to be influenced by the partition coefficients as well as the pK values. For further work with organic solvents and organic compounds see also Kornberg and Pricer[77], Kennedy[78] and Savary and Desnuelle[79] and pages 132–139.

4. Theories of chromatographic elution on ion exchange columns

A mathematical theory of chromatographic adsorption was developed by Wilson[80] and DeVault[81] and later extended by Glueckauf[82–86], Weiss and his collaborators[87] and others. It has not contributed to practical chromatography and has served mainly for the calculation of adsorption isotherms from elution data. The theory of column processes was first developed in analogy to fractional distillation by Martin and Synge[88]; its results and principles are stated in Part C (pp. 151, 154). Using a similar approach Mayer and Tompkins[89] obtained an equation relating the volume of solvent necessary to elute the peak of a band with the equilibrium constant. This was expressed by them as

$$F_{max} = C \quad \text{(see also p. 154)} \tag{1}$$

where F_{max} = number of V's that have passed through the column, when the peak of a band is eluted.

V = the volume of solution in the column.

C = distribution of solute in any plate, *i.e.* the equilibrium constant corrected for resin volume and solvent volume ratio.

Beukenkamp *et al.*[90] express this equation as

$$U^X = CV \tag{2}$$

where U^X = the volume that has passed through the column when the concentration of the solute is maximum, *i.e.* when the peak is eluted. As they prefer to measure the volume which collects till the peak is eluted, which is the volume added to the column + the volume already contained in it they express this as

$$U^X = CV + V$$

where U^X is defined as the volume eluted when the concentration of the solute is maximum.

Eqns. (1) and (2) merely express mathematically that the least adsorbed substance is first eluted and permits the calculation of the volume required to elute a peak of a band when certain data on the resin and column dimensions are known.

Both Martin and Synge[88] and Mayer and Tompkins[89] proceed then to calculate the number of *theoretical plates, i.e.* the length of column required for one equilibrium process between the dissolved and the adsorbed solute. Their work was criticised by Glueckauf[91] who points out that a discontinuous treatment may introduce errors which are obviated by his continuous flow model of a column. He constructed tables giving the purity of the separated products as function of the separation factor and the number of theoretical plates of the column for special conditions when equilibrium is practically obtained, that is with very small particles and low flow rates.

We shall only give the results of a simplified model due to Beukenkamp *et al.*[90] which assumes that the elution curves resemble very closely the Gaussian equation. In this case the number of theoretical plates p of a column is

$$p = \left(\frac{2C}{C + 1}\right)\left(\frac{U^x}{U_a - U^x}\right) \tag{3}$$

where U_a is the volume required to elute that part of the band where the concentration of the solute equals the peak concentration divided by e (base of the natural system of logarithms). As all terms of this equation may be obtained from an experimental elution graph (provided V is known), this equation permits the calculation of the number of theoretical plates from experimental data. A similar equation is cited by Schubert

$$p = \frac{2C(C + 1)}{W^2} \tag{4}$$

where W is the half width of the elution curve at an ordinate of $1/e$ of the maximum. Beukenkamp *et al.*[90] then proceed also to calculate the relation of C (the equilibrium constant) to the pH and the concentration of the eluant for the general case of a weak tribasic acid H_3A through a column saturated with Cl^-; for details see the original paper.

The column height required for a given separation was calculated by the above authors[90] still on the assumption of the elution curve of Gaussian shape. If the separation is *quantitative* that is, that 99.9% of A is separated from 99.9% of B then an approximation formula

$$\sqrt{H} = \frac{3.29}{C_2 - C_1}\left(\frac{C_2 + 0.5}{\sqrt{P_2}} + \frac{C_1 + 0.5}{\sqrt{P_1}}\right) \tag{5}$$

may be used, where H = the height of the column, P = the number of plates per centimeter (this of course depends on U_a, see eqn. 3, and hence varies for each substance) and $C = b$ (as before) the equilibrium constant. For the use of this equation an experimental elution curve must be available and then it serves to calculate:

(*a*) if the separation is incomplete what column length must be used for a complete separation or

(*b*) if the separation is complete, how much smaller a column may be used while maintaining a quantitative separation.

Thus the main use of this expression will be in the calculation of conditions used in routine analyses where such exact information would be valuable. This equation was confirmed for the elution of a mixture of tetrametaphosphate and trimetaphosphate with 0.500 M KCl as shown in Fig. 8.

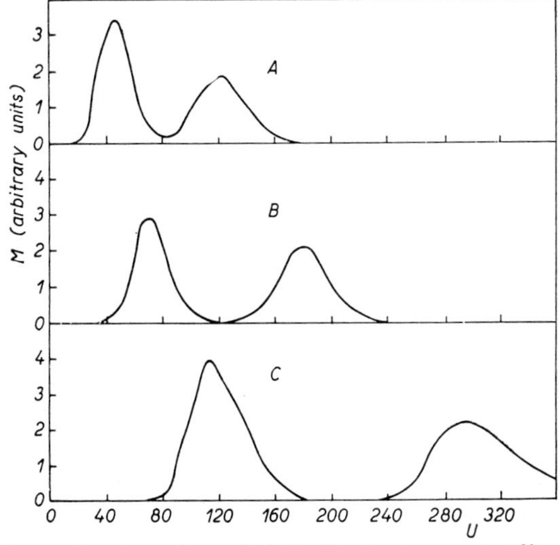

Fig. 8. Test of equation for column height (Beukenkamp *et al.*[90]). Elutions of tetrametaphosphate and trimetaphosphate with 0.500 M KCl.

The first column used was 5.8 cm long and 3.8 cm^2 cross section, as shown in Fig. 8A. From this elution graph a column height of 8.0 cm was calculated and the experimental results with a column 8.3 cm long are shown in Fig. 8B. Fig. 8C shows an elution with a 13.8 cm column. Beukenkamp *et al.*[90] recommend that the actual column used should be slightly larger than that calculated by eqn. (5), in this particular case 8.5 cm.

To summarise: the various theories may be used for calculating adsorption isotherms and equilibrium constants (instability constants of complexes, dissociation constants of weak acids and bases, etc.) from elution data. It is also possible to calculate the number of theoretical plates, the amount of contamination of one substance in another on a given part of the elution curve, the minimum length of a column for a given separation and, if certain constants of the substance, are known even the optimum eluant conditions. Nevertheless for the separation or identification of unknown substances most data are preferably employed on the usual empirical basis and column lengths, etc. conveniently judged by trial and error.

5. Ion exchange papers

Ordinary filter paper contains usually a certain amount of COOH groups the effect of which may not be negligible in chromatography at least in some cases, as has been shown by Schoenfeld and Broda[92], Burma[93], Boscott[94], Schute[95] and also by Ultée and Hartel[96] who determine the COOH content of paper chromatographically. It is, however, desirable to increase the ion exchange capacity of filter paper if it is to be used for ion exchange chromatography.

Carboxyl groups in the paper were formed by Wieland and Berg[97] by oxidation with N_2O_4 after Yackel and Kenyon[98] which produces a paper containing up to 5% of COOH groups. This paper is then readily soluble in alkali and has to be used only with acid solvents. Wieland and Berg employed this paper for separations of amino acids, inorganic ions (Ag + Pb—Bi—Hg and Sb—As—Sn) as well as for curare alkaloids. This work has been continued by Ströle[99] who studied in detail the variables (pH, buffers, COOH content) for the separation of the basic amino acids. Commercial oxycellulose is used for chromatography of peptides. For the preparation of carboxyl, *sulphonic* and *pyridinium* papers see Lautsch *et al.*[100]. Sober and Peterson[101] prepare a carboxyl cellulose by treating strongly alkaline cellulose with chloroacetic acid. Proteins are separated on this cellulose (in columns) using phosphate buffers as eluant.

Phosphorylated papers were described by various authors (for example Walravens[102]). Inorganic separations with such a paper were carried out by Kember and Wells[103], for example Fe—Cu—Ni with 2 *N* NaCl as solvent. A paper obtained from cotton which had been treated with 2-aminoethylsulphuric acid (also prepared by Whatman) was used for cation exchange separations such as Au—Pt—Pd—Rh with 2 *N* HCl as developer.

Jermyn and Thomas[104] prepare a basic paper by oxidation with periodate and condensation with 2-aminoethylhydrazine. Hydrophobic paper which contains free COOH groups was synthesised by Micheel and Albers[105].

Micheel and Schminke[106] describe the preparation of a β-aminoethyl cellulose paper. A good range of commercial ion exchange papers is now available. Whatman prepares papers with phosphate, carboxymethyl, citrate, aminoethyl, diethylaminoethyl and another containing tertiary amino (Ecteola) groups.

Table IX shows their ion exchange capacity in mequiv./g and their *reference number*. Schleicher and Schüll market "Carboxylpapier I and II" containing 0.8% and 1.1% COOH groups respectively.

TABLE IX

ION EXCHANGE CAPACITIES OF WHATMAN ION EXCHANGE PAPERS

Reactive groups	*Reference number*	*Ion exchange capacity*
Phosphate	P 20	2.1 (maximum) 1.0 (for strongly acidic groups only)
Carboxymethyl	CM 50	0.5
Citrate	CT 60	2.4
Aminoethyl	AE 30	0.6
Diethylaminoethyl	DE 20	0.4
Ecteola	ET 20	0.3

Ion exchange resin papers

A simple way to prepare an ion exchange paper is by dipping paper strips into colloidal suspensions of the respective Dowex resin. These papers have been shown[73] to behave like the corresponding resin column. Thus mixtures of rare earths could be separated with citrate solutions on Dowex-50 paper and mixtures of Cu—Fe—Co with HCl on Dowex-2 paper. Essentially the same work with Zeo-Karb 225 or Amberlite IRA-400 incorporated into paper (home-made from pulp mixed with resin on a Buchner funnel) was reported by Hale[107].

It can be shown that in absence of complex formation, fully ionised cations developed with mineral acids obey the equation $x\text{pH} = R_M + \text{constant}$[108] or that the law of mass action holds on ion exchange papers. This was later

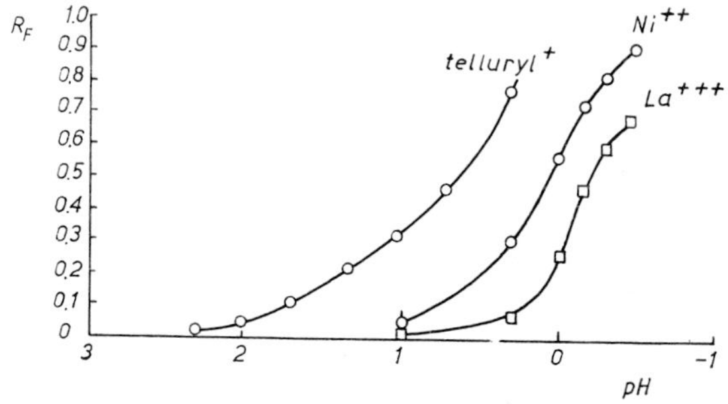

Fig. 9. The R_F–pH relationship of typical mono-, di- and tri-valent cations when eluted with H_2SO_4 (data from ref.[108]).

References p. 146

verified with several tri- and tetravalent cations and the relation of pH and R_F shown graphically[109] in Figs. 9 and 10. Dowex-50 papers were also used as a rapid test for determining the adsorbability of metal ions in HF solutions on Dowex-50[110]. Amino acids were successfully separated on ion exchange resin papers by Tuckerman[111] and Roberts and Koler[112]. Schleicher and

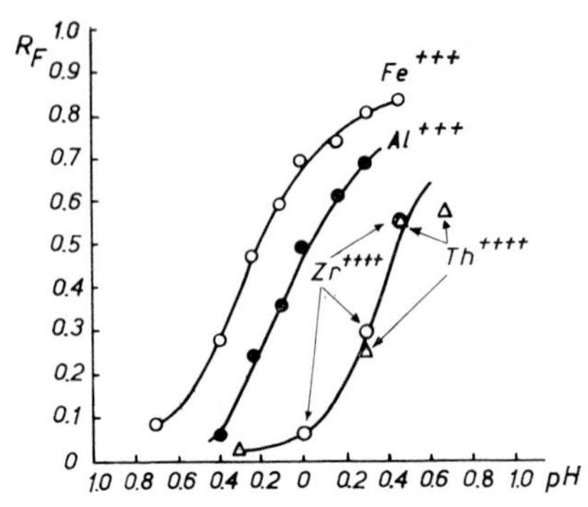

Fig. 10. The R_F–pH relationship of tri- and tetra-valent cations when eluted with HCl. Fe^{+++} has a curve rather like a divalent cation, presumably owing to the preponderance of $FeCl^{++}$ ions. Ti(IV), not shown here, precedes Fe(III) and is also not present as Ti^{4+}.

Schüll market cation and anion exchange papers containing 5% Dowex-50 and 5% Dowex 2-X8 respectively. The latter was tried by the author and found to contain insufficient resin for most purposes. Binzer also market ion exchange resin papers, which contain, however, 10 % of resin. Rohm and Haas supply four ion exchange resin papers holding about 45 % of the resin: Amberlite SA-2 paper containing fine particles of Amberlite IR-120, Amberlite WA-2 paper containing Amberlite IRC-50 a weakly acidic carboxylic resin, Amberlite SB-2 paper containing Amberlite IRA-400 and Amberlite WB-2 paper containing Amberlite IR-4B, a weakly basic, polyamine type anion exchange resin.

A similar range of papers is also available from the manufacturers of the Whatman papers. Comparative studies of the separations of amino acids on resin papers and ion exchange cellulose papers were carried out by Knight[232,233].

6. Cellulose ion exchangers

A series of new ion exchangers based on modified cellulose has been first described by Sober and Peterson[101]; these exchangers have shown particular usefulness for the purification of proteins, nucleoproteins and other high molecular compounds, including even viruses. One of the reasons for this seems to be that, due to the fibrous nature of these exchangers, the majority of functional groups is on the surface and is therefore readily available for exchange with large molecules, which normally could not penetrate the closely cross-linked structure of the synthetic ion exchange resins (see the reviews by Sober and Peterson[101,113,114]).

Cation exchangers. Sober and Peterson[101] prepared *carboxymethylcellulose* (CM-cellulose) by treating alkali-swollen α-cellulose with chloroacetic acid. It is generally considered that this reaction replaces principally the $-CH_2OH$ group of cellulose by the $-CH_2OCH_2COOH$ group.

The exchange capacity of CM-cellulose is greatest at low salt concentration. Horse carbon monoxide haemoglobin can be adsorbed by an equal weight of CM-cellulose (0.7 mequiv. carboxyl groups per g). Elution from this and similar cellulose exchangers can be accomplished with a single eluant at suitable conditions of pH and salt concentration. Since the range of adsorption affinities of proteins is generally too great to permit differential elution of all components with a single eluant, stepwise or continuous increase in salt concentration or change in pH are most frequently used. Mitz and Yanari[115] have used dissolved carbon dioxide as an eluting agent (with DEAE-cellulose columns).

Sober and Peterson[114] have studied the influence of the gradient on elution of proteins from cellulose exchange columns and have described a mixing device called "Varigrad" which makes it possible to effect any desired adjustment in the gradient.

CM-cellulose has been used for the purification of transaminases[101], of haemoglobins (Huisman *et al.*[116]) and of egg white proteins (Rhodes *et al.*[117]).

Cellulose phosphate, essentially cellulose dihydrogen phosphate, is a bi-functional exchanger containing both strong and very weak acid groups.

Micheel and Leifels[118] have described the preparation of succinylcellulose (where the active groups are $-CH_2OOCCH_2CH_2COOH$) and have used it for separation of amino acids and alkaloids.

Anion exchangers. Sober and Peterson[101] have prepared a *diethylamino ethylcellulose* (DEAE-cellulose) by treating strongly alkaline cellulose with 2-chloro-N,N-diethylamine. This exchanger, having a content of basic groups of 1 mequiv./g, adsorbs three-quarters of its own weight of bovine plasma albumin from 0.2% solution at pH 7.0 in 0.01 *M* sodium phosphate.

DEAE-cellulose has been used for a large number of purifications of proteins, *e.g.* bovine pancreatic juice (Keller *et al.*[119]), amidases (Sober and Peterson[101]), separations of complement components in guinea pig serum (Sober and Peterson[114]) and pituitary gonadotropins (Steelman and Segaloff[120]).

Ecteola cellulose has a more complex structure, produced by the action of epichlorohydrin and triethanolamine on cellulose and has a relatively small capacity for the fixation of proteins, but has proven useful for the chromatography of nucleotides, nucleic acids, nucleoproteins (Hoyer *et al.*[121]),

References p. 146

bacteriophages (Creaser and Taussig[122,123]) and mammalian viruses and rickettsiae (Hoyer *et al.*[121]).

Porath[123] has described the preparation of *triethylaminoethyl* (TEAE) cellulose which has been used for chromatography of phosphatases (Boman and Westlund[124]), phosphoproteins and nucleotides (Glomset[125]).

For separation of enzymic extracts it may sometimes be useful to perform chromatography in the absence of oxygen; Cochran *et al.*[126] have described such experiments, conducted under nitrogen gas pressure.

7. Thin layer chromatography on ion exchangers

Thin layer chromatography on layers of Ecteola cellulose on glass was recently described by Randerath[234] for the separation of nucleobases, nucleosides and nucleotides. Two-dimensional separations are obtained with 0.15 *M* NaCl and 0.01 *N* HCl as solvents and the technique offers advantages in speed and improved separation over both columns and paper chromatography.

8. The behaviour of organic compounds on ion exchange columns

In this chapter some special features pertaining to the separations of organic substances on ion exchange columns will be discussed.

Such separations have been achieved with numerous groups of ionised substances such as *amino acids, purine* and *pyrimidine bases, nucleotides* and borate complexes of *carbohydrates* (see p. 140).

(*a*) *Adsorption effects*

With amino acids, the equilibria involved in the exchange reaction are those between the unionised, the ionised and the *exchanged* forms. Davies[127] discussed the mechanism of this exchange and found that *molecular adsorption* is very large and increases with molecular weight. Similarly, organic acids and bases have been shown to be adsorbed in the unionised form by Davies and Thomas[128].

Aromatic substances are much more strongly adsorbed than aliphatic ones. This has been studied in detail by Davies and Thomas[129] for acids such as benzoic and phenylacetic as compared to citric and tartaric. The amount adsorbed is independent of particle size except for large molecules.

The affinity of straight chain fatty acids on Duolite A-2 (anion exchanger) was examined by Robinson and Mills[129] and was found to increase depending on the solvent, from acetone → water → shell solvent.

Molecular adsorption of indicators on ion exchange resins was observed by

Weiss[130] and by Idler[131]. The latter employs adsorbed phenolphthalein as an indicator to detect a band of aspartic acid on the column.

(b) *Adsorption chromatography on ion exchange resins*

The possibility of separations depending on adsorption rather than ion exchange on the surface of ion exchange resins has been discussed in a series of papers from the research laboratories of the Dow Chemical Company. One may divide such separations into two types: (*1*) the separation of organic substances from inorganic salts called *ion exclusion* and (*2*) the separation of two or more organic non-ionised substances. As has been shown in ion exchange work, the resins have a very large surface, being completely permeable and thus offer also good possibilities for reversible adsorption.

(*i*) *Ion exclusion*

Tompkins *et al.*[132] have reported in their work on fission products that a cation exchange resin allows an acid, *e.g.* HCl or HI to pass through the column without any adsorption. Wheaton and Bauman[133] were able to show

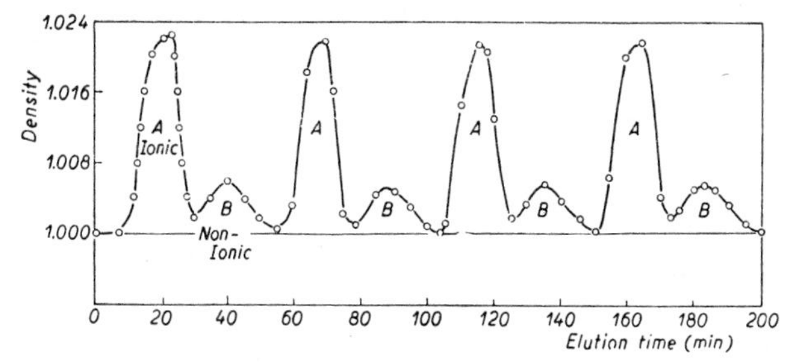

Fig. 11. Ion exclusion: semi-continuous cycles. Flow rate: 0.62 gpm/ft.^{2}, 1 vol. feed: 3 vol. rinse (Wheaton and Bauman[133]).

that weakly ionised organic acids, such as acetic acid or neutral organic molecules such as polyhydric alcohols are more or less strongly adsorbed and hence if a mixture of HCl and CH_3COOH is passed over a Dowex-50 H^+ column, HCl is first eluted followed by the organic substance, the separation depending on the adsorption affinity of the organic substance to the resin surface.

With the sodium form of Dowex-50 such separations as NaCl from ethanol are possible; industrial applications for this process are suggested.

The Dow Chemical Company[134] recommends for ion exclusion operations Dowex-50 resin with 4–12% cross-linkage. Pilot plant operations with columns of 35 gallons capacity have been operated and the following separations were achieved in a *cyclic*, *i.e.* semi-continuous process (see Fig. 11): HCl from acetic acid, HCl from dichloroacetic acid, trichloroacetic

References p. 146

from dichloroacetic acid, NaCl from ethylene glycol and from higher glycols, NaCl from ethyl alcohol, from formaldehyde, from alkanolamines, from ethylene diamine, from higher amines and ammonium chloride from amino acids. A typical separation is shown in Fig. 12.

(ii) Non-ionic separations with ion exchange resins

Since it was shown that weakly or unionised substances are retained on ion exchangers it was also evident that they could be separated from each other. Wheaton and Bauman[135] discuss in detail the effect of cross-linking and particle size on the adsorption of numerous substances. Equilibration rates were also investigated in relation to these two factors. To illustrate the possible separations we shall reproduce a table of the K_d values (see p. 119) of organic substances on Dowex resins (Table X).

TABLE X

DISTRIBUTION CONSTANTS OF ORGANIC SUBSTANCES ON DOWEX RESINS
(Wheaton and Bauman[135])

Solute (in aqueous solution)	*resin*	*Kd*
Ethylene glycol	Dowex-50-X8 H^+	0.67
Sucrose		0.24
D-Glucose		0.22
Glycerol		0.49
Triethylene glycol		0.74
Phenol		3.08
Acetic acid		0.71
Acetone		1.20
Formaldehyde		0.59
Methanol		0.61
Formaldehyde	Dowex-1-X7.5 Cl^-	1.06
Acetone		1.08
Glycerol		1.12
Methanol		0.61
Phenol		17.7
Formaldehyde	Dowex-1-X8 SO_4^{--}	1.02
Acetone		0.66
Xylose	Dowex-50-X8 Na^+	0.45
Glycerol		0.56
Pentaerythritol		0.39
Ethylene glycol		0.63
Diethylene glycol		0.67
Triethylene glycol		0.61
Ethylene diamine		0.57
Diethylene triamine		0.57
Triethylene tetramine		0.64
Tetraethylene pentamine		0.66

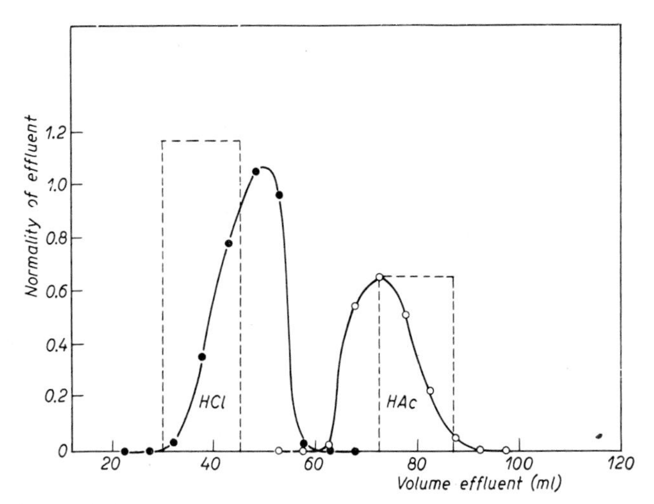

Fig. 12. Ion exclusion: complete separation. Resin: Dowex 50X 8% 50–100 mesh. Feed: 15 ml at 1.17 N HCl and 0.66 N acetic acid (Wheaton and Bauman[133]). ●—●—● HCl; ○—○—○ HAc; ----- theoretical.

(iii) *Salting-out chromatography*

Salting-out chromatography was defined by Sargent and Rieman[136] as a process in which non electrolytes may be separated by elution through a column of ion exchange resin with aqueous salt solutions as eluants. In other words the salting out effect usually used in solvent extraction or precipitation is employed to enhance the adsorption of non-electrolytes on the resin surface.

These authors separated alcohols[137,138], amines[136], aliphatic ethers, polyglycol ethers and carboxylic acids[139] and aldehydes and ketones[140]. An

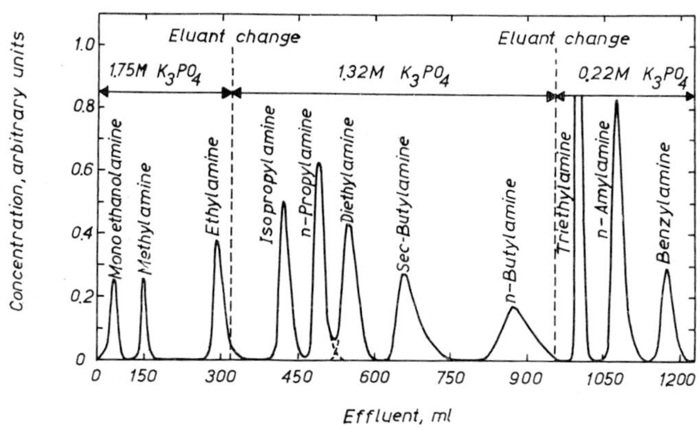

Fig. 13. The separation of an eleven-component mixture. 27.5 cm × 2.28 cm² Dowex 50-X4, 200–400 mesh, 0.4 cm/min. Potassium phosphate eluant changed at 324 and 960 ml.

References p. 146

intermediate amount of cross-linking (4% DVB) was found to give the best separations for amines on Dowex-50. Slow flow rates (0.5 cm/min) were found superior to faster rates (1 cm/min).

The electrolyte used for the salting-out depends on the class of compounds, for example K_3PO_4 (1.8 M–0.22 M) was used for amines, ammonium sulphate (3.0 M–0.01 M) for glycol ethers, aldehydes and ketones. Typical separations are shown in Figs. 13 and 14.

A theoretical interpretation of salting-out chromatography was given by the equation $\log C = \log C_0 + kM$ where C is the distribution ratio of the solute (see equation on p. 125), C_0 the distribution ratio with water as eluant, k the salting-out constant and M the molarity of salt in the eluant. The salting-out constant k was shown to be identical with the constant obtained by solubility measurements and the Setschenow equation[141].

(iv) Solubilization chromatography

While in salting-out chromatography salts are added to water to decrease the affinity of the compounds to be separated to the aqueous phase and

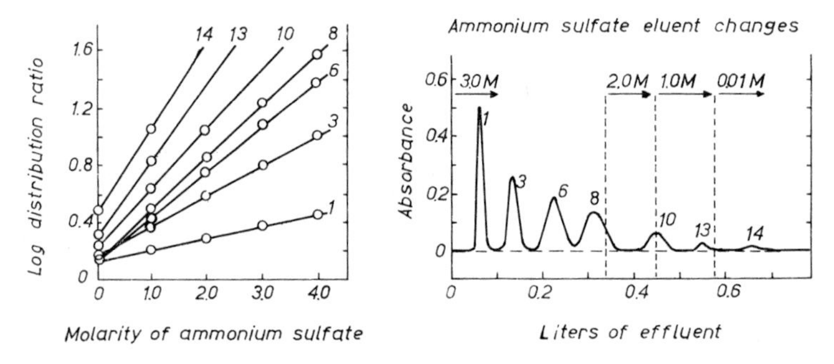

Fig. 14. Log C plots of the separation of a mixture of ethers on Dowex 50-X4, 200–400 mesh, 14.0 cm × 3.90 cm², 0.7 cm/min. Simplified structural formula of ethers and alcohols:

(1) HO—C—C—OH; (2) C—O—C—C—OH; (3) C—O—C—C(OH)—C—;

(4) C—O—C—C—O—C; (5) C—C—O—C—C; (6) (C)(C)C—O—C(C)(C);

(7) C—C—C—O—C—C—C.

thus increase their adsorption, exactly the opposite is used in solubilization chromatography, namely the addition of organic compounds to the aqueous phase, to desorb compounds too strongly held on the resin surface.

This type of chromatography was developed by Sherma and Rieman[142] to elute higher alcohols and phenols from Dowex-50 or Dowex-1. The relation between log C and the concentration of acetic acid in the eluant is not linear as in salting-out chromatography; as shown in Figs. 15 and 16. In the case of the adsorption of phenols on Dowex-1, actual ion exchange may also occur.

For typical separations of alcohols and phenols see Figs. 17 and 18. Higher ketones[143] and ethers, carboxylic acids and hydrocarbons[144] were also studied.

(v) *Salting-in chromatography*

Since such good correlation between salting-out (precipitation) and salting-out adsorption on resins was observed, Sherma and Rieman[143] also investigated whether the phenomenon of salting-in could be applied to adsorption on the resin surface. Although the phenomenon of salting-in could be observed on Dowex-1 with ketones and tetramethylammonium bromide as electrolyte, the authors concluded that salting-in chromatography does not follow the theory and would seem useless as a separation technique for organic compounds of large molecular weight.

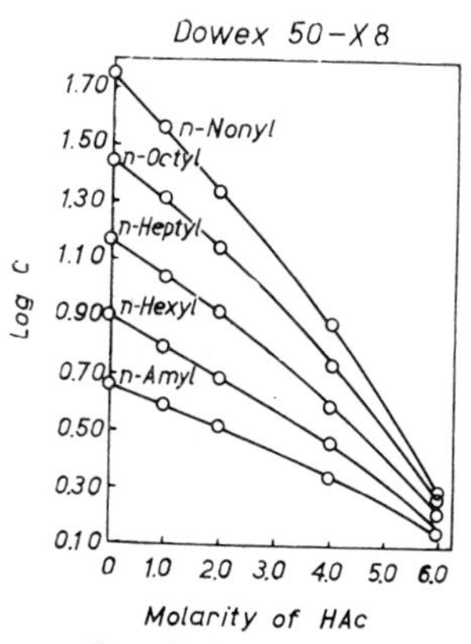

Fig. 15. Log C plots of alcohols against the molarity of acetic acid.

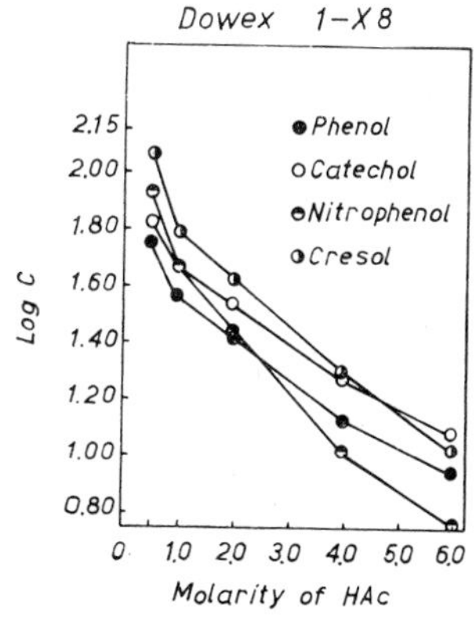

Fig. 16. Log C plots of some phenols against the molarity of acetic acid.

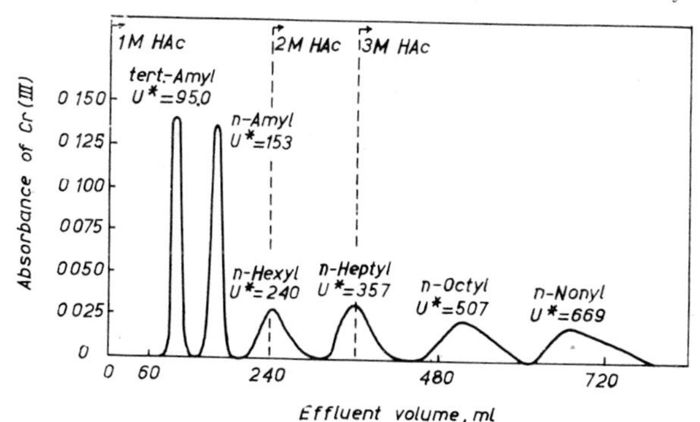

Fig. 17. Separation of alcohols on Dowex 50-X8, 200–400 mesh, hydrogen form, 39.0 × 2.28 cm², 0.45 cm/min.

(c) *Molecular sieve action of ion exchange resins*

Detailed studies on the different behaviour of polymers and monomers on ion exchange resins were made by Deuel *et al.*[145,146]. Thus clupein, polygalacturonic acid, polymannuronic acid and polymetaphosphoric acid are

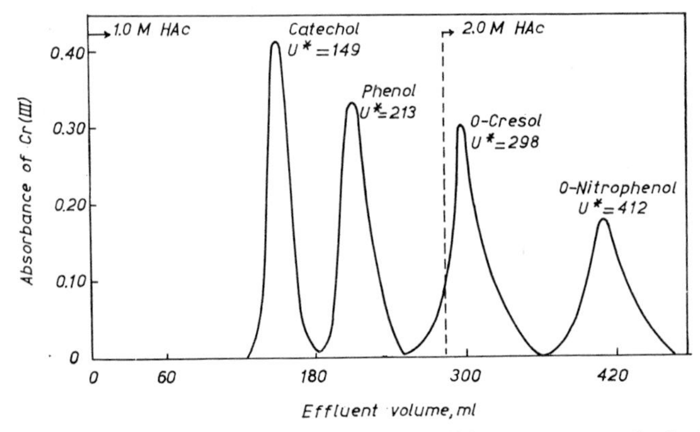

Fig. 18. Separation of phenols on Dowex 50-X8, 200–400 mesh, hydrogen form, 51.6 cm × 2.28 cm², 0.45 cm/min.

not exchanged, being too large to penetrate the pores of the exchanger (Amberlite IR-4B), whilst the corresponding monomers are readily exchanged. The catalytic hydrolysis of esters and disaccharides (with Amberlite IR-120) proceeds with small molecules, *e.g.* maltose, ethyl acetate, galacturonic methyl ester, but not with their polymers: glycogen, polyvinyl acetate and polygalacturonic methyl ester. On resins with very large pore size, both reaction and exchange with the polymers can take place.

The inability of exchange resins to adsorb large molecules was used by Richardson[147] to purify direct cotton dyes. All inorganic salts may be removed by passage through a cation and an anion exchanger.

Protein molecules, even high molecular peptides, may be unable to penetrate the pores of resins of sufficiently high cross-linkage (see Gilbert and Swallow[148], Thompson[149] and Partridge[150]).

Cellulose xanthate (viscose) is not adsorbed on anion exchangers and can thus be freed from contaminating inorganic anions (Samuelson and Gärtner[151]).

(d) *Occlusion*

While dealing with the relation of molecular size to pore size, a mention should be made of numerous effects which have been observed with porous zeolites. The term occlusion is usually employed here and differentiation between relatively small molecules was observed. Chabazite for example absorbs all the *n*-heptane from a mixture of heptane and toluene, whilst the toluene does not enter the pores of the mineral at all (see ref. [152]).

(*e*) *Specific ion exchange resins*

Suitable modifications of the active groups of synthetic ion exchange resins have been proposed for the preparation of more or less specific or selective resins.

Mercuration of a phenol–formaldehyde polymer produces a resin that selectively removes *mercaptans* from aqueous solutions (Miles *et al.*[153]). Reduced glutathione and cysteine are quantitatively retained by the resin and are recovered by elution with 2-mercapto-ethanol. Coenzyme A is also retained and can be eluted with 0.1 *M* potassium sulfide at pH 7.7. The marked influence of pH on the retention of different compounds by the resin, as well as the differences in the effectiveness of various eluting agents offer interesting possibilities for chromatographic separations of mercaptans.

Grubhofer and Schleith[154] have treated Amberlite XE-64 with quinine and have used the "asymmetric column" thus obtained for the *resolution* of the optical antipodes of mandelic acid.

The same authors[155] have diazotized the —NH_2 groups of a basic resin and then coupled it with proteins. *Enzymes* are said to have kept their activity after thus being fixed to the resin.

Isliker[156] has described the purification of *antibodies* by means of antigens linked to ion exchange resins; after fixing the stromata of erythrocytes on anion exchange resins, columns were obtained which adsorbed specifically the iso-agglutinins; similarly, cation exchange resins were transformed into their acid chlorides which were made to react with serum albumin; the thus modified resin fixes specifically the homologous antibody. Viruses can also be fixed on carboxylic resins in the acid chloride form, which are thus made specific for adsorption of the corresponding virus antibodies. Elution of the adsorbed antibodies was possible either by pH changes, or by the action of different carbohydrates having special affinities with the antibodies.

Similarly Manecke and Gillert[157] prepared immunologically specific resins by diazotizing polyaminostyrene and coupling the diazonium salt with antibodies (anti-cows' milk serum); the resins so obtained adsorbed specifically the homologous *antigen*.

Manecke *et al.*[158] have developed this idea further and have prepared an antibody-combined resin which has a certain specificity for a haptene. As haptene they used for instance *p*-aminobenzoic acid. This was diazotised and combined with a protein, (*e.g.* ovalbumin) and the azoprotein was injected into rabbits, thus producing antibodies against the protein and the haptene. The serum of these animals was then combined with a poly-*p*-isocyanate–styrene.

References p. 146

Separation of neutral carbohydrates in presence of borate. Khym and Zill[160] have developed a new method of column separation of carbohydrates, by using the reaction of polyhydroxy compounds with borate ions to form

```
   |                        [   |                 ]-
 —C—O                       [ —C—O       OH       ]
   |    \B—OH               [   |    \B/          ]  H+
 —C—O/                      [ —C—O/     \OH       ]
   |                        [   |                 ]
  (I)                            (II)
```

acidic borate complexes (I or II); these borate complexes are easily separated on columns of strong base anion exchange resins (Dowex-1) with boric acid–borate buffers (pH 8 to 9). The particular order of elution of the sugars suggests that several factors affecting the affinity of the sugar-borates for the exchanger are involved (mutarotation, furanose–pyranose interconversion, etc.). Disaccharides are readily separated from monosaccharides and the components of hexose and pentose mixtures are easily resolved. Zill *et al.*[160] have applied this method to the separation of various mono- and oligosaccharides and polyols; after elution, boric acid can be eliminated as the volatile methyl borate. Noggle and Zill[161] have applied the borate method to the analysis of sugars in plant extracts (Fig. 19). (See also ref.[162].) Lampen[163] has used the method of Khym and Zill[159] for the separation of pentoses.

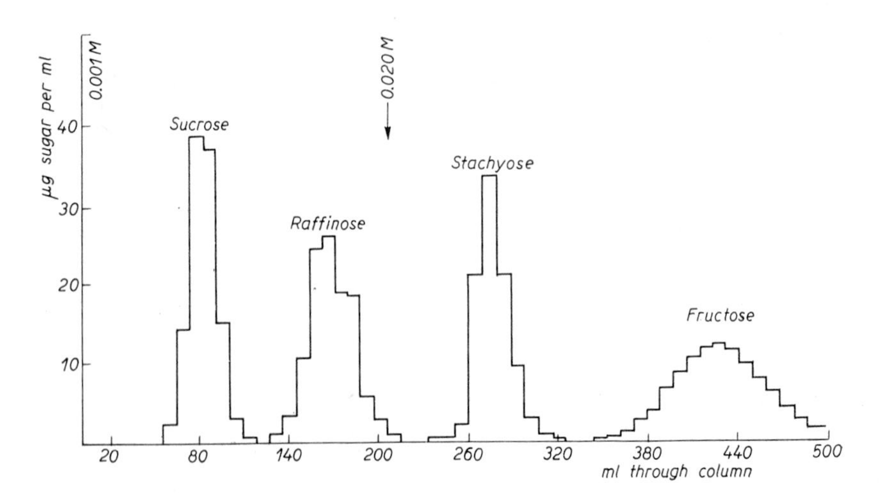

Fig. 19. Separation and recovery of 1 mg each of sucrose, raffinose, stachyose and fructose; Dowex-1 column (0.85 cm^2 × 2.5 cm). Flow rate: 60 ml/h. Elution started with 0.001 *M* potassium tetraborate and changed to 0.02 *M* at 210 ml. Found: 1.01 mg sucrose, 1.02 mg raffinose, 0.89 mg stachyose and 1.01 mg fructose (Noggle and Zill[161]).

(f) *Chromatography of proteins on ion exchange resins*

Amberlite IRC-50 has recently been used by different authors for the successful purification of basic proteins of low molecular weight.

Paléus and Neilands[164,165] obtained a good separation of *cytochrome c* from several iron-containing impurities, by eluting with 0.1 M NH_4OH–ammonium acetate at pH 10.8. Margoliash[166,167] has described in detail a method for obtaining pure cytochrome *c* by elution with an ammonium acetate buffer by ion exchange on Amberlite IRC-50 and has separated the reduced and oxidized forms. The variables involving the purification of cytochrome *c* on this resin have also been studied by Boardman and Partridge[168,169].

Hirs *et al.*[170] obtained a separation of crystalline *ribonuclease* into two peaks by chromatography on Amberlite IRC-50, thus confirming the presence of the two active components found by Martin and Porter[171] by partition chromatography on kieselguhr columns (see p. 159). Elution of the enzyme was carried out with a 0.2 M sodium phosphate buffer of pH 6.45 and proceeded without loss of enzymatic activity. Crystalline

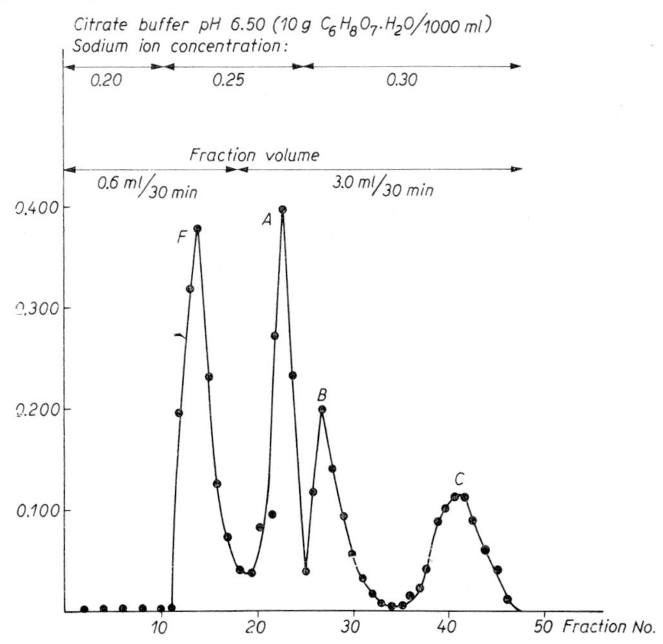

Fig. 20. Elution curves of four different kinds of human haemoglobin, chromatographed on Amberlite IRC-50 (XE-64). 48.5 mg carboxyhaemoglobin (in 0.5 ml) was chromatographed; from each fraction, after dilution to 4 ml, the extinction was measured at 5700 Å. Temp. 10°; recovery 85%. The carboxyhaemoglobins are indicated by F (foetal); A (adult), B (sickle cell), and C (Prins and Huisman[180]).

lysozyme carbonate was chromatographed under similar conditions and also yielded two active peaks, though one of these seemed to be an artefact (Tallan and Stein[172]; Stein[173]). A lysozyme-like protein from spleen of rabbit has been separated into two active fractions on columns of Amberlite XE-64 (Jollès and Fromageot[174]).

Chymotrypsinogen α has been purified on Amberlite IRC-50 by Hirs[175], by elution with a sodium phosphate buffer of pH 6, *hyaluronidase* by Rasmussen[176] and by Högberg[177], *thrombin* by Rasmussen[178].

Boardman and Partridge[169] have shown that Amberlite IRC-50 can also be used for the purification of neutral proteins; they have separated sheep foetal carbon monoxide *haemoglobin* from sheep maternal CO haemoglobin and from bovine CO haemoglobin and bovine CO haemoglobin from bovine methaemoglobin; these separations are sharply dependent on the pH and sodium ion concentration of the eluting buffer. The proteins can be recovered unaltered from the column and are readily crystallized, if the necessary precautions are taken (working at 0°, using freshly prepared proteins). Jollès and De Repentigny[179] have purified metmyoglobin on Amberlite XE-64. Prins and Huisman[180] have described a very good separation of different kinds of *human haemoglobin*, eluting with sodium citrate buffers (Fig. 20). See also the review of Prins[46].

Boman[181] has obtained good separations of *serum proteins* on columns of the anion exchange resin Dowex-2 in the chloride form, eluting by stepwise increase of buffer concentration and keeping the pH constant at 7.2; several other proteins (phosphatases, haemoglobins, phycoerythrin and phycocyanine) could also be purified. Boman[182] has also purified prostatic phosphatase on Dowex-50 by elution with a pH gradient.

(g) *Chromatography of nucleotides and nucleic acids*

Ion exchange has been extensively used for the separation and preparation of nucleotides. Cohn[183] separated the four mononucleotides of yeast nucleic acid, first by cation exchange on Dowex-50, then by an improved method by anion exchange on Dowex-1 or Dowex-2, by successive elution with weak acids and buffers of controlled pH and anion concentration[183,184]. Three isomeric adenylic and inosinic acids were separated. This method was applied by Volkin and Carter[185] to the analysis of the mononucleotides of rat liver ribonucleic acid. Two adenylic acid and two guanylic acid peaks were obtained (Fig. 21). Heterogeneity of pyrimidine nucleotides was also reported, as indicated by the formation of two peaks in ion exchange elution diagrams[186].

Cohn and Carter[187] have described the preparation of uridylic and cytidylic acids from yeast ribonucleic acid by anion exchange on Amberlite

IRA-400. Loring *et al.*[188] have separated isomeric cytidylic acids on a preparative scale by chromatography on Dowex-1 or Dowex-2.

The enzymic degradation of ribonucleic acid by crystalline ribonuclease has been studied by Carter and Cohn[189], by applying ion exchange and paper chromatographic methods to the products of hydrolysis.

More recently, gradient elution methods using Dowex-1 in the formate form with elution by increasing concentrations of formic acid or formic acid + formate have been described by Bergkvist and Deutsch[190], Hurlbert *et al.*[191]; Schmitz *et al.*[192,193]; these methods permit the successive elution of most of the mono-, di- or triphosphates of adenosine, inosine, guanosine, cytidine and uridine. These and similar methods have been largely used in recent years for the isolation of different nucleotides: inosine-phosphates (Schulman and Buchanan[194]; Deutsch and Nilsons[195]), guanosine-triphosphate (Bergkvist and Deutsch[196]), uridine-triphosphate (Bergkvist and Deutsch[197]), uridine-diphosphate glucuronic acid (Storey and Dutton[198]), cyclic phosphates of adenosine, uridine and cytidine (Brown *et al.*[199]),

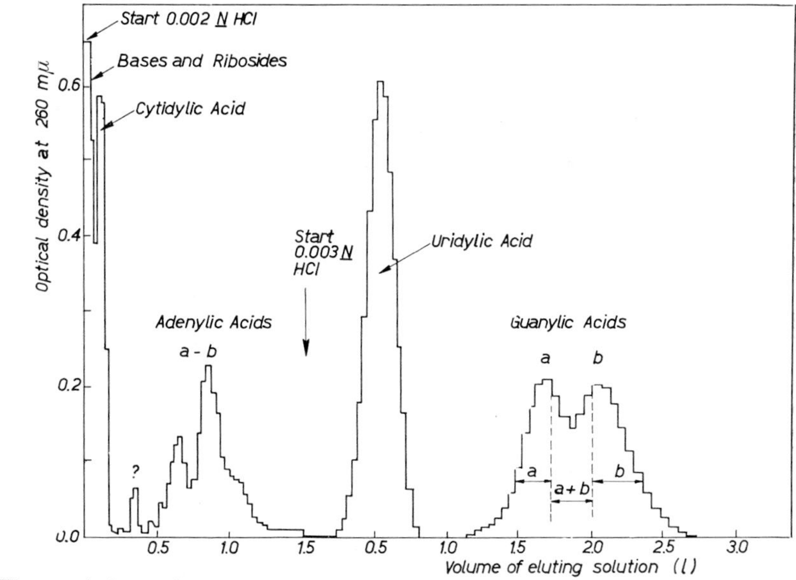

Fig. 21. Anion-exchange chromatography on Dowex-1 of rat liver ribonucleic acid mononucleotides (Volkin and Carter[185]).

pyrimidine-diphosphates (Cohn and Volkin[200]), guanosine-diphosphate-mannose from yeast (Cabib and Leloir[201]), cytidine-phosphates (Whitfeld *et al.*[202]). See also Sacks *et al.*[203].

A detailed discussion of physico-chemical factors governing separation in this field can be found in the review by Cohn[204].

References p. 146

Volkin *et al.*[205] have described the preparation of *deoxyribonucleotides* by anion exchange on Dowex-1. A similar method using Dowex-A1 has been reported by Sinsheimer and Koerner[206].

The isolation and identification of deoxy-5-methyl-cytidylic acid from thymus nucleic acid has been effected by Cohn[207], using Dowex-1. See also Potter *et al.*[208].

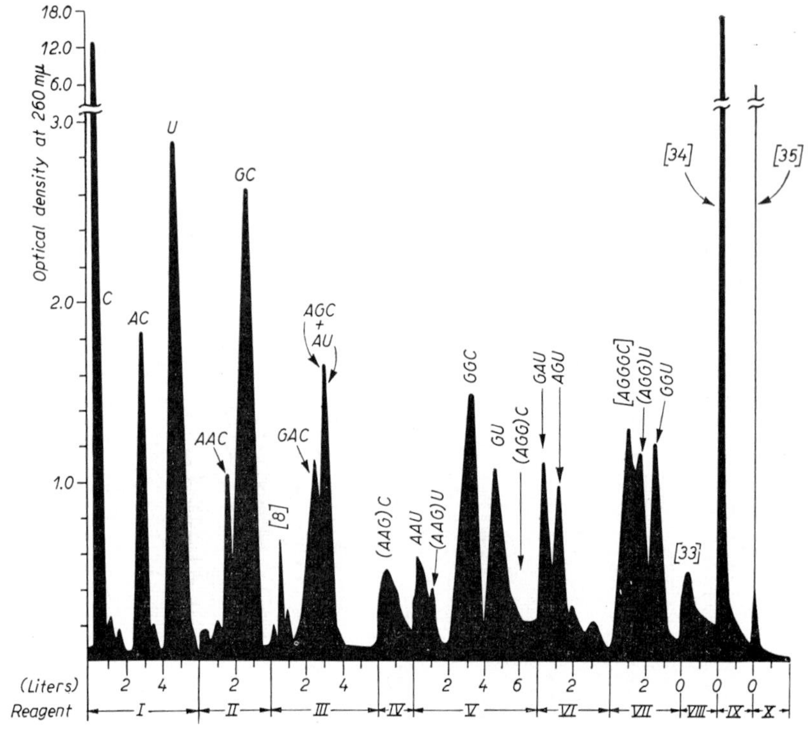

Fig. 22. Separation of the products of ribonuclease digestion of ribonucleic acid. Exchanger: Dowex-1 (2% DVB)-chloride, 400 mesh, 15 cm × 3.7 cm². Solution: HCl + NaCl as follows: I, 0.005 *N* HCl; II, 0.01 *N* HCl; III–IX, 0.01 *N* HCl + 0.0125, 0.025, 0.05, 0.1, 0.2, 0.3 and 1 *N* NaCl, respectively; X, 2 *N* HCl. Sorbed material: 700 mg calf liver RNA + 10 mg ribonuclease in 105 ml H_2O, 22 h at 37°, + NaOH as required to keep at pH 7.0; pH lowered to 2.0; chilled; centrifuged; supernatant made alkaline with NH_4OH; sorbed (Volkin and Cohn[209]). A = adenosine, C = cytidine, G = guanosine, U = uridine.

In a study of the products of ribonuclease action on ribonucleic acid, Volkin and Cohn[209] have used Dowex-1 with only 2% cross-linking (400 mesh); the low degree of cross-linking seems essential for the equilibration of the larger oligonucleotides with the active groups of the resin (Fig. 22); in this experiment the concentration of HCl was held at 0.01 *N* with stepwise increments in NaCl to remove the more strongly adsorbed oligonucleotides. Cohn[204] has discussed the relative positions of the latter in regard to the positions of the corresponding mononucleotides.

Sinsheimer[210] has separated a mixture of nineteen mono- and dinucleotides obtained by the action of deoxyribonuclease on highly polymerized deoxyribonucleic acid, by successive elutions from Dowex-1-8X and Dowex-1-2X.

(*h*) *Secondary reactions of organic compounds on ion exchange resins*

In working with ion exchange resins, it should be remembered that they are insoluble acids or bases and that a whole series of reactions can be brought about by their action on organic compounds, under more or less drastic conditions: hydrolysis of esters (Bernhard and Hammet[211]), hydrolysis or synthesis of glycosides (Mowery[212]); hydrolysis of peptide bonds (Paulson *et al.*[213]; Dixon[214]); aldolization, ketolization, crotonization and condensation of aldehydes and ketones (Durr[215]; Mastagli and Durr[216], Austerweil and Pallaud[217]), hydration of acetylenic bonds (Heilman and Glénat[218]), etc.

Carbohydrates are especially susceptible to the action of the strong base resins; Phillips and Pollard[219], Woolf[220] and Hulme[221] report destruction of sugars on Amberlite IRA-400 (OH) or Dowex-2 (OH) with formation of lactic and glycolic acids. Rebenfeld and Pacsu[222], Turton and Pascu[223] and Sowden[224] have observed isomerisation of D-glucose on Amberlite IRA-400, fructose and mannose being formed to approximately the same extent as from D-glucose in presence of dilute aqueous NaOH.

Buhler *et al.*[225] have studied the epimerization and fragmentation of glucose by quaternary ammonium base type anion exchange resins with the aid of [2-^{14}C]-glucose. Richardson and Hulme[226] have found that even weakly basic anion exchange resins, such as Deacidite G, react in the OH form with sugars to give several acids, including glyceric acid. This difficulty was overcome by using Deacidite G in the acetate form (for the separation of acids from sugars in plant extracts freed from amino acids).

Nucleosides and *nucleotides* can be partly hydrolysed by cation exchange resins; Anderson *et al.*[227] report that Dowex-50, even in the ammonium form produces extensive hydrolysis of the glycosidic linkage of deoxyribonucleosides, particularly of adenine deoxyriboside, which remains on the column for the longest period. No such hydrolysis occurred on anion exchange resins (Dowex-2 in the formate form). Lund *et al.*[228] observed partial hydrolysis of ATP to ADP on cation exchange resins, Stadtman and Kornberg[229] decomposition of coenzyme A on Dowex-50 and Kenner *et al.*[230] destruction of uridine nucleotides on anion exchange resins.

Azaserine, containing the labile aliphatic diazo group is destroyed (or irreversibly adsorbed) on Dowex-50 (H^+), Zeo Rex (H^+), Amberlite IRA-400 (OH^-), XE97 (H^+) or XE98 (OH^-) (Fusari *et al.*[231]).

References p. 146

REFERENCES

[1] F. C. Nachod, *Ion Exchange*, Academic Press, New York, 1949.
[2] F. C. Nachod and J. Schubert, *Ion Exchange Technology*, Academic Press, New York, 1956.
[3] O. Samuelson, *Ion Exchangers in Analytical Chemistry*, Almquist & Wiksell, Stockholm, 1952.
[4] O. Samuelson, in *Handbuch der Mikrochemischen Methoden*, Springer, Wien, in preparation.
[5] R. Kunin and R. J. Myers, *Ion Exchange Resins*, John Wiley & Sons, New York, 1950.
[6] H. G. Cassidy, *Adsorption and Chromatography*, Interscience, New York, 1951, 360 pp.
[7] G. H. Osborn, *Synthetic Ion Exchangers, Recent Developments in Theory and Application*, Chapman & Hall, London, 1955.
[8] G. V. Austerweil, *L'échange d'ions et les échangeurs*, Gauthier-Villars, Paris, 1955.
[9] F. Helfferich, *Ionenaustauscher*, Vol. I, *Grundlagen*, Verlag Chemie, Weinheim, 1959.
[10] G. J. Martin, *Ion Exchange and Adsorption Agents in Medicine*, Little, Brown & Co., Boston, 1955.
[11] C. Calmon and T. R. E. Kressman, *Ion Exchangers in Organic Chemistry and Biochemistry*, Interscience, New York, 1957.
[12] E. Blasius, *Chromatographische Methoden in der analytischen und präparativen Chemie unter besonderer Berücksichtigung der Ionenaustauscher*, Ferdinand Enke Verlag, Stuttgart, 1958.
[13] A. G. Jones, *Analytical Chemistry, Some New Techniques*, Butterworths, London, 1959, p. 118–154.
[14] *Research in Ion Exchange Chromatography*, (in English translation), Consultants Bureau, New York, 1958.
[15] P. Meunier and A. Vinet, *Bull. soc. chim. biol.*, 24 (1942) 365.
[16] B. Riegel, C. E. Schweitzer and P. G. Smith, *J. Biol. Chem.*, 129 (1939) 495.
[17] B. W. Lew, M. L. Wolfrom and R. M. Goepp, *J. Am. Chem. Soc.*, 68 (1946) 1449.
[18] S. B. Binkley, D. W. MacCorquodale, S. A. Thayer and E. A. Doisy, *J. Biol. Chem.*, 130 (1939) 219.
[19] R. T. Conner and G. J. Straub, *Ind. Eng. Chem., Anal. Ed.*, 13 (1941) 385.
[20] P. Ellinger and R. A. Coulson, *Nature*, 152 (1943) 383.
[21] E. E. Hays, I. C. Wells, P. A. Katzman, C. K. Cain, F. A. Jacobs, S. A. Thayer, E. A. Doisy, W. L. Gaby, E. C. Roberts, R. D. Muir, C. J. Carroll, L. R. Jones and N. J. Wade, *J. Biol. Chem.*, 159 (1945) 725.
[22] P. A. Katzman, E. E. Hays, C. K. Cain, J. J. van Wyck, F. J. Reithel, S. A. Thayer, E. A. Doisy, W. L. Gaby, C. J. Carroll, R. D. Muir, L. R. Jones and N. J. Wade, *J. Biol. Chem.*, 154 (1944) 475.
[23] P. A. Katzman, M. Godfrid, C. K. Cain and E. A. Doisy, *J. Biol. Chem.*, 148 (1943) 501.
[24] T. Wieland, *Z. physiol. Chem.*, 273 (1942) 24.
[25] K. A. Kraus, T. A. Carlson and J. S. Johnson, *Nature*, 177 (1956) 1128.
[26] B. A. Adams and E. L. Holmes, *J. Soc. Chem. Ind. (London)*, 54 (1935) 1.
[27] O. Liebknecht, *U.S. Pat.*, 2,191,060; 2,206,007; *C.A.*, 34 (1940) 4501-1; 7503-6.
[28] P. Smit, *U.S. Pat.*, 2,191,063; 2,205,635; *C.A.*, 34 (1940) 4500-7, 7504-3.
[29] G. F. D'Alelio, *U.S. Pat.*, 2,366,007 (1945); *C.A.*, 39 (1945) 4418-3.
[30] P. N. Craig, *Ann. N.Y. Acad. Sci.*, 57 (1953) 67.
[31] W. C. Bauman, *Ind. Eng. Chem.*, 38 (1946) 46.
[32] W. C. Bauman and J. Eichhorn, *J. Am. Chem. Soc.*, 69 (1947) 2830.
[33] E. R. Tompkins, *Anal. Chem.*, 22 (1950) 1352.
[34] N. E. Topp and K. W. Pepper, *J. Chem. Soc.*, (1949) 3299.
[35] Dow Chemical Company, Midland, Mich., U.S.A., *Dowex Fine Mesh Resins*, Publication No. 2, 1954.
[36] E. R. Tompkins, *J. Chem. Educ.*, 26 (1949) 32; 92.

[37] A. Skogseid, *Thesis*, University of Oslo, 1948.
[38] D. P. Mellor, *Australian J. Sci.*, 12 (1950) 183.
[39] F. P. Dwyer, N. S. Gill, E. C. Gyarfas and F. Lyons, *Australian J. Sci.*, 13 (1950) 52.
[40] H. G. Cassidy, *J. Am. Chem. Soc.*, 71 (1949) 402.
[41] I. H. Updegraff and H. G. Cassidy, *J. Am. Chem. Soc.*, 71 (1949) 407.
[42] M. Ezrin and H. G. Cassidy, *Ann. N.Y. Acad. Sci.*, 57 (1953) 79.
[43] F. H. Spedding, A. F. Voigt, E. M. Gladrow and N. R. Sleight, *J. Am. Chem. Soc.*, 69 (1947) 2777.
[44] K. A. Kraus and F. Nelson, *Peaceful Uses of Atomic Energy*, Conference, Geneva, 1955, Vol. 7.
[45] E. R. Tompkins, J. X. Khym and W. E. Cohn, *J. Am. Chem. Soc.*, 69 (1947) 2769.
[46] H. K. Prins, *J. Chromatog.*, 2 (1959) 445.
[47] K. A. Kraus, R. J. Raridon and D. L. Holcomb, *J. Chromatog.*, 3 (1960) 178.
[48] G. E. Boyd, J. Schubert and A. W. Adamson, *J. Am. Chem. Soc.*, 69 (1947) 2818.
[49] R. Kunin and R. J. Myers, *J. Am. Chem. Soc.*, 69 (1947) 2874.
[50] W. A. Selke, in: *Ion Exchange Technology*, Academic Press, New York, 1956, p. 52.
[51] H. P. Gregor, *J. Am. Chem. Soc.*, 70 (1948) 1293.
[52] H. P. Gregor, *J. Am. Chem. Soc.*, 73 (1951) 642.
[53] D. Reichenberg, K. W. Pepper and D. J. McCauley, *J. Chem. Soc.*, (1951) 493.
[54] J. F. Duncan and B. A. J. Lister, *Discussions Faraday Soc.*, 7 (1949) 104.
[55] H. F. Walton, *J. Franklin Inst.*, 232 (1941) 305.
[56] H. Jenny, *Kolloid-Beih.*, 23 (1927) 428.
[57] G. Wiegner, *J. Soc. Chem. Ind. (London)*, 50 (1931) 65T.
[58] G. Wiegner and K. W. Müller, *Z. Pflanzenernähr., Düng. u. Bodenk.*, 14A (1929) 321.
[59] R. G. Russell and D. W. Pearce, *J. Am. Chem. Soc.*, 65 (1943) 595.
[60] R. Kozak and H. F. Walton, *J. Phys. Chem.*, 49 (1945) 471.
[61] B. H. Ketelle and G. E. Boyd, *J. Am. Chem. Soc.*, 69 (1947) 2800.
[62] B. H. Ketelle and G. E. Boyd, *J. Am. Chem. Soc.*, 73 (1951) 1862.
[63] J. A. Marinsky, L. E. Glendenin and C. D. Coryell, *J. Am. Chem. Soc.*, 69 (1947) 2781.
[64] R. Kunin and R. J. Myers, *J. Am. Chem. Soc.*, 69 (1947) 2874.
[65] E. R. Tompkins and S. W. Mayer, *J. Am. Chem. Soc.*, 69 (1947) 2859.
[66] G. E. Boyd, A. W. Adamson and L. S. Myers, *J. Am. Chem. Soc.*, 69 (1947) 2836.
[67] E. N. Gapon and T. B. Gapon, *Zhur. Fiz. Khim.*, 22 (1948) 979.
[68] D. K. Hale and D. Reichenberg, *Discussions Faraday Scc.*, 7 (1949) 79.
[69] T. R. E. Kressman and J. A. Kitchener, *Discussions Faraday Soc.*, 7 (1949) 90.
[70] E. Ekedahl, E. Högfeldt and L. G. Sillen, *Nature*, 166 (1950) 723.
[71] G. E. Boyd, L. S. Myers and A. W. Adamson, *J. Am. Chem. Soc.*, 69 (1947) 2849.
[72] G. Carleson, *Acta Chem. Scand.*, 8 (1954) 1673.
[73] M. Lederer, *Anal. Chim. Acta*, 12 (1955) 142.
[74] N. F. Kember, P. J. McDonald and R. A. Wells, *J. Chem. Soc.*, (1955) 2273.
[75] J. D'Ans, E. Blasius, H. Guzatis and U. Wachtel, *Chem.-Ztg.*, 76 (1952) 841.
[76] K. K. Carroll, *Nature*, 176 (1955) 398.
[77] A. Kornberg and W. E. Pricer, *J. Biol. Chem.*, 204 (1953) 345.
[78] E. P. Kennedy, *J. Biol. Chem.*, 201 (1953) 399.
[79] P. Savary and P. Desnuelle, *Bull. soc. chim. France*, (1954) 936.
[80] J. N. Wilson, *J. Am. Chem. Soc.*, 62 (1940) 1583.
[81] D. DeVault, *J. Am. Chem. Soc.*, 65 (1943) 532.
[82] E. Glueckauf, *Nature*, 160 (1947) 301.
[83] E. Glueckauf, *J. Chem. Soc.*, (1947) 1321; *J. Chem. Soc.*, (1949) 3280.
[84] E. Glueckauf, *Discussions Faraday Soc.*, 7 (1949) 12.
[85] E. Glueckauf, *J. Am. Chem. Soc.*, 73 (1951) 849.
[86] J. I. Coates and E. Glueckauf, *J. Chem. Soc.*, (1947) 1302.
[87] A. C. Offord and J. Weiss, *Discussions Faraday Soc.*, 7 (1949) 26.
[88] A. J. P. Martin and R. L. M. Synge, *Biochem. J.*, 35 (1941) 1358.
[89] S. W. Mayer and E. R. Tompkins, *J. Am. Chem. Soc.*, 69 (1947) 2866.

[90] J. Beukenkamp, W. Rieman III and S. Lindenbaum, *Anal. Chem.*, 26 (1954) 505.
[91] E. Glueckauf, *Trans. Faraday Soc.*, 51 (1955) 34.
[92] T. Schönfeld and E. Broda, *Mikrochemie ver. Mikrochim. Acta*, 36/37 (1951) 537.
[93] D. P. Burma, *Anal. Chem.*, 25 (1953) 549.
[94] R. J. Boscott, *Chem. & Ind. (London)*, (1952) 472.
[95] J. B. Schute, *Nature*, 171 (1953) 839.
[96] A. J. Ultée Jr. and J. Hartel, *Anal. Chem.*, 27 (1955) 557.
[97] T. Wieland and A. Berg, *Angew. Chem.*, 64 (1952) 418.
[98] E. C. Yackel and W. O. Kenyon, *J. Am. Chem. Soc.*, 64 (1942) 121.
[99] U. Ströle, *Z. anal. Chem.*, 144 (1955) 256.
[100] W. Lautsch, G. Manecke und W. Broser, *Z. Naturforsch.*, 8b (1953) 232.
[101] H. A. Sober and E. A. Peterson, *J. Am. Chem. Soc.*, 76 (1954) 1711.
[102] J. Walravens, *Arch. intern. physiol.*, 60 (1952) 191.
[103] N. F. Kember and R. A. Wells, *Nature*, 175 (1955) 512.
[104] M. A. Jermyn and R. Thomas, *Nature*, 172 (1953) 728.
[105] F. Micheel and P. Albers, *Mikrochim. Acta*, (1954) 489.
[106] F. Micheel and W. Schminke, *Ber.*, 91 (1958) 984.
[107] D. K. Hale, *Chem. & Ind. (London)*, (1955) 1147.
[108] M. Lederer and S. Kertes, *Anal. Chim. Acta*, 15 (1956) 226.
[109] M. Lederer, *J. Chromatog.*, 1 (1958) 314.
[110] M. Lederer, *J. Chromatog.*, 2 (1959) 209.
[111] M. M. Tuckerman, *Anal. Chem.*, 30 (1958) 231.
[112] H. R. Roberts and M. G. Koler, *Anal. Chem.*, 31 (1959) 565.
[113] H. A. Sober and E. A. Peterson, in: C. Calmon and T. R. E. Kressman, *Ion Exchangers in Organic Chemistry and Biochemistry*, Interscience, New York, 1957, p. 318.
[114] H. A. Sober and E. A. Peterson, *Federation Proc.*, 17 (1958) 1116.
[115] M. A. Mitz and S. Yanari, *J. Am. Chem. Soc.*, 78 (1956) 2649.
[116] T. H. J. Huisman, E. A. Martis and A. Dozy, *J. Lab. Clin. Med.*, 52 (1958) 312.
[117] M. B. Rhodes, P. B. Azari and R. E. Feenay, *J. Biol. Chem.*, 230 (1958) 399.
[118] F. Micheel and W. Leifels, *Ber.*, 91 (1958) 1212.
[119] P. J. Keller, E. Cohen and H. Neurath, *J. Biol. Chem.*, 233 (1958) 344.
[120] S. L. Steelman and A. Segaloff, *Recent Progr. in Hormone Research*, 15 (1959) 115.
[121] B. H. Hoyer, E. T. Bolton, Richard A. Ormsbee, G. Le Bouvier, D. B. Ritter and C. L. Larson, *Science*, 127 (1958) 859.
[122] E. H. Creaser and A. Taussig, *Virology*, 4 (1957) 418: *C.A.*, (1958) 10261-e.
[123] J. Porath, *Arkiv kemi*, 11 (1957) 97.
[124] H. G. Boman and L. E. Westlund, *Arch. Biochem. Biophys.*, 70 (1957) 572.
[125] J. Glomset, *Acta Chem. Scand.*, 12 (1958) 641.
[126] G. W. Cochran, J. L. Chidester and G. W. Welkie, *Biochim. Biophys. Acta*, 35 (1959) 190.
[127] C. W. Davies, *Biochem. J.*, 45 (1949) 38.
[128] C. W. Davies and G. G. Thomas, *J. Chem. Soc.*, (1951) 2624.
[129] D. A. Robinson and G. F. Mills, *Ind. Eng. Chem.*, 41 (1949) 2221.
[130] D. E. Weiss, *Roy. Australian Chem. Inst. J. & Proc.*, 17 (1950) 141.
[131] D. R. Idler, *J. Am. Chem. Soc.*, 71 (1949) 3854.
[132] E. R. Tompkins, J. X. Khym and W. E. Cohn, *J. Am. Chem. Soc.*, 69 (1947) 2769.
[133] R. M. Wheaton and W. C. Bauman, *Ind. Eng. Chem.*, 45 (1953) 228.
[134] Dow Chemical Company, Midland, Mich., U.S.A., *Ion Exclusion*, Technical Service and Development Pamphlet, 1952.
[135] R. M. Wheaton and W. C. Bauman, *Ann. N.Y. Acad. Sci.*, 57 (1953) 159.
[136] R. Sargent and W. Rieman III, *Anal. Chim. Acta*, 17 (1957) 408.
[137] R. Sargent and W. Rieman III, *J. Org. Chem.*, 21 (1956) 594.
[138] R. Sargent and W. Rieman III, *J. Phys. Chem.*, 61 (1957) 354.
[139] R. Sargent and W. Rieman III, *Anal. Chim. Acta*, 18 (1958) 197.
[140] A. Breyer and W. Rieman III, *Anal. Chim. Acta*, 18 (1958) 204.
[141] I. Setschenow, *Z. physik. Chem.*, 4 (1889) 117.
[142] J. Sherma and W. Rieman III, *Anal. Chim. Acta*, 18 (1958) 214.

[143] J. Sherma and W. Rieman III, *Anal. Chim. Acta,* 19 (1958) 134.
[144] J. Sherma and W. Rieman III, *Anal. Chim. Acta,* 20 (1959) 357.
[145] H. Deuel, J. Solms and L. Anyas-Weisz, *Helv. Chim. Acta,* 33 (1950) 2171.
[146] H. Deuel, J. Solms, L. Anyas-Weisz and G. Huber, *Helv. Chim. Acta,* 34 (1951) 1849.
[147] R. W. Richardson, *J. Chem. Soc.,* (1951) 910.
[148] G. A. Gilbert and A. J. Swallow, *Biochem. J.,* 47 (1950) 502.
[149] A. R. Thompson, *Nature,* 169 (1952) 495.
[150] S. M. Partridge, *Nature,* 169 (1952) 496.
[151] O. Samuelson and F. Gärtner, *Acta Chem. Scand.,* 5 (1951) 596.
[152] H. G. Cassidy, *Adsorption and Chromatography,* Interscience, New York, 1951, 360 pp.
[153] H. T. Miles, E. R. Stadtman and W. E. Kielley, *J. Am. Chem. Soc.,* 76 (1954) 4041.
[154] N. Grubhofer and L. Schleith, *Z. physiol. Chem.,* 296 (1954) 262.
[155] N. Grubhofer and L. Schleith, *Naturwiss.,* 40 (1953) 508.
[156] H. C. Isliker, *Ann. N.Y. Acad. Sci.,* 57 (1953) 225.
[157] G. Manecke and K. E. Gillert, *Naturwiss.,* 42 (1955) 212.
[158] G. Manecke, S. Singer and K. E. Gillert, *Naturwiss.,* 45 (1958) 440.
[159] J. X. Khym and L. P. Zill, *J. Am. Chem. Soc.,* 73 (1951) 2399; 74 (1952) 2090.
[160] L. P. Zill, J. X. Khym and G. M. Chenial, *J. Am. Chem. Soc.,* 75 (1953) 1339.
[161] G. R. Noggle and L. P. Zill, *Arch. Biochem. Biophys.,* 41 (1952) 21.
[162] G. R. Noggle and L. P. Zill, *Plant Physiol.,* 28 (1953) 731: *C.A.,* 48 (1954) 2166-b.
[163] J. O. Lampen, *J. Biol. Chem.,* 204 (1953) 999.
[164] S. Paléus and J. B. Neilands, *Acta Chem. Scand.,* 4 (1950) 1024.
[165] J. B. Neilands, *J. Biol. Chem.,* 197 (1952) 701.
[166] E. Margoliash, *Nature,* 170 (1952) 1014.
[167] E. Margoliash, *Biochem. J.,* 56 (1954) 529; 535.
[168] N. K. Boardman and S. M. Partridge, *J. Polymer Sci.,* 12 (1954) 281: *C.A.,* 48 (1954) 5900-e.
[169] N. K. Boardman and S. M. Partridge, *Biochem. J.,* 59 (1955) 543.
[170] C. H. W. Hirs, W. H. Stein and S. Moore, *J. Am. Chem. Soc.,* 73 (1951) 1893.
[171] A. J. P. Martin and R. R. Porter, *Biochem. J.,* 49 (1951) 215.
[172] H. H. Tallan and W. H. Stein, *J. Am. Chem. Soc.,* 73 (1951) 2976.
[173] W. H. Stein, in: *The Chemical Structure of Proteins,* Ciba Foundation Symposium, 1953, p. 17.
[174] G. Jollès and C. Fromageot, *Biochim. Biophys. Acta,* 11 (1953) 95.
[175] C. H. W. Hirs, *J. Biol. Chem.,* 205 (1953) 93.
[176] P. S. Rasmussen, *Biochim. Biophys. Acta,* 14 (1954) 567.
[177] B. Högberg, *Acta Chem. Scand.,* 8 (1954) 1098.
[178] P. S. Rasmussen, *Biochim. Biophys. Acta,* 16 (1955) 157.
[179] P. Jollès and J. de Repentigny, *Biochim. Biophys. Acta,* 15 (1954) 161.
[180] H. K. Prins and T. H. J. Huisman, *Nature,* 175 (1955) 903.
[181] H. G. Boman, *Nature,* 175 (1955) 898.
[182] H. G. Boman, *Biochim. Biophys. Acta,* 16 (1955) 245.
[183] W. E. Cohn, *Science,* 109 (1949) 377; *J. Am. Chem. Soc.,* 71 (1949) 2275.
[184] W. E. Cohn, *J. Am. Chem. Soc.,* 72 (1950) 1471.
[185] E. Volkin and C. E. Carter, *J. Am. Chem. Soc.,* 73 (1951) 1516.
[186] W. E. Cohn, *J. Am. Chem. Soc.,* 72 (1950) 2811.
[187] W. E. Cohn and C. E. Carter, *J. Am. Chem. Soc.,* 72 (1950) 2606.
[188] H. S. Loring, H. W. Bortner, L. W. Levy and M. L. Hammell, *J. Biol. Chem.,* 196 (1952) 807.
[189] C. E. Carter and W. E. Cohn, *J. Am. Chem. Soc.,* 72 (1950) 2604.
[190] R. Bergkvist and A. Deutsch, *Acta Chem. Scand.,* 8 (1954) 1877.
[191] R. B. Hurlbert, H. Schmitz, A. F. Brumm and V. R. Potter, *J. Biol. Chem.,* 209 (1954) 23.
[192] H. Schmitz, *Biochim. Biophys. Acta,* 14 (1954) 160.
[193] H. Schmitz, R. B. Hurlbert and V. R. Potter, *J. Biol. Chem.,* 209 (1954) 41.
[194] M. P. Schulman and J. M. Buchanan, *J. Biol. Chem.,* 196 (1952) 513.

[195] A. Deutsch and R. Nilsson, *Acta Chem. Scand.*, 7 (1953) 1288.
[196] R. Bergkvist and A. Deutsch, *Acta Chem. Scand.*, 8 (1954) 1889.
[197] R. Bergkvist and A. Deutsch, *Acta Chem. Scand.*, 8 (1954) 1880.
[198] I. D. E. Storey and G. J. Dutton, *Biochem. J.*, 59 (1955) 279.
[199] D. M. Brown, C. A. Dekker and A. R. Todd, *J. Chem. Soc.*, (1952) 2715.
[200] W. E. Cohn and E. Volkin, *J. Biol. Chem.*, 203 (1953) 319.
[201] E. Cabib and L. F. Leloir, *J. Biol. Chem.*, 206 (1954) 779.
[202] P. R. Whitfeld, L. A. Heppel and R. Markham, *Biochem. J.*, 60 (1955) 15.
[203] J. Sacks, L. Lutwak and P. D. Hurley, *J. Am. Chem. Soc.*, 76 (1954) 424.
[204] W. E. Cohn, in: *The Nucleic Acids*, Vol. I, Academic Press, New York, 1955, p. 211.
[205] E. Volkin, J. X. Khym and W. E. Cohn, *J. Am. Chem. Soc.*, 73 (1951) 1533.
[206] R. L. Sinsheimer and J. F. Koerner, *Science*, 114 (1951) 42.
[207] W. E. Cohn, *J. Am. Chem. Soc.*, 73 (1951) 1539.
[208] J. L. Potter, K. D. Brown and M. Laskowski, *Biochim. Biophys. Acta*, 9 (1952) 150.
[209] E. Volkin and W. E. Cohn, *J. Biol. Chem.*, 205 (1953) 767.
[210] R. L. Sinsheimer, *J. Biol. Chem.*, 208 (1954) 445.
[211] S. A. Bernhard and L. P. Hammett, *J. Am. Chem. Soc.*, 75 (1953) 1798.
[212] D. F. Mowery jr., *J. Am. Chem. Soc.*, 77 (1955) 1667.
[213] J. C. Paulson, F. E. Deatherage and E. F. Almy, *J. Am. Chem. Soc.*, 75 (1953) 2039.
[214] A. S. J. Dixon, *Biochem. J.*, 60 (1955) 165.
[215] G. Durr, *Compt. rend.*, 235 (1952) 1314.
[216] P. Mastagli and G. V. Durr, *Bull. soc. chim. France*, (1955) 268.
[217] G. V. Austerweil and R. Pallaud, *J. Appl. Chem. (London)*, 5 (1955) 213.
[218] R. Heilman and R. Glénat, *Compt. rend.*, 240 (1955) 2317.
[219] J. D. Phillips and A. Pollard, *Nature*, 171 (1953) 41.
[220] L. I. Woolf, *Nature*, 171 (1953) 841.
[221] A. C. Hulme, *Nature*, 171 (1953) 610.
[222] L. Rebenfeld and E. Pascu, *J. Am. Chem. Soc.*, 75 (1953) 4370.
[223] C. N. Turton and E. Pacsu, *J. Am. Chem. Soc.*, 77 (1955) 1059.
[224] J. C. Sowden, *J. Am. Chem. Soc.*, 76 (1954) 4487.
[225] D. R. Buhler, R. C. Thomas, B. E. Christensen and C. H. Wang, *J. Am. Chem. Soc.*, 77 (1955) 481.
[226] A. Richardson and A. C. Hulme, *Nature*, 175 (1955) 43.
[227] A. S. Anderson, G. R. Barker, J. M. Gulland and M. V. Lock, *J. Chem. Soc.*, (1952) 369.
[228] N. A. Lund, F. S. M. Grylls and J. S. Harrison, *Nature*, 173 (1954) 544.
[229] E. R. Stadtman and A. Kornberg, *J. Biol. Chem.*, 203 (1953) 47.
[230] G. W. Kenner, A. R. Todd and R. F. Webb, *J. Chem. Soc.*, (1954) 2843.
[231] S. A. Fusari, R. P. Frohardt, A. Ryder, T. H. Haskell, D. W. Johannessen, C. C. Elder and Q. R. Bartz, *J. Am. Chem. Soc.*, 76 (1954) 2878.
[232] C. S. Knight, *Symposium on paper chromatography*, Prague, 1961.
[233] C. S. Knight, *Chromatog. Reviews*, 4 (1962) 69.
[234] K. Randerath, *Angew. Chem.*, 73 (1961) 674.

Chapter II

PART C

Partition Chromatography

Introduction

When a solution of a substance is shaken with an immiscible solvent, the solute will distribute itself between two phases and when equilibrium is reached, the coefficient $\frac{\text{concentration in solvent A}}{\text{concentration in solvent B}}$ is a constant α, where α is termed the *partition coefficient.*

In order to effect a separation of a mixture of amino acids, Martin and Synge[1] utilised the difference of partition coefficients with a battery of solvent-solvent extractors. Although this work with solvent-solvent extractors (counter-current distribution) has been further developed, notably by Craig[2], Martin and Synge[3] found that a far more efficient, fractional solvent-solvent extraction is possible by packing columns with silica gel, holding about 50% water, placing the solution of a mixture on the column and developing with water-immiscible solvents *e.g.* chloroform containing small amounts of butanol. The liquid held on the column is termed the stationary phase and the eluant the mobile phase. Other materials are also capable of holding water as a stationary phase and columns of starch, cellulose powder, cotton linters, even asbestos and glass beads will be mentioned in the special sections.

This process has been called *partition chromatography* as distinct from adsorption chromatography.

Consden, Gordon and Martin[4] showed that filter paper sheets and strips can also be used as support of a stationary phase in partition chromatography. This technique, called *paper chromatography*—other names proposed: papyrography[5] and partography[6]—is probably the most versatile method for analytical work on a micro scale. Generally water or hydroxylated polar solvents are used as stationary solvents and more or less non-polar solvents as mobile phases. For lipid-soluble substances with very low solubility in hydroxylated solvents (higher fatty acids, weakly polar steroids, etc.) it is preferable to hold a lipid phase stationary on such materials as rubber latex (Boldingh[7,8]), glass powder (Partridge and Chilton[9]), silicone-treated kiesel-

References p. 208

guhr[10] and silicone- or vaselin-treated filter paper[11]. The mobile phase in this type of chromatography, called *reversed phase chromatography*, is usually a hydrophilic solvent.

Theory. A theory of partition chromatography, developed by Martin and Synge[3] considers chromatography analogous to fractional distillation with total reflux. By employing the concept of a theoretical plate, they developed an equation to correlate the rate of movement of a zone with the partition coefficient, *viz.*

$$R_F = \frac{A_L}{A_L + \alpha A_S} \tag{1}$$

where α = partition coefficient $\frac{\text{concn. in water phase}}{\text{concn. in lipid phase}}$

A_S = the cross sectional area occupied by the stationary phase

A_L = the cross sectional area occupied by the mobile phase

$R_F = \frac{\text{distance travelled by the zone}}{\text{distance travelled by the liquid front}}$

The R_F values of amino acids have been shown to agree well with those calculated from the partition coefficients measured by static methods. Also the degree of separation of two substances of known partition coefficients can be calculated for a given length of column or paper strip.

In a later paper Martin[12] developed the theory of partition displacement chromatograms along similar lines to his original theory and arrived at the following equations for the movement of zones in a *buffered column*.

$$R = \frac{T}{M + \alpha S\left(1 + \frac{K_a}{H^+}\right)}$$

where R = ratio of rate of movement of zones divided by rate of movement of developing liquid in tube above column

T = cross sectional area of total area in column

M = cross sectional area of mobile phase in column

α = partition coefficient of unionised acid

S = cross sectional area of stationary phase in column

K_a = dissociation constant of acid.

From this relationship the optimum pH range for the separation of two acids, A and B, with partition coefficients α and β is given:

when $\beta/\alpha < 1$ and $K_b/K_a < 1$, a high pH is desirable.

when $\beta/\alpha < K_a/K_b < 1$, a low pH is desirable.

when $K_a/K_b < \beta/\alpha < 1$, a high pH is desirable.

The factors governing enrichment by passing from one phase to another were also considered by the same authors. Martin and Synge[3] calculated the number of theoretical plates in a silica gel column and found the height equivalent to a theoretical plate to be 0.002 cm. Later estimates are only 0.02 cm (Verzele[13]). Thus a column a few cm high has a few hundred theoretical plates, compared to 20 for the best distillation columns, 20 for a column of alumina in Lindner's *radiometric analysis*[14] and a few hundred for ion exchange columns (Nachod[15]).

A relationship similar to equation (1) was also developed for ion exchange columns (see p. 125).

A simple and non-mathematical approach can be developed along the kinetic approach first used by Cremer and Müller[16]. A kinetic picture of the chromatographic process is necessary: the molecules of a given solute are continually moving from the stationary phase to the moving phase and back and, depending on the partition coefficient, spend a certain average time in each phase. As all molecules do not have the same energy, some will spend more time than the average in the moving phase and some less, thus producing a band with the characteristic concentration curve, similar to the normal distribution curve.

Now consider the column or paper strip, Fig. 1, and let x be the distance

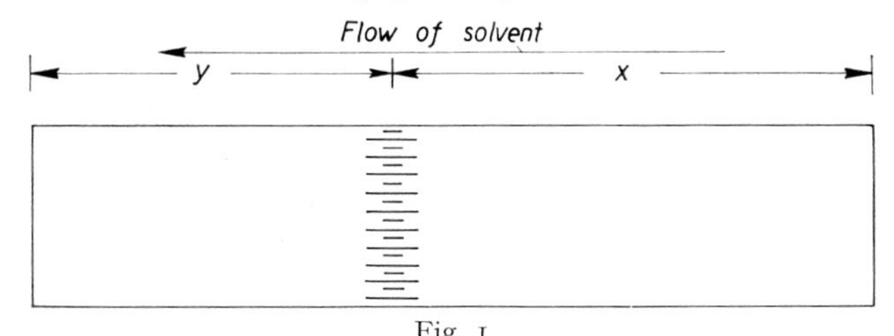

Fig. 1.

the center of a band of solute has travelled and $x + y$ the distance the solvent has travelled; then x is proportional to the solubility of the solute in the moving phase and y proportional to its solubility in the stationary phase, *i.e.* $\frac{x}{y} \propto \frac{1}{\alpha}$ (α is the partition or more generally the equilibrium coefficient) and $\frac{x}{y} = \frac{1}{\alpha} k$ where k is a constant accounting for the ratio of the cross section of the moving and stationary phase. Also

$$R_F = \frac{x}{x + y} \quad \text{and} \quad \frac{1}{R_F} = \frac{x + y}{x} = 1 + \frac{\alpha}{k}$$

where k as in the equation of Martin and Synge $= \dfrac{A_L}{A_S}$

then $$\frac{1}{R_F} = 1 + \alpha \frac{A_S}{A_L} = \frac{A_L + \alpha A_S}{A_L} \quad \text{and} \quad R_F = \frac{A_L}{A_L + \alpha A_S}$$

an expression identical with that obtained from the theory of fractional distillation.

Also the volume necessary to elute the peak of a band of a solute may be obtained in a similar manner. In Fig. 1, consider x now as the length of a column with the peak of the band just about to flow out. Assume y to be another section of column which is used to collect the effluent. Then as before, $k\alpha = \frac{y}{x}$ but y is now proportional to the volume that has to flow out to elute the peak of the band and x proportional to the volume held in the column; thus $\frac{\text{peak effluent volume}^{*}}{\text{column volume}} = k\alpha$ or the peak effluent volume $= K\alpha$.

An equivalent expression was obtained by Mayer and Tompkins[17] who eliminate K by expressing the volume in terms of the column contents (see p. 125).

The above theory establishes a correlation between the partition coefficient of a substance and its rate of movement in a chromatogram, considering only the rate of movement of the peak of the band.

Two further theoretical topics have received much attention: the shape of the band and the correlation of chemical structure and movement on the chromatogram.

The shape of the band has been dealt with first by Martin and Synge[3] for linear partition isotherms (ignoring diffusion) and a simplified method for its calculation was derived for the analogous problem in ion exchange by Beukenkamp *et al.*[18] (see p. 126). The problems associated with diffusion are almost exclusively considered in relation to spot size in paper chromatograms and are hence dealt with on p. 198.

Correlation of structure and movement on the chromatogram was first discussed by Martin[12] and has since received its main application in paper chromatography (see p. 165).

The behaviour of homologous series on partition columns was treated by Van Duin[19,20]; the problem is essentially the same as in paper chromatography.

I. PARTITION CHROMATOGRAPHY ON COLUMNS

1. Silica gel

The terms *silica gel*, or *silicic acid* refer to hydrated silica precipitates, the properties of which can vary rather widely according to the precipitation and purification method used.

Silica gel is usually prepared by precipitation of sodium silicate (water-glass) with 10 N HCl, followed by exhaustive washing and drying (Gordon *et al.*[21], also Martin[22]). For the preparation of columns it is mixed with 53% of water and poured into the column as a slurry with the mobile phase. The exact method as given by Gordon *et al.*[21] is as follows:

"Commercial water-glass (140° Tw.-Jos. Crosfield, Ltd., Warrington) is diluted to 3 vol. with distilled water containing a little methyl orange. 10 N HCl is added in a thin stream with vigorous stirring, addition being interrupted at

* Peak effluent $= F_{max}$, see p. 125.

intervals and stirring continued to get efficient mixing. The solution changes first slowly then rapidly to a thick porridge and all but the smallest lumps are broken up by stirring. When the mixture is permanently acid to thymol blue, addition of HCl is stopped and the mixture is kept three hours. It is filtered on a Büchner funnel and washed with distilled water (approx. 2 l/250 g dry gel) without allowing the precipitate to crack. The gel is then suspended in *N*/5 HCl and aged 2 days at room temperature. It is again filtered and washed in the same way with distilled water (approx. 5 l/250 g dry gel) until the washings are free from methyl orange. Finally, the gel is crumbled and dried at 110° in an air oven. With such a preparation the addition of 53% w/w of indicator solution to the dry gel should be satisfactory with the butanol–chloroform or propanol–cyclohexane mixtures. The dry gel can be stored in a closed vessel for long periods without deterioration.

The gel prepared in this way contains nitrogen. If it is wished to use it for the adsorption of the hexone bases further purification is necessary[23] as follows: 100 g of silica gel is treated for 48 to 55 hours with 500 ml of 20% acetic acid. After filtration on a Büchner funnel the gel is washed with 200 ml of 20% acetic acid and then with boiling water until the filtrate reaches pH 6. Drying is carried out at 110° for 6 h. The gel then contains approx. 20 μg of N per g. The complete removal of nitrogenous material is achieved by treating the silica gel in the column in which it is to be used with 200 ml of 0.1 *N* HCl and then with 200 ml of water."

Columns containing too much water can give rise to a phenomenon similar to water logging on paper chromatograms and a single substance may yield more than one band, as part of the band moves down the column and part is held in a "wet" zone at the top of the column (Lester Smith[24] and Ovenston[25]).

The adsorptive powers of silica gel also vary considerably from batch to batch and testing with standard mixtures of known substances for sharpness of the eluted zone is necessary.

The role of water in the chromatographic behaviour of silicic acid was subjected to a study by Kay and Trueblood[26] who concluded that depending on the amount of water held, silicic acid may act as an adsorbent or partition support; usually, both properties contribute to varying degrees to the separation effects obtained.

Tristram[27], Isherwood[28] and Harris and Wick[29] have described the preparation of silica gel for partition chromatography.

In order to render the zones of acidic substances (acetyl amino acids, fatty acids) visible on the column, indicators can be incorporated in the aqueous phase. Methyl orange was first used, but was too soluble in the mobile phase. Anthocyanins, also 3,6-disulpho-β-naphthalene-azo-N-phenyl-α-naphthylamine[30] have been found more satisfactory.

Commercial *silica gel* can be purified as follows:

"A 50-gram sample of silica gel (80- to 120-mesh) was suspended in 300 ml of concentrated hydrochloric acid and allowed to stand overnight. The yellow supernatant solution was decanted, fresh concentrated hydrochloric acid was

References p. 208

added, and the mixture was shaken, and again allowed to stand. This process was repeated until the solution was colorless. The mixture was next filtered with suction on a sintered-glass funnel. The residue on the filter was suspended in water and washed by decantation until free of chloride, filtered as before, and the material was then suspended in 95% ethyl alcohol. This suspension was filtered and washed with 200 ml of 95% ethyl alcohol on the sintered-glass disk. The gel was then washed with 200 ml of absolute ethyl alcohol, suspended in anhydrous ether, filtered, and washed with 500 ml of anhydrous ether. The gel was heated for 24 hours at 100° and finally dried for 24 hours in a desiccator over phosphorus pentoxide in vacuo."

"Davison Chemical Corp. Grade 70 silica gel, purified and dried in this way, will adsorb its weight of water and still remain dry enough to "gel" with chloroform. (This property is desirable because it allows solutions of organic acids to be taken up with a relatively small amount of gel. The mixture of gel and acids can then be placed on top of the major portion of the column in a compact zone, which permits sharp eluate fractions.)"

"Treatment with hydrochloric acid is necessary to remove inorganic cations which form insoluble salts with organic acids; incomplete washing with hydrochloric acid leads to low recoveries of the acids. The adsorbent properties which are present in some silica gels also are removed in the purification process." (Resnik *et al.*[31]).

Silicic acid (Merck or Mallinckrodt) can be purified as follows:

"500 g of reagent grade silicic acid (Merck or Mallinckrodt) are thoroughly mixed with 800 ml of acid ethanol (400 ml of c.p. hydrochloric acid diluted to 2400 ml with 95% ethanol). The mixture is filtered through a Büchner funnel, and the washing procedure is repeated at least three times. The filtrate from the final washing should be colorless. The silicic acid is then washed three times in the same manner with 700 ml portions of 95% ethanol, and finally three times with 800 ml portions of diethyl ether. It is then spread on clean white paper and allowed to dry for 24 to 48 hours. The material is then passed through an 80 mesh sieve and dried in a vacuum desiccator." (Morrison and Stotz[32]).

For separation of fatty acids or penicillins *buffered silica columns* are used. The bands are either made visible with indicators or eluted portions are titrated with alkali. Such gels may be prepared in the following way:

Buffered silica gel (for the purification of penicillin, after Levi and Terjesen[33]): 30 g of silica gel prepared as described by Martin and Synge[21] is well mixed in a mortar with 15 or 20 ml of a solution of potassium phosphate at pH 6.6 (the buffer is prepared by titrating a solution of 25 parts of KOH in 100 ml of water with an aqueous solution of 30% of phosphoric acid to pH 6.6 as measured potentiometrically). In this way a dry powder is obtained which is poured into the column with amyl acetate (the solvent used for the adsorption of penicillin). 100 g of gel are sufficient for the adsorption of 3.2 g of the calcium salt of penicillin.

Some examples of the use of silicic acid columns in partition chromatography may be quoted: Ramsey and Patterson[34] have used a column of silicic acid saturated with methanol (containing bromocresol green as indicator) and a mobile phase of isooctane to give good separations of the straight-chain fatty acids from C_5 to C_{10}; in a later publication[35] the range was extended to the C_{11} to C_{19} acids by using a silicic acid column with a mixture of furfuryl alcohol and 2-aminopyridine as the stationary phase and *n*-hexane as the mobile phase. The method of Ramsey and Patterson[34,35] has been modified by Vandenheuvel and Hayes[36] who use two different columns, the first for the acids C_2 to C_7, the second for the acids C_7 to C_{12}.

New solvent systems for separating monocarboxylic acids from C_2 to C_{16}, (and dicarboxylic acids from C_2 to C_{22}) have been described by Zbinovsky[37] (Fig. 2).

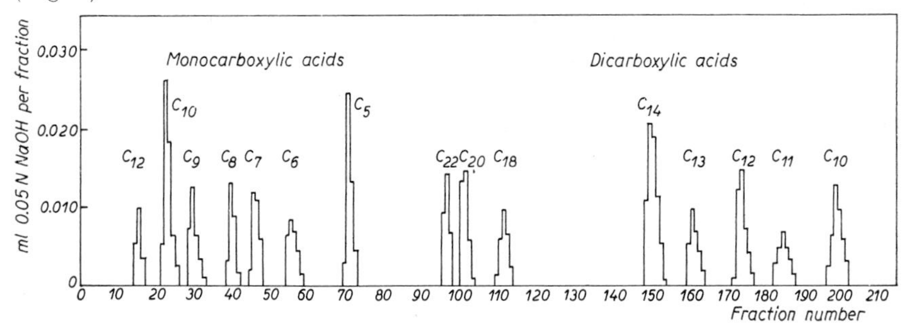

Fig. 2. Separation of monocarboxylic acids (1.8 mg of total acids) and dicarboxylic acids (2.0 mg of total acids) on 6-g silicic acid column (Zbinovsky[37]). Fractions 1–39, 0.5 ml; 40–69, 1.0 ml; 70–73, 2.0 ml; 74–171, 0.5 ml and 172–202, 1.0 ml. Solvents: Fraction 1–73, Skellysolve B; 74–127, Skellysolve B–*n*-butyl ether mixture (1:1); 128–202, *n*-butyl ether.

Van Duin[19] has separated primary and secondary amines as 2,4-dinitrophenyl derivatives, on columns of silica gel with nitromethane as stationary and petrol ether as mobile phase.

2. Kieselguhr

Kieselguhr (Celite, Hyflo Supercel) is an excellent, quite inert support for partition chromatography. Owing to the compact, crystalline nature of the silica in kieselguhr, practically no adsorption occurs. Some examples of the utilisation of kieselguhr follow.

Quantitative separations of the straight-chain fatty acids from C_2 to C_{10} have been obtained by Peterson and Johnson[38] using a Celite column with 27–37 *N* sulphuric acid as the stationary phase and benzene as the mobile phase.

A large number of di- and tri-carboxylic and keto- and hydroxy-acids have been separated on columns of Celite containing 0.5 *N* sulfuric acid, using two successive solvent systems: butanol in chloroform, followed by ether (Phares *et al.*[39]) (Fig. 3).

References p. 208

Martin and Porter[40] used the system ammonium sulphate–water–cellosolve (ethylene glycol monoethyl ether) for partition chromatography of *ribonuclease* on kieselguhr. The crystalline enzyme was found to contain two enzymatically active components (Fig. 4).

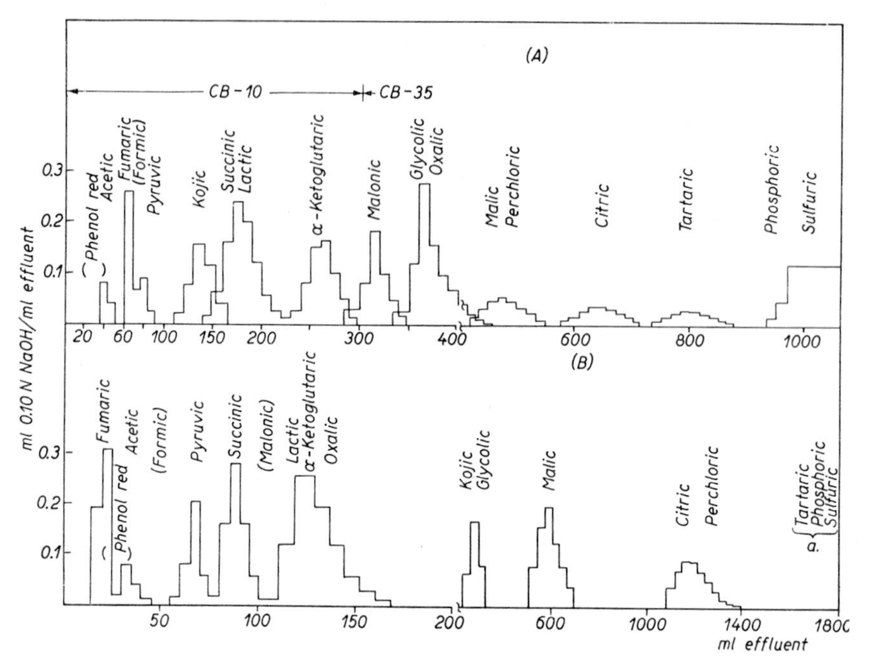

Fig. 3. Comparison of elution bands of acids with (A) chloroform–butanol and with (B) ethyl ether as the mobile phases on 45 × 1.0 cm Celite partition columns (20 ml per volume). CB-10 = 10% butanol in $CHCl_3$, CB-35 = 35% butanol in $CHCl_3$, (a) these acids not eluted at 2000 ml (Phares *et al.*[39]).

Martin and Porter[40] found that the rate of movement of the bands was much slower than would be expected from the partition coefficients of the substances. Since in the absence of the stationary phase kieselguhr shows no adsorption, the authors conclude that adsorption must occur at the interfaces between the two liquid phases. This might explain the efficiency of the separation obtained.

Porter[41] has studied in detail partition systems for chromatography of proteins, and has used three of these, containing water, ethyl and butyl cellosolve and sodium or potassium phosphate for the purification of *insulin* on silane treated kieselguhr. The behaviour of *ribonuclease, avidine, bovine serum albumin* and *penicillinase* was also studied; in the latter cases, however, some irregularities were observed, the rate of movement of the principal peaks varying considerably from one chromatogram to the next. *Glucagon, chymotrypsin* and *chymotrypsinogen* could also be purified (Porter[42]).

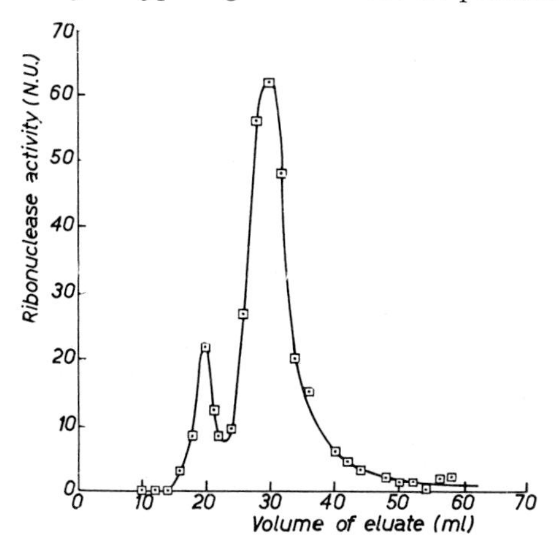

Fig. 4. Chromatogram of ribonuclease. System: 20 g ammonium sulphate, 20 g cellosolve, 56 g water, 6 g kieselguhr column (Martin and Porter[40]).

Porter[43] has studied the partition chromatography of *γ-globulin*, using the same system as described before, but working at —3° to avoid denaturation. It was concluded that a large number of components was present whose chromatographic behaviour ranges about a mean value.

3. Starch

Starch columns were employed some time ago for separations of amino acids by Moore and Stein[44] and for purines and pyrimidines by Daly and Mirsky[45]. In recent years the use of starch as support of stationary phases for chromatography has been abandoned.

4. Cellulose

Cellulose columns were used by Hough *et al.*[46] for separating macroquantities of sugars. They recommend the following for testing the efficiency of the column: "The performance of the column may be observed visually by placing a suitable mixture of the following dyes on the column and noting the appearance and the separation of the coloured materials as they advance down the column. It has been found that various dyes move at different rates on sheet-filter-paper chromatograms. The R_G values (see p. 198) of a number of the more suitable of these coloured materials have been determined on sheet-paper chromatograms, using the top layer of a mixture of *n*-butanol

References p. 208

(40 %), ethanol (10 %), water (50 %) as the mobile phase. R_G values determined were as follows: auramine 1.00, dimethyl yellow 0.95, bromothymol blue 0.83, brilliant cresyl green 0.73, metanil yellow 0.48, cresol red 0.41, methyl red 0.38, bromocresol green 0.30, bromophenol blue 0.26 and methyl orange 0.23. If the coloured materials travel through the column in the form of regular horizontal bands, the column is regarded as satisfactory for use, the uniformity of packing being thus indicated. These dyes can also be used as markers, since a dye that moves slightly faster than the fastest-moving component of the sugar mixture, can be incorporated in the mixture to be resolved, and it is then only necessary to examine the eluate after the coloured material has emerged from the column."

Both starch and cellulose columns have essentially the same general behaviour as paper strips; however, in general solvents with high R_F values are used for columns in order to keep the volume necessary for elution within reasonable limits. For displacement analysis on partition columns see Levi[47]. Solka-Floc cellulose columns were used for amino acid separations by Carter *et al.*[48]. *Ascending development* on cellulose columns was employed successfully by Fischer and Behrens[49] for the separation of indole derivatives.

A very useful cellulose column for preparative chromatography is the *Chromax** column consisting of a ready-made paper roll which is inserted into a pressure mantle which is inflatable by means of a pressure ballast flask. Such columns exist in varying sizes and are capable of separating gram quantities of mixtures.

For partition chromatography of steroid derivatives on cellulose columns, Kuritzkes *et al.*[50] use a glass column which is cut in two all the length and the two halves of which are held together with scotch tape. After development of the column, it is opened and a print is taken of the moist cellulose, with filter paper; the print can be developed with colour reagents and then the zones of compounds thus located are cut out from the column.

Cellulose acetate has been proposed by Boscott[51] for separations of phenols and aromatic acids.

5. Rubber

Rubber columns can be used for *reversed phase* partition chromatograms, *i.e.* for the separation of lipophilic substances.

Boldingh[7,8] has used a column of moderately vulcanized Hevea rubber saturated with benzene for the separation of higher fatty acids (elution with aqueous methanol, see also Hirsch[52]). Nyc *et al.*[53] and Bosch[54] have used a powdered vulcanized rubber ("Mealorub", Andresen Corp., Chicago) for the separation of oestrogens.

---

* LKB-Produkter, Stockholm 12, Sweden.

Partridge and Swain[55] have developed a reversed-phase chromatogram using a commercial chlorinated rubber ("Alloprene", I.C.I. Ltd.; extra high viscosity grade E) for the separation of 2,4-dinitrophenylderivatives of amino acids (butanol as stationary, aqueous buffers as mobile phase).

6. Polyethylene

A reversed phase system with polyethylene columns* has been used by Wiss and Gloor[56] for the separation of the fat soluble vitamins and by Morton *et al.*[57] for the analysis of the ubiquinones (homologous isoprenoid benzoquinone derivatives).

7. Partition chromatoplates (Thin layer chromatography)

The advantages of chromatoplates over columns and papers in adsorption chromatography (see p. 44) have induced several authors to try partition

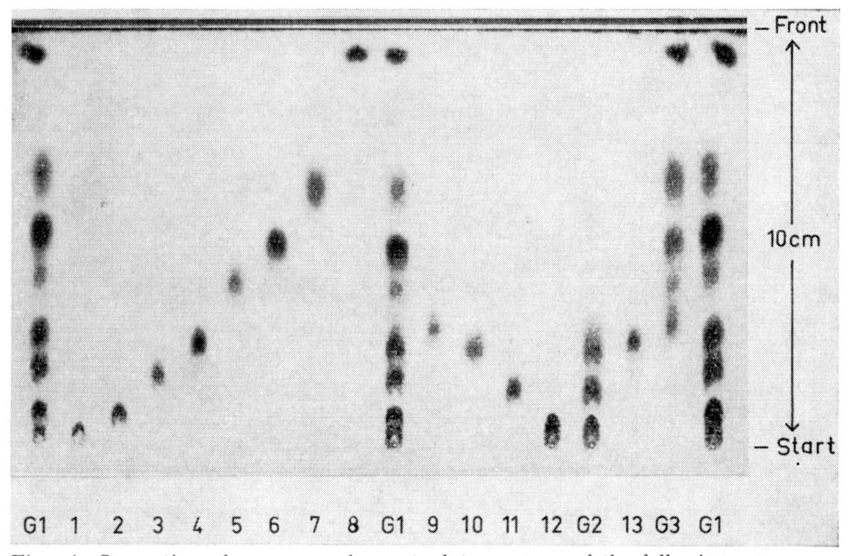

Fig. 4A. Separation of sugars on chromatoplates. 0.5 μg of the following sugars are separated on acetate-buffered kieselguhr G (Merck) and detected with anisaldehyde: 1 = lactose, 2 = sucrose, 3 = glucose, 4 = fructose, 5 = xylose, 6 = ribose, 7 = rhamnose, 8 = digitoxose, 9 = arabinose, 10 = mannose, 11 = galactose, 12 = maltose and 13 = sorbose. G1 is a mixture of 1–8, G2 a mixture of 9–12 and G3 a mixture of 5–9. (Stahl and Kaltenbach [499]).

separations on chromatoplates. The various separations achieved have been reviewed by Demole[496], Stahl[497] and Wollish *et al.*[498]. A typical illustration of the possibilities of partition chromatoplates is given in the separation

* Hostalen W., a polyethylene powder produced by Farbwerke Hoechst A.G.

of sugars by Stahl and Kaltenbach[499]. Buffered kieselguhr G (Merck) is applied on glass plates by means of the Desaga-equipment No. 600, and ethyl acetate–isopropanol–water used as solvent. The separations obtained with only 0.5 μg of each sugar and detected with anisaldehyde (in ethanol–H_2SO_4) are shown in Fig. 4A and the sensitivity for sugars was noted to be 100 times as great as on filter paper.

II. PAPER CHROMATOGRAPHY

Literature

The literature of paper chromatography has become rather large in the last few years and requires explanatory comments.

Treatises which deal with all aspects of paper chromatography were published by Hais and Macek[58] (now in a revised German edition), Opienska-Blauth *et al.*[59] (in Polish) and Lederer and Lederer[60] (in English). These treatises offer a more or less complete bibliography of the subject.

Handbooks and laboratory guides which only select material from the literature were written by Balston and Talbot[61] (now rather out of date), Block, Durrum and Zweig[62], Cramer[63] (both English and German) and a rather theoretical discussion by Cassidy[64].

Specialised books dealing with certain applications of paper chromatography were written by Linskens[65] (applications to botany), Smith[66] (clinical chemistry), Neher[67] (sterols, steroids and related compounds).

The paper chromatography of inorganic substances is treated in the following books: Lederer[68] (now out of date, but a revised edition is included in [60]), Pollard and McOmie[69], Blasius[70] as well as in a small laboratory text by Tamura[71].

In addition to the numerous general reviews (such as in *Anal. Chem.*) a series of specialised reviews appears in the *Journal of Chromatography*. These are also available in bound volumes, under the title *Chromatographic Reviews*[72].

1. Mechanism

Filter paper in an atmosphere saturated with water vapour absorbs approximately 22% of water[73]. Consden, Gordon and Martin[4] considered filter paper as an inert support of an aqueous stationary phase and explained the observed separations as a result of continuous partitions of the substances between the aqueous stationary phase and the water-immiscible organic solvent flowing down the paper. This approach was criticized later by numerous authors[74–77]. Craig[75] thought that an equilibrium could not be established sufficiently fast in a system without agitation and hence the separations could not be explained by simple solvent-solvent extraction.

Martin[78], however, points out that on the basis of known diffusion constants the efficiency of paper chromatograms is of the right order.

A more important objection is as follows: if the separations obtained are due to partition between two solvents, it should be impossible to employ water-miscible solvents, where only one phase exists and hence no partition is possible. However, numerous authors have effected separations of amino acids and other substances with water-soluble solvents such as propanol, acetone, ethanol or even with pure water[77, 79–82]. Before deciding on this point it is necessary to examine in detail the exact state of the water-saturated filter paper.

If one exposes dry cellulose to water vapours, a quantity of water, approx. 6%, is absorbed with a high heat of sorption and high apparent density and a low velocity of diffusion. As more water is absorbed these properties change and become more and more like those of liquid water, especially the diffusion rate. Martin[78] compares the aqueous phase on the paper with a concentrated solution of carbohydrate: "The stationary phase in a cellulose chromatogram should be compared with say a strong solution of glucose, or better of some soluble polysaccharide rather than water saturated with the organic phase. It should therefore cause no surprise that solvents miscible with water can be used. A strong solution of glucose will form two phases with aqueous propanol, the carbohydrate-rich phase containing a relatively higher proportion of water, the other phase a relatively higher of organic solvent."

Hanes and Isherwood[76] adopted a point of view analogous to Martin's; they consider the stationary phase as a water–cellulose complex. A substance in solution will be held more or less strongly in this complex, depending on its hydrophilic properties.

It is thus mainly a matter of definition of terms whether the mechanism of paper chromatography is called an adsorption on, or a partition in the *water cellulose complex*.

Horner *et al.*[83] studied the distribution of water between the paper and the solvent refractometrically with various water-solvent mixtures. See also the review of Moore and Stein[84].

Burma and Banerjee[85] chromatographed a number of amino acids and sugars with water as solvent and found in most cases that the spots moved with the liquid front. They thus concluded that no adsorption occurs.

Paper chromatography with aqueous solvents has, however, been successful with dyestuffs, alkaloids, phenols, anthocyanins and many other groups of compounds. Typical solvents are dilute acetic acid, acetate buffers (sometimes containing small amounts of amyl alcohol) and aqueous potassium chloride solution. There seems to be no doubt that the separations are due to molecular adsorption in most cases. Inorganic anions (such as CrO_4^{--}) were shown to be adsorbed on paper in a way resembling salting-out[86]. For the paper chromatography of antibiotics with aqueous solvents see Uri[87].

References p. 208

The existence of carboxylic groups in the cellulose has been demonstrated by several authors[88-92] and some of the ion exchange mechanisms were recently studied by Miranda and Lissitzky[93].

Real partition chromatography

Tschesche *et al.*[94] call *real partition chromatography* the development on paper which has been thoroughly moistened with the stationary phase and thus does not absorb its stationary phase from the atmosphere or the developing solvent. This technique is advantageous when the stationary phase is organic and the aqueous phase is mobile as used for the separation of cardiac glycosides. Disappearance of otherwise unavoidable comets is claimed in this technique.

2. Correlation of chemical constitution and R_F value

As shown (p. 153), the R_F value depends on the partition coefficient and the relative amounts of the two phases in contact. For a given column or paper it depends solely on the partition coefficient, which is a thermodynamic property of a given molecular species, as specific and distinctive as other phase transition points such as boiling and melting points.

Whilst for the identification by boiling or melting point a pure specimen is required, the R_F value is not influenced by the presence of many impurities. Further, only micro quantities are required for a paper chromatographic identification. To identify a substance one usually measures the R_F value with a number of suitable solvents, as well as the R_F values of reference substances run on the same paper at the same time. It is not possible, however, to identify an unknown substance by R_F value alone. Numerous mixtures of isomers

$$\text{for example}\quad \begin{array}{l} CH_2OH \\ | \\ CHNH_2 \\ | \\ CH_3 \end{array} \quad\text{and}\quad \begin{array}{l} CH_2NH_2 \\ | \\ CHOH \\ | \\ CH_3 \end{array}$$

produce only one spot in all solvents examined[95].

On the other hand two spots need not necessarily mean the presence of two substances in a sample. See section on multispots, p. 170.

(a) The R_M value

A new R value proposed by Bate-Smith and Westall[96] is

$$R_M = \log\left(\frac{1}{R_F} - 1\right)$$

It is proportional to the free energy of moving a molecule from one phase to the other. Both Bate-Smith and Westall[96] and Marnit[12] have shown that the R_M value is made up of additive values representing the groups in the molecule and a constant for the given solvent system, paper, etc. Recently several attempts were made to use R_M values to calculate the R_F values of given compounds[97] or even to determine structures from a given number of R_F values in different solvents[98]. For this purpose *group constants* must be calculated for the solvent system from R_F values of known compounds as well as the constant for the solvent system (Grundkonstante).

We shall cite one example from Reichl[97] (see Table I).

TABLE I

SOME ΔR_M VALUES CALCULATED BY REICHL[97]

Solvent: amyl alcohol–5 N HCOOH, Paper: Whatman No. 1, Ascending method

Constant for solvent system (Grundkonstante)	0.97
Each carbon atom	0.12
Each branched chain	0.25
Primary OH	—0.73
Secondary OH	—0.50
Tertiary OH	—0.58
Carboxyl group	—0.63
Amino group	—1.65
Keto group	—0.39

	R_F	
	Measured	*Calculated by adding the above constants and converting R_M to R_F*
Adipic acid	0.75	0.73
Citric acid	0.23	0.23
Glycolic acid	0.43	0.41

In numerous cases, for example peptides, the correlation is not as satisfactory. For determination of structures Schauer and Burlisch[98] propose the calculation using determinants. This requires the R_F values in sufficient solvent systems and by analysis a knowledge of the number of each group present.

Another limitation of the determination of structures from R_F values lies in the fact that the group constants are only constant in a relatively small range of aliphatic, low molecular compounds. Franc and Jokl[99] have shown that the ΔR_M for the CH_2 group decreases logarithmically over a certain chain length. This, however, is rather in contradiction with the findings of Holness and Stone[100].

Relations between the R_M value and molecular properties such as intermolecular hydrogen bond energies, dipole moments, etc. were noted by

References p. 208

Franc and Latinák[101], Franc and Jokl[102–104], Franc[105], Calvo[106] and Dikstein[107].

The calculation of R_F values of *peptides* has received considerable attention (Martin[12]). Sanger[108] states that although not always accurate, the R_M value calculations may be applied in most cases and was found to be a useful check on the identity of a peptide. Numerous theoretical R_F values of peptides were calculated by Pardee[109] and Moore and Baker[110].

A straight line relationship between the *molecular weight* of tannins and the R_M value was reported by Roux and Evelyn[111] both in partition solvents (butanol–acetic acid–water) and aqueous solvents (2% acetic acid).

(b) *The* ΔR_M *method*

Substances such as acids and bases can be chromatographed, depending on the solvent, in the ionised or non-ionised form. If a solvent pair is chosen in which most other groups than the ionisable ones have low group constants the difference in R_M values will be proportional to the number of the ionisable

TABLE II

THE ΔR_M METHOD, NUMERICAL EXAMPLES (REICHL [112])

	Solvent 1		*Solvent 2*		
1 COOH	R_F	$-R_M$	R_F	$-R_M$	ΔR_M
Glycine	0.41	−0.17	0.24	−0.49	0.32
Lactic acid	0.76	0.50	0.52	0.04	0.46
2 COOH					
Aspartic acid	0.39	−0.19	0.06	−1.20	1.01
Fumaric acid	0.86	0.78	0.14	−0.79	1.57
Oxalic acid	0.40	−0.17	0.04	−1.33	1.16
3 COOH					
Aconitic acid	0.82	0.65	0.02	−1.62	2.27
Citric acid	0.59	0.16	0.01	−1.92	2.08

(or complexed, etc.) forms in the molecule. Reichl[112] bases a method for determining the number of COOH groups on this principle. Using ethyl acetate–acetic acid–water (2:1:1) as the acid solvent and acetone–0.5 *N* ammonium acetate as a neutral one he obtains the following results (Table II, examples are cited only).

Thus it is apparent that the ΔR_M value varies with the number of COOH groups and the estimation of the number of COOH groups may be made. For the determination of free glycol systems in veratrum alkaloids by the same method see Macek and Vejdelek[113].

(c) *Homologous series*

Fatty acids and their derivatives show a regular increase in their R_F values with the increase in the number of C atoms. In the partition chromatography of amino acids on paper the relationship between chemical structure and partition coefficient is shown clearly by certain regularities in the position of the spots. Fig. 5 of Polson[114] illustrates this relationship.

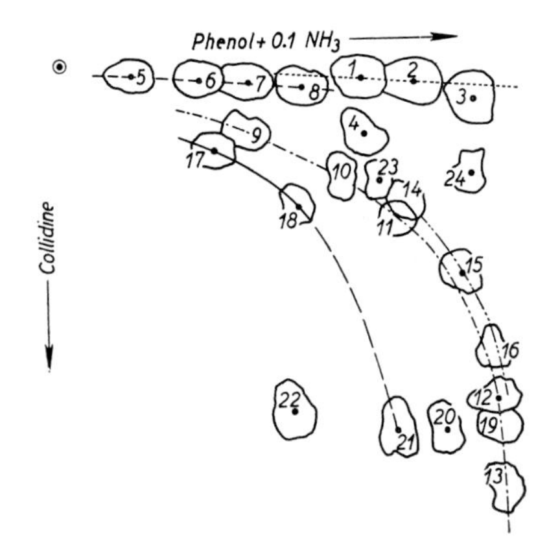

Fig. 5. Tracing of a two-dimensional chromatogram of a mixture of amino acids. Spots due to acids of related composition fall on smooth curves (Polson[114]). ...... Basic amino acids; ----- Dicarboxylic amino acids; —·—·— Normal aliphatic; —··—··— Iso-aliphatic; ——— Hydroxyaliphatic.

On a two-dimensional chromatogram (*e.g.* phenol and collidine) the mono-amino aliphatic acids (glycine, alanine, α-amino butyric acid, valine and leucine) appear on a curve, the hexone bases occur together and the di-carboxylic acids are very close to one another (Consden *et al.*[4]). The position of an unknown spot thus allows, to a limited extent, the drawing of conclusions on the chemical structure of the substance in question.

The partition coefficients of members of a homologous series are sufficiently different to allow complete separation. That changes in the constitution of the carbon chain have only small effects on the partition coefficient is shown by the difficulty encountered in the separation of leucine, iso-leucine and nor-leucine, and also of valine and nor-valine.

If the R_M values are plotted, for example, against number of C atoms, straight lines are obtained for all homologous series. This makes the calculation of R_F values of unknown members rather accurate as shown in Table III.

There are of course solvents and series where this relationship seems to fail (Franc and Jokl[99]).

References p. 208

TABLE III

FATTY ACID HYDRAZIDES (Satake and Seki[115])

Number of C atoms	*R_F measured*	*R_F calculated from graphical average of a R_M-CH_2 line*
1	0.11	0.10
2	0.18	0.18
3	0.37	0.33
4	0.54	0.52
5	0.70	0.70
6	0.77	0.83

3. The organic solvent

Still the most commonly employed solvents in paper chromatography are butanol (with various additions), collidine, phenol and benzyl alcohol. Instead of collidine a less expensive collidine–lutidine mixture is sometimes employed. As the purity of the solvent is rather important these solvents are now commercially available in a *for chromatography* grade. For laboratory methods of purification of phenol and collidine see Draper and Pollard[116] and Mars[117].

Water miscible solvents such as propanol, furfuryl alcohol, acetone, pyridine and tetrahydrofuran are also used.

In discussing the effect of the organic solvent on the movement of substances on the chromatogram two variables must be considered: (1) The R_F value, *i.e.* the solubility in the organic solvents, and (2) The separability or the difference in partition coefficients between members of a homologous series or between substances with various functions.

The R_F value increases generally as the amount of water in the solvent or as the polarity of the organic solvent increases. This was shown by Bentley and Whitehead[118] with numerous amino acids and by Lacourt *et al.*[119] and Walker and Lederer[120] for inorganic ions. Isherwood and Jermyn[121] obtained an empirical relationship between the molar concentration of water in the solvent and the R_M value of sugars. Briner[122] proposes the equation $R_M = a - b \log N$ (a and b are constants, N the molar concentration of water) from numerous experiments with amino acids, amines and water soluble organic solvents (such as acetone).

For homologous series the separability, *i.e.* the distance between two spots, has been shown to decrease with the polarity of the solvents. Osteux *et al.*[123] found this relationship for the separation of volatile fatty acids. The increase in ΔR_M of the CH_2 group (in numerous homologous series) with the number of carbon atoms in the alcohol used as solvent has been shown to be linear (M. Lederer[124]).

Coch-Frugoni (unpublished) observed the same for ΔR_M of the OH group. Thoma and French[125] also showed that oligo-saccharides had a better separability in solvents containing little water compared to those containing more water.

Thus the selection of the solvent is a compromise between one which gives optimum R_F ranges and a solvent which gives the highest ΔR_M value (or distance between the spots).

(a) *Additions of acids to the solvent*

Weak acids and weak bases can be chromatographed either in the ionised form, or in the unionised form or as an equilibrium mixture of the ionised and unionised forms. Usually the unionised form is more solvent-soluble and the ionised form more water soluble. Hence the partition coefficient will vary with the pH according to the Henderson–Hasselbach equation

$$\text{pH} = \text{p}K + \log \frac{\text{ionised}}{\text{unionised}}$$

It is thus obvious that separations of weak acids, bases or amphoteric compounds are possible in two different ways. (1) If both have the same degree of ionisation, by selecting a solvent which separates them due to the structural differences of the compounds, and (2) by choosing a pH value at which there is a difference in the ionisation of the substances.

Usually both these factors contribute to the separation. Extensive experimental work on the improvement of separations of amino acids, by buffering the paper, has been carried out by Landua *et al.*[126] and McFarren[127].

The mixture butanol–acetic acid–water has found wide application for separations of weak acids (non-volatile), amines, amino acids, anthocyanins, etc., since the pH of the mixture permits numerous substances to be separated by differences in ionisation.

Waksmundski and Soczewinski[128] derive the equation

$$R_F = \frac{\alpha \dfrac{A_L}{A_S}}{\alpha \dfrac{A_L}{A_S} + 1 + \dfrac{K_a}{[\text{H}^+]}}$$

where α = partition coefficient of the unionised substance and K_a is the ionisation constant of the acid, and propose its use for calculating the pK

References p. 208

values of weak acids and bases from the R_F values measured at various pH values.

For an application in the separation of chelidonine and protopine see Debska[129].

(b) *Comet formation*

When organic acids and bases are chromatographed with neutral solvents, instead of the usual round spots, long trails (comets) are formed. This phenomenon was first observed by Lugg and Overell[130,131] in the chromatography of organic acids and is due to the dissociation of these acids into one or more ionised forms. As each ionised form has a different R_F value such dissociation results in a continuous deposition of material from the spot travelling on the paper.

Addition of an acid to the solvent (swamping acid) can prevent this formation of a comet by inhibiting ionisation.

Munier and Macheboeuf[132] observed the same trailing of spots with alkaloids and other weak bases (K between 10^{-3} and 10^{-10}) (Fig. 6).

Other reactions beside ionisation can also produce a comet. Hanes and Isherwood[134] consider traces of Ca^{++} and Mg^{++} responsible for the trailing and low R_F values of many acids and employ *acid-washed papers* to obviate this effect. For techniques of washing filter paper see Isherwood and Hanes[135]. Inorganic ions can either be hydrolysed (*e.g.* Sb^{+++}) or reduced (*e.g.* Au^{+++} and Ir^{++++}) and then form comets. In the first instance an increased acid concentration and in the second the addition of oxidising agents can prevent comet formation[136].

Adsorption comets occur especially with dyes (Zahn[137]).

A recent review by Keller and Giddings[138] presents a mathematical treatment of comet and multispot formation.

(c) *Multispots*

One extreme case of comet formation is the formation of two or more discrete spots (*multispots*) of one substance. Multispots may be caused by non-equilibrium between various complexed and ionised forms as shown by Curry[139] for mono- and dihydrogen phosphate and by Erdem and Erlenmeyer[140] for ammine complexes. Adsorption multispots were recorded by Hassall and Magnus[141] with monamycin and dyes. See also Waldron-Edward[142].

Traces of heavy metals, especially copper, have been noted to cause double spots with amino acids and amino compounds, due to complex formation with part of the substance. Additions of stronger complexing

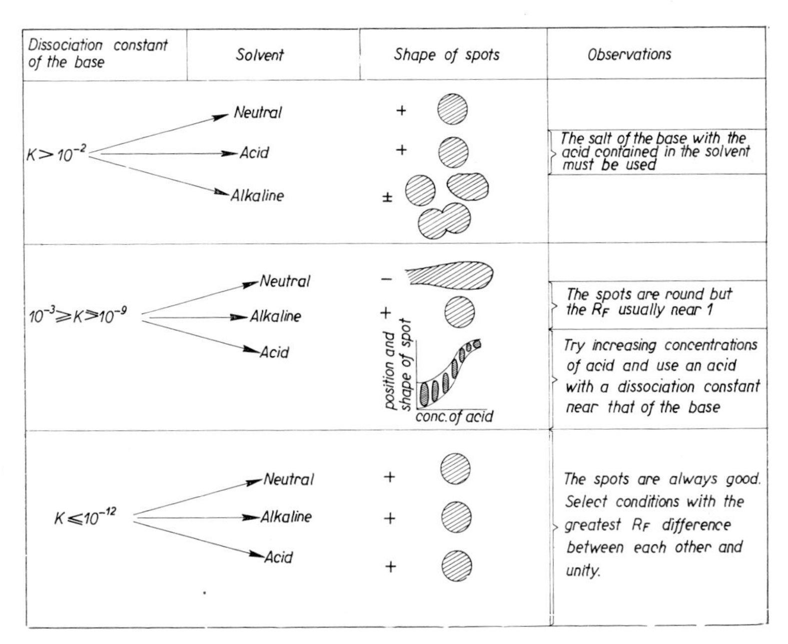

Fig. 6. The shape of spots of weak bases with solvents of various pH (Munier[133]).

agents such as 8-hydroxyquinoline or HCN can inhibit this interference[4]. Metal traces are also complexed with EDTA in some of the work with organic and inorganic polyphosphates.

4. The effect of temperature variation

Wark[143] has shown that the partition coefficient varies with the temperature according to an isochore of the type of Van 't Hoff's isochore. In paper chromatography not only the effect of temperature on the actual partition coefficient but also on the composition of the solvent phases, the hydration of the cellulose, adsorption equilibria and further factors must be considered.

Consden *et al.*[4] demonstrated already very early that the main factor influencing R_F value changes with temperature was the water content of the organic phase which in some solvents (*e.g.* phenol) varies little and in others (*e.g.* collidine) considerably. Experimental data for sugars and amino acids for 17°, 37° and 57° were reported by Counsell *et al.*[144]; for water-soluble solvents a similar study was carried out by Burma[145]; for inorganic ions by Tewari[146].

References p. 208

Isherwood and Jermyn[147] and later Alcock and Cannell[148,149] pointed out that a linear relation between the R_M value and the logarithm of the water content of the solvent may be used for those solvents, where the water content is known at various temperatures.

As R_M is a function of log α (the logarithm of the partition coefficient) a direct relationship between R_M and the absolute temperature may be obtained which has been shown (Lederer[124]) to hold well for the usual range of room temperatures namely

$$R_M = \frac{-\Delta H}{2.303R} \cdot \frac{1}{T} + C$$

where ΔH = heat of partition
R = universal gas constant
T = absolute temperature
C = constant

In examining the experimental data of the workers cited above it appears that ΔH is almost the same for a group of similar substances. Thus a change of R_M between two temperatures for one sugar may in most cases be used to predict the R_F of another sugar at a given temperature, providing the R_F is known at one temperature.

The above relation may be used to calculate the maximum temperature variation for a given precision in R_F values. It was found empirically of such a magnitude that thermostatically controlled or insulated chromatography chambers are recommended by many authors (*e.g.* ref. [150]).Development at elevated temperatures (60–70°) has been proposed repeatedly for faster results. See for example Roberts and Koler[151], also Roberts[152] and Roberts and Bucek[153].

5. The paper

(*a*) *Common papers*

The commonly used papers are Whatman No. 1 (specially prepared *for chromatography*), Whatman Nos. 3 and 4, Schleicher and Schüll (SS) 589 and 595, and Munktell (Swedish) Nos. OA and OB.

Kowkabany and Cassidy[154] compared 22 commercial brands of filter paper and classified them by considering the following:

Degree and clarity of separation of amino acid spots
Diffuseness of spots
Formation of a brown front (due to impurities in the paper)
Extent of tails and beards (comets)
Rate of movement of the solvent in descending development.

For amino acids, the papers were classified according to the usefulness in the solvent as follows (the best placed first):

Collidine: Whatman No. 3, SS595, Whatman No. 4, Whatman No. 1.

Phenol: Whatman No. 3, SS595, Whatman No. 1, Whatman No. 4.

1-Butanol: SS589 Black Ribbon, SS595, SS598, Whatman No. 3.

2-Butanol–formic acid: Whatman No. 3, Whatman No. 1, Whatman No. 2, SS602.

2-Butanol–ammonia: SS589 Blue Ribbon, -Red Ribbon, -White Ribbon, Whatman No. 1.

Reeve Angel papers No. 202, 226 and 230 were found unsuitable. Kowkabany and Cassidy[154] also observed that the R_F values differed considerably from paper to paper, also that aspartic acid is adsorbed to a different degree on various papers. Thus on SS507, 576, 589 Black, 589 Blue and 589 White Ribbon, aspartic acid gives circular spots; on all other papers an elongated spot.

A comparison of R_F values of amino acids on various papers is shown in Fig. 7. The authors recommend Whatman No. 3 as a generally useful paper with sharply resolved spots; SS595 also gives excellent separations with generally higher R_F values.

A similar study by Burma[155] compares Whatman papers 1, 2, 4, 7, 11, 40, 42, 54 and 3MM for phenol and collidine. Here Whatman No. 1 paper was found most satisfactory followed by 4 and 54.

It must always be kept in mind that paper is a product of natural origin. Many constituents of living cells can thus be present as impurities and as some cells are not broken during manufacture they may yield such substances as amino acids, peptides or even fatty materials[157] on development or washing. It appears impossible to wash paper completely free of certain impurities as each wash may induce a further release of impurities by loosening some fibres. A *glass fibre paper* developed by the Whatman manufacturers may overcome some of these problems.

The usual impurities in filter papers are Ca^{++} and Mg^{++} ions (see comets, p. 170), also Fe^{+++} and Cu^{++} ions; the latter two produce a dark background when H_2S is used as a reagent for inorganic cations. A peptide-like contaminant in filter paper has been noted by Wynn[158].

In addition to the properties examined by Kowkabany and Cassidy[154], uniformity is essential when the paper is used for quantitative determinations by spot area measurements (see Quantitative methods, p. 198).

Balston and Talbot[61] consider the suitability of Whatman papers with special regard to flow rates. The flow rate is faster in the machine direction, *i.e.* in the direction of the orientation of the fibres, in certain machine-made papers. In other papers an even flow rate in two directions is possible and then produces rounder spots.

The Tables IV and V (taken from the Whatman Buyer's guide, folder *Chromatography papers*) contain the maximum impurity limits and capillary properties of Whatman papers.

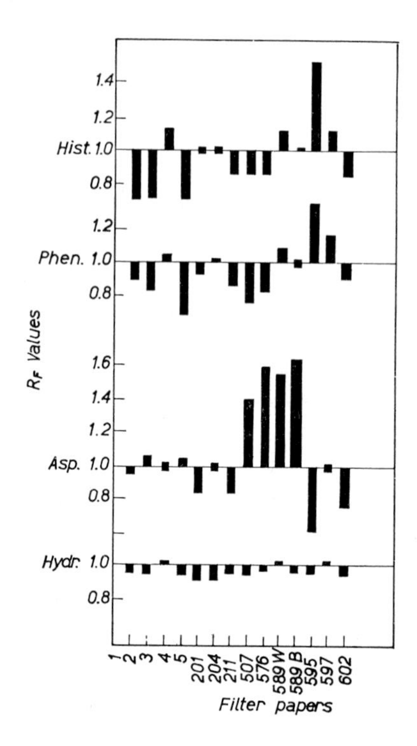

Fig. 7. R_F values of amino acids on various papers. R_F values for four amino acids, two each in two different solvents, are shown for fifteen filter papers. In each group the papers were run at the same time in the same cabinet and the same mixture of amino acids was used with each paper. The R_F values are plotted on the ordinate relative to Whatman No. 1, which is taken as the norm. Hist.: histidine in 1-butanol–ammonia. Phen.: phenylalanine in 1-butanol–ammonia. Asp.: aspartic acid in phenol. Hydr.: hydroxyproline in phenol. On the abscissa are listed the filter papers: *W* refers to White ribbon, *B* to Blue ribbon. The first five are Whatman papers, the next three are Reeve Angel, the rest are Schleicher and Schuell papers (Kowkabany and Cassidy[154]).

Recently a new brand of chromatography papers has appeared on the market. Binzer Filtrierpapier-Fabrik (Hatzfeld/Eder, Germany) proposes several papers with properties similar to the Whatman and Schleicher & Schüll papers. They also prepare a paper without machine direction, which might have advantages in centrifugal chromatography.

TABLE IV

MAXIMUM IMPURITIES OF WHATMAN CHROMATOGRAPHY PAPERS

	Grade	*Mean basis weight g/100 cm²*	*Av. ash g per 100 g*	*Av. ash µg per cm²*	*Max. Fe µg per cm²*	*Max. Cu µg per cm²*	*Ammonia N µg per cm²*	*Organic N µg per cm²*	*Ether extract µg per cm²*
Fast	17	4.4	0.05	22	0.44	0.11	0.7	< 4	10
Qualitative	4	0.92	0.06	5	0.14	0.02	0.1	< 1	2
Qualitative	15	1.40	0.06	8	0.21	0.03	0.2	< 1.4	3
Qualitative	3	1.85	0.05	9	0.28	0.05	0.3	< 1.8	4
Qualitative	1	0.87	0.06	5	0.13	0.02	0.1	< 0.9	2
Qualitative	3 MM	1.80	0.06	11	0.27	0.05	0.3	< 1.8	4
Qualitative	2	0.97	0.06	6	0.15	0.02	0.1	< 1	3
Slow	20	0.93	0.06	5	0.14	0.02	0.1	< 1	3
Fast	ET 31	1.90	0.015*	3	0.19	0.04	1.1	< 1.9	4
Ashless	41	0.91	0.010*	0.9	0.04	0.008	0.5	< 0.9	2
Ashless	40	0.95	0.010*	1	0.05	0.01	0.6	< 0.9	2
Slow	42	1.00	0.010*	1	0.05	0.01	0.6	< 1	2
Fast	54	0.93	0.025*	2	0.09	0.009	0.6	< 0.9	2
Slow	52	1.00	0.025*	2.5	0.10	0.01	0.6	< 1.0	2
Fast	541	0.82	0.008*	0.7	0.04	0.008	0.5	< 0.8	2
Hardened ashless	540	0.88	0.008*	0.7	0.04	0.008	0.5	< 0.9	2
Slow	542	1.00	0.008*	0.8	0.05	0.01	0.6	< 1	2
Fast	ET 31 (H)	1.96	0.010						
Slow	3 MM (H)	1.92	0.020						

(*b*) *Purified papers*

Purified papers often give faster flow rates due to irreversible swelling on purification. The Whatman papers are shown below in the order of diminishing flow rate:

Fast	No. 15	a thick paper
	No. 4	
Medium	No. 1	
	No. 3 MM	a thick paper
	No. 29	a black paper
Medium Slow	No. 11	a thin paper
	No. 2	
Slow	No. 20	

References p. 208

TABLE V

SOME PHYSICAL CHARACTERISTICS OF WHATMAN CHROMATOGRAPHY PAPERS

	Grade	Mean basis weight g/100 cm²	Apparent density g/ml	Upward flow rate index Time (t) variable	Upward flow rate index–distance $(d)^2$ variable (0 10 20 30 40 50 60 70 80 90 100 110 120 130 140)
Qualitative	17	4.4	0.5	13	
	4	0.92	0.45	15	
	15	1.40	0.45	17	
	3	1.85	0.49	26	
	1	0.87	0.53	30	
	3MM	1.80	0.56	32	
	2	0.97	0.54	32	
	20	0.93	0.60	70	
Ashless	ET31	1.90	0.36	11	
	41	0.91	0.43	15	
	40	0.95	0.46	30	
	42	1.00	0.49	74	
Hardened ashless	54	0.93	0.54	15	
	52	1.0	0.64	46	
	541	0.82	0.54	15	
	540	0.88	0.65	43	
	542	1.0	0.69	107	
	ET31 (H)	1.96		13	
	3MM (H)	1.92		32	

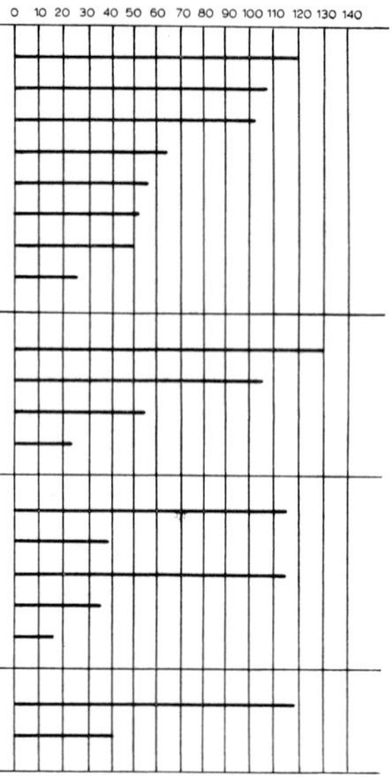

To prevent tearing of wet paper sheets during manipulations, Whatman "*wet strength paper*", more dense than the ordinary papers, can be used. In order of diminishing absorbancy these are:

		Acid washed	
Very fast	Separa DHC	—	slightly creped surface
	Separa DH	—	
Fast	No. 54	No. 541	
Medium Slow	No. 52	No. 540	
Slow		No. 542	
		No. 544	a little thinner than 542
Very slow	No. 50	—	very smooth surface

Whatman also produces singly and doubly acid washed papers with approximately equal flow rates in the two directions, with slightly grained surface and less dense than the quantitative papers (except No. 120):

	Singly acid washed	*Doubly acid washed*
Fast	No. 31 good for amino acids and paper electrophoresis	No. 41
		No. 43
Medium	No. 30	No. 40
Slow	—	No. 120 very thick and dense
		No. 44 slightly thinner than No. 42
Very Slow	No. 32	No. 42

A comprehensive treatise of the physics and chemistry of cellulose fibres was written by Hermans[73].

(c) *Chemically modified paper*

(i) *Acetylated papers*

For reversed phase chromatography (see p. 152) acetylated papers are often preferred to papers impregnated with silicone or vaseline. Methods for the acetylation were reported by Burton[159], Micheel and Schweppe[160], Micheel and Albers[161], Buras and Hobart[162] and Zijp[163], while Micheel and Albers[164] describe the attachment of butyl-, benzoyl- and phthaloyl groups to the paper.

Spotswood[165] recommends the following method for obtaining a high degree of acetylation. Ten strips of Whatman No. 1 paper 14 × 50 cm are rolled together and placed in a widemouthed Erlenmeyer flask. Glass spacing rods were inserted into the roll at intervals to insure even acetylation and the papers covered with an acetylating mixture comprising 800 ml of acetic anhydride, 1000 ml of thiophen-free benzene and 0.6 g of concentrated sulphuric acid. The mixture was then heated under reflux at 60 to 65° for six hours with occasional shaking. After this time the acetylating mixture was poured off and the flask filled with absolute ethanol and allowed to stand overnight. The ethanol was poured off and the paper washed several times with distilled water and air dried. The nature of the paper obtained was found to depend on the purity of the benzene used and on the ratio of sulphuric acid to acetic anhydride.

The benzene used must be free from sulphur compounds if reproducible results are to be obtained. More than 5% sulphuric acid does not produce a superior paper.

Acetylated papers are also available commercially from the Binzer Filtrierpapier-Fabrik (see p. 175) who also indicate the acetyl content of each batch. Schleicher and Schüll offer a paper with 20–25 % and one with 90 % of the theoretical acetyl content.

(ii) *Impregnated water-repellent papers*

The usual impregnation for water repellent papers is either rubber, silicones, vaseline or sometimes chromyl stearate. (See for example Kovacz[166] or Morin *et al.*[167].)

Silicone impregnated papers are sold by Schleicher and Schüll (2043 a Mgl hy and 2043 b Mgl hy) as well as by Macherey and Nagel (brand "WA"). Chromyl stearate papers may be obtained from the Papeterie d'Arches (No. 306).

(iii) *Glass papers*

Since a few years the manufacturers of Whatman papers have prepared sheets of a "paper" made entirely of glass fibres. These were intended for filtration (*e.g.* in Gooch crucibles) and do not produce good chromatograms as their capillary properties are not suitable. However, paper electrophoresis is usually successful. Two glass fibre papers with extremely fast flow rates are also marketed by Schleicher and Schüll (Glasfaserpapier No. 6 and No. 8).

(iv) Ion exchange papers

Cellulose has been given cation and anion exchange properties by suitable reactions and most paper manufacturers list a good selection of such papers (for details see section on ion exchange, p. 128).

(v) Redox papers

Redox papers were prepared by Ezrin and Cassidy[168], also by Sansoni[169], but so far no chromatographic application has been found for them.

6. The movement of the solvent during development

Müller and Clegg[170–172] carried out extensive work on the movement of solvents through filter paper. They confirmed the previous findings of Goppelsroeder in the years 1888–1904[173,174], Jermyn and Isherwood[175] and Karnovsky and Johnson[176], namely that the rate of travel of the solvent depends on the viscosity of the solvent and slows down with time.

Müller and Clegg[172] showed that for short development the height h to which a solvent rises in time t obeys the equation:

$$h^2 = Dt - b$$

where h is in mm, t the time in seconds, b a constant and equivalent to an h^2 term and D a constant for a given paper and liquid. This constant D, called the diffusion coefficient, varies with the surface tension, viscosity and density of the solvent and obeys the equation:

$$D = \alpha\, \gamma/\eta\, d + b$$

where a and b are constants depending on the filter paper. Good confirmation of these equations was obtained with water, methanol, ethanol and higher alcohols. Temperature variations of the rate of flow of a solvent could be explained by the temperature variation of the term $\gamma/\eta\, d$. The flow of fluid in the paper was also critically reviewed by Cassidy[177,178]. See also Erdos and Vavruch[179]. A cinematographic study of the kinetics of development was carried out by Dixmier *et al.*[180].

The importance of the rate of solvent flow on the R_F value has only been recently pointed out by Giddings *et al.*[181]. Since the speed of movement decreases along the paper, the distance between the solvent level and the original spot will be able to alter the R_F value. This effect is very small with the usual length of development but can be considerable when short chromatograms are run.

In another paper Giddings[182] derives mathematical equations for the movement of a single liquid in papers of different geometries (tapered in both directions, circular etc.) and confirms his work with experimental measurements.

7. Formation of more than one liquid front

When a solvent is allowed to run over a strip of filter paper, the paper dehydrates the solvent to some extent, absorbing about 20% of water of hydration. In a saturated atmosphere this dehydration is made up by some water vapour condensing on the paper and the composition of the solvent remains uniform. It is essential, therefore, to keep the atmosphere saturated with all the constituents of the solvent. This is readily achieved with solvents of which all the constituents are volatile, by placing a lower layer, obtained from the preparation of the solvent, into the developing tank. It is not possible, however, when the solvent (*e.g.* butanol) contains non-volatile constituents such as hydrochloric or nitric acids. In such solvents, a band poor in hydrochloric acid will precede the main portion of the solvent flowing over the paper and thus two distinct liquid fronts will be formed; the first being mainly that of butanol, the second being butanol with water and hydrochloric acid in the proportions found in the bulk of the solvent. Certain, not yet determined, impurities in the paper give the second front a dark border and leave a dark line which does not fade on drying. The height of the hydrochloric acid ascent depends on the temperature and acid concentration of the solvent. In butanol shaken with 0.3 N HCl, the acid or water front does not travel far at all. In concentrations above 1 N it usually travels 60–75% of the total distance travelled by the butanol. A good account of demixion was published by Munier and Macheboeuf[183].

Often a substance moves with the second front, *i.e.* is completely extracted as soon as the new constituent moves over it. Such spots usually have a flattened shape.

8. Technique

In the following pages the operations required for a paper chromatographic analysis are discussed.

(*a*) *Desalting*

Large quantities of HCl or alkalies are usually present in solutions of amino acids and sugars prepared by the hydrolysis of large molecules. Their

References p. 208

presence can cause the formation of large spots of high water content (water logging) and can interfere with the reagents used (*e.g.* $AgNO_3$ reacts with Cl^- instead of the sugar). Thus pyrex tubes should be used for the hydrolysis to keep the electrolyte concentration low[184].

In addition to the usual chemical methods for the removal of electrolytes (such as precipitation with $BaCO_3$, etc.) an electrolytic method was developed by Consden *et al.*[185] which utilises a circulating mercury cathode and a graphite anode (Fig. 8); this apparatus has been modified by Acher *et al.*[186]; see also Joseph[187], Astrup *et al.*[188] and Katz and Chaikoff[189].

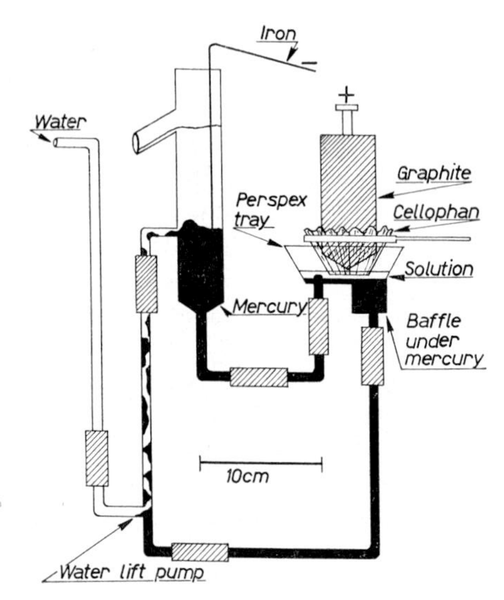

Fig. 8. Diagram of desalting apparatus (Consden *et al.*[185]).

It was observed by Stein and Moore[190] that by this method low results were obtained for arginine, which is converted to ornithine.

Ion exchange resins have been used for desalting the neutral amino acids by Brenner and Frey[191] who percolate the solution through a column of Amberlite IR-4B and then through a column of Amberlite IRC-50. This yields an eluate containing all the neutral amino acids, with the anions and cations on their respective exchangers. A column of Nalcite SAR to adsorb the amino acids from samples of saliva (except arginine and lysine, which are lost) is used by Piez *et al.*[192]. See also Drèze and DeBoeck[193], Drèze *et al.*[194].

In a study of the amino acids and polypeptides of biological liquids, Boulanger and Biserte[195] achieved the desalting of amino acids and oligopeptides by chromatography on the sulfonated polystyrene resin Permutit-50. This resin retains all cations, all amino acids and some oligopeptides; the adsorbed organic compounds can be eluted by displacement with dilute ammonia; the inorganic cations are not eluted. Some losses of arginine seem inevitable.

Boulanger and Biserte[196] extract free amino acids from dry plasma with acetone containing 1% HCl in which the inorganic salts are insoluble. Lipids are removed from this extract with ether.

Sugars can be dissolved from dry residues of hydrolysates with pyridine in which the electrolytes are insoluble (Malpress and Morrison[197]). This operation may not be without danger to the sugar molecules.

In numerous instances the removal of electrolytes is not essential. Berry and Cain[198] describe the analysis of amino acids in urine without desalting. Ishii and Andô[199] show that the R_F of amino acids is not affected by HCl in phenol or lutidine; there is, however, an effect with butanol as solvent. See also Baliga *et al.*[200]; commercial desalters are now available.

Zweig and Hood[201] describe an electrolytic desalting apparatus in which a mercury cathode and an anode are applied directly to the spot on the paper previous to development.

(*b*) *Concentration and extraction of the substances to be chromatographed*

Unless the concentration is effected during the process of placing the sample on the paper (see next section) a concentration is often necessary, for, although minimal quantities are employed, they must be dissolved in correspondingly small volumes. In the author's laboratory concentration on specially shaped watchglasses (Fig. 9) or in conical test-tubes was found adequate.

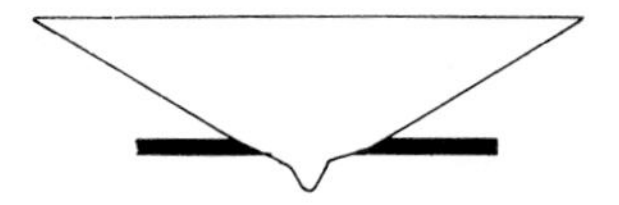

Fig. 9. Watchglass for concentrating small volume without loss. The black border indicates where the rim of the water bath is best placed.

Watzke[202] recommends freeze drying in a vacuum desiccator for labile substances.

It is also obvious that partition chromatograms necessitate the absence of insoluble particles at the starting point, as gradual extraction during development will cause streaking.

Zimmermann[203] proposes a micro soxhlet apparatus specially for extraction previous to chromatography. A micropercolator for extracting alkaloids out of plant material and placing them on paper in an air current was used

References p. 208

by French and Gibson[204]. List[205] constructed a rather complicated apparatus in which he places the sample to be extracted on a cotton wad through which a solvent is run by a refluxing system. Antoszewski[206] destroys cell material by hammering on the paper, which is placed between two metal blocks. Several such extracts on the periphery of a circle of paper are then concentrated and placed on the chromatogram by conical development. Simple pressing of the plant sap on the chromatogram was found satisfactory by Greenshields[207] but can not be generally recommended. When large amounts of material are available, usual extraction procedures should be used.

(c) *Placing the sample on the paper*

Solutions are usually placed on the paper by means of a micropipette, capillary tube or micrometer syringe. The usual volumes employed are 0.002–0.02 ml. The spots should be placed at such distances (2–3 cm) that the chromatograms do not interfere with each other. Numerous authors prefer to place the sample on the paper as a thin line rather than a round spot; see for example Boser[208] and Fig. 10.

Holzer[210] recommends a micropipette with a right angle bend for easier application to the paper. Urbach[211] developed a special pipette with a platinum wire fitted inside the capillary, which delivers a solution slowly onto the paper and thus permits evaporation of large volumes directly onto the paper as a small spot. A similar technique was employed by Glazko *et al.*[212].

Duncombe and Peaple[213] apply large volumes by means of an Agla syringe which is driven by a synchronous motor. See also Levenbook[214].

For the application of regular lines, Merz[215] designed a simple apparatus in which the end of the micropipette is made to move at a regular speed over the paper. Essentially the same apparatus is being sold by Research Specialties Co. (Calif., U.S.A.).

Yanovsky *et al.*[216] apply large volumes of solutions with a stationary pipette to a sheet of paper, revolving on a kymograph, which is dried with an infrared lamp. Novellie[217] prefers to apply the solution (in large amounts) to the paper by folding the sheet on the line of application and dipping into a trough holding enough solution for several chromatograms. Von Euler and Eliasson[218] first apply the solution to be separated onto a thin strip of paper which is clamped to the sheet used for the chromatographic run with glass rods. Thus relatively large amounts may be concentrated on thin lines. The method was successful with Grycksbo OB paper but not with Whatman No. 1 or No. 4 papers. See also Barker and Perry[219] who place the paper on a specially constructed frame for faster drying of large volumes.

Other designs have been proposed by Porteous[220], Duruisseau[221], Van

Gulik[222] and Van der Sijde and De Flines[223]. Wiegand and Schrank[224] suggest paraffin barriers around the spot to permit evaporation on a limited area.

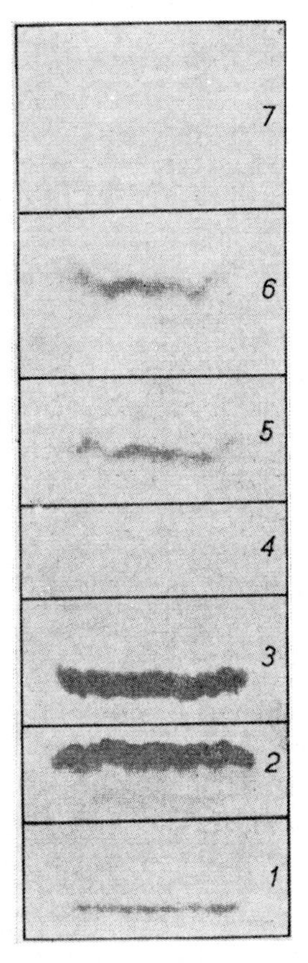

Fig. 10. Radioautogram of ascending chromatogram from hydrolysate of thyroid of chicken injected for 24 h with ^{131}I: exposure time 5 h. Solvent: collidine 125 ml, water 44 ml; atmosphere of ammonia (Taurog *et al.*[209]). 1, unhydrolysed thyroglobulin (?); 2, diiodotyrosine; 3, monoiodotyrosine; 5, thyroxine; 6, inorganic iodine.

(*d*) *Transferring spots from one sheet to another*

Usually equipment similar to that used for the elution of spots is also employed for transferring samples from one chromatogram (or electropherogram) to another. Thus in most techniques a tongue-shaped piece of paper is cut out, clamped between papers and/or glass slides and a liquid allowed to move the spot to its pointed end, which is either first exposed to

References p. 208

evaporation or directly placed on the sheet. (See for example Moore and Boylen[225], Reith[226] and French and Gibson[227]).

Some authors also have confidence that a spot placed in close contact with a new sheet by sewing on, weaving into, etc., will behave normally on a second paper sheet (Stöckli[228], Boggs[229], Marini-Bettolo *et al.*[230]. See also Gregory[231]).

Carrying-out of reactions on the paper before separation

Numerous authors were led by decomposition reactions during drying to perform irradiations directly on the spots on the paper and detecting the products formed after various amounts of irradiation after development.

Even enzymatic reactions may be carried out on the paper (See Chargaff and Kream[232] and Williams and Bevenue[233]).

Several papers by Prey *et al.*[234,235] concern themselves with the creation of a scheme of organic qualitative analysis by means of paper chromatography. The preparation of most derivatives is carried out on squares of glass-fibre paper, from which the substances are transferred to the chromatogram.

(*e*) *Development*

Usually, solvents such as phenol or butanol are first saturated with water. The water-rich phase so formed is placed into the development chamber in a dish to prevent evaporation of water from the paper or the solvent trough. It is recommended to *equilibrate* the development chamber for 24 hours before commencing development. With very volatile solvents such as ether, continuous recycling of the solvent over the walls of the container may be necessary to maintain a constant atmosphere (see Baker *et al.*[236], also Münz[237]). Devices for shorteningt he equilibration period were described by Head and Canaway[238] and by Ensgraber[239]. Cases have been noted[240] where the sequence of two substances has been inverted by presaturation of the paper, the sequence on dry paper being due to gradient effects.

(*i*) *Atmospheric contaminants*

Shaw and Trevarthen[241] have shown that considerable destruction of indoles placed on chromatograms may occur when *smog* conditions prevailed in the area where the laboratory was situated (Pasadena, Calif.). Filtering of the air over charcoal to create a smog-free room was necessary.

(*ii*) *Descending development*

Consden *et al.*[4] allowed the liquid to run down the paper by gravity, employing a glass trough to hold the solvent and enclosing the whole

Fig. 11. Development chamber: duralumin frame and glass sides (Institut de Biologie Physico-Chimique, Paris).

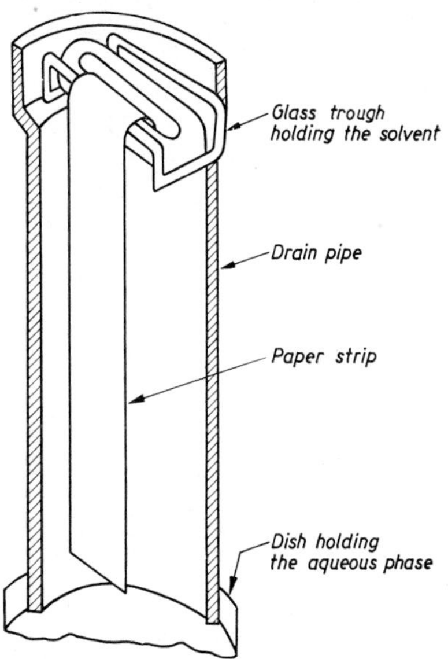

Fig. 12. Apparatus for uni-dimensional descending development. The lid is not shown.

apparatus in a drain pipe. Many kinds of development chambers are now used (*e.g.* Figs. 11, 12): Block and Bolling[242]; Toennies and Kolb[243]; Heyns and Anders[244]; Yamaguchi and Howard[245]; Alcock and Cannell[246]; Irrevere and Martin[247]; Mitchell[248]; Fink *et al.*[249]; Hunter *et al.*[250]; Kowala[251].

Winsten[252] developed several strips simultaneously from a petri dish holding the solvent; Miettinen and Virtanen[253] staple a piece of absorbent cotton to the lower end of the filter paper strip for the solvent to run over the paper where it is adsorbed by the cotton. Spots of low R_F value may thus be separated. Hird[254] reported a similar technique in which the same problem is solved by merely allowing the solvent to drip off the end of the filter paper (cut in zig-zag at the lower end) for 5 to 6 days. The construction of glass troughs for descending development appears to be difficult: several methods have been described[4,255-257]. Troughs made of polythene and supported by a metal frame, or stainless steel troughs may by used in place of the glass troughs. See also Porter[258] and Thompson and Marion[260]. For a trough in sections see Wunderly[259].

(*iii*) *Ascending development*

Williams and Kirby[261] simplified the technique of development by allowing the solvent to run up the filter paper by capillary action instead of running down the paper. A cylinder of the filter paper, with up to ten

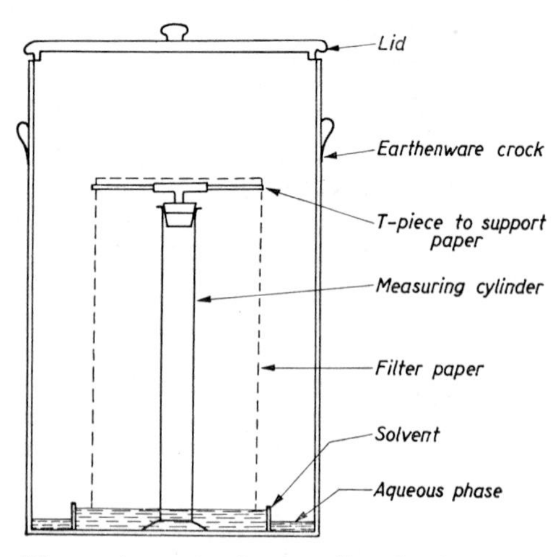

Fig. 13. Apparatus for ascending development.

samples on one sheet, is stood in a dish containing the solvent and the whole enclosed in a battery jar, or earthenware pot (Fig. 13). Usually the same R_F

values are obtained by the ascending and descending techniques. In order to decrease the space required by each chromatogram, Ma and Fontaine[262] wind the paper round a specially constructed steel coil; the rolled-up paper is then placed in a measuring cylinder for development (Fig. 14). For other techniques employing paper wound around coils to diminish their size see Alcock and Cannell[148,149] and Simek[263]. Another *space-saving* equipment

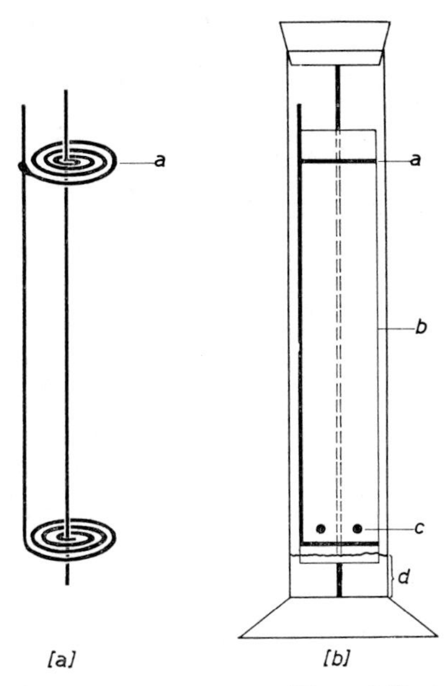

Fig. 14. Apparatus for ascending development (Ma and Fontaine[262]) A, paper holder with adjustable coil (a); B, assembled apparatus, showing adjustable coil (a), paper (b), position of test spots (c), and liquid volume (d).

rolls the paper in layers of hydrophobic plastic sheeting and then into a coil[264]. It is doubtful whether this is universally applicable. Stapling and strengthening with strips of adhesive is recommended by Wolfson *et al.*[265] (Fig. 15). Other supports for paper strips are described by Singer and Kenner[266] and by Kawerau[267] (Fig. 16). A frame capable of holding numerous two-dimensional chromatograms for routine purposes is described by Datta *et al.*[268] (Fig. 17), also by Brockmann *et al.*[269]. A simple wooden frame was described by Borkowski and Trojnar[270]. The frame of Datta *et al.*[268] is now commercially available.

Longenecker[271] uses very thin strips of paper, 4–5 mm wide, as well as mercerised cotton, glass wool and thin asbestos paper.

Rockland and Dunn[272] carry out very short chromatograms with small drops using test tubes as containers for the solvent and the paper strip

References p. 208

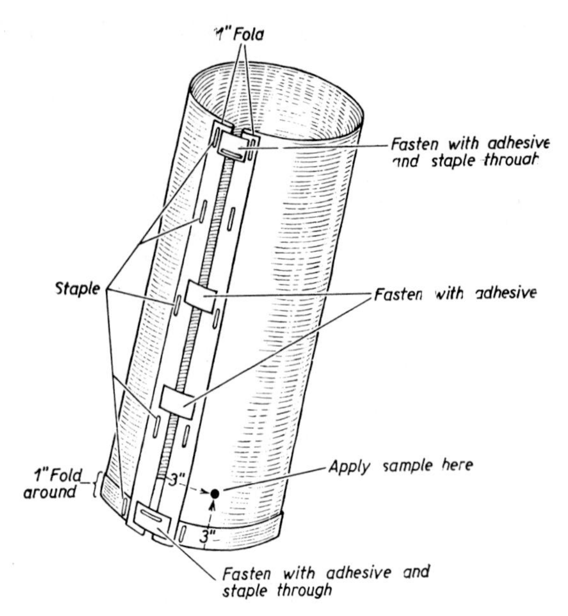

Fig. 15. Technique of folding and fastening large filter paper sheets. When the run is completed, the staples are carefully removed and the adhesive tape cut. The sheet is hung for drying; if a two-dimensional chromatogram is contemplated, it is reformed into a cylinder and refastened after drying. At this time, excess adhesive from the first run is removed. Spots of material to be fractionated are best applied about 2 in. above the lower border and 2 in. from the vertical border which is to be the lower border when the sheet is run in the second direction (Wolfson *et al.*[265]).

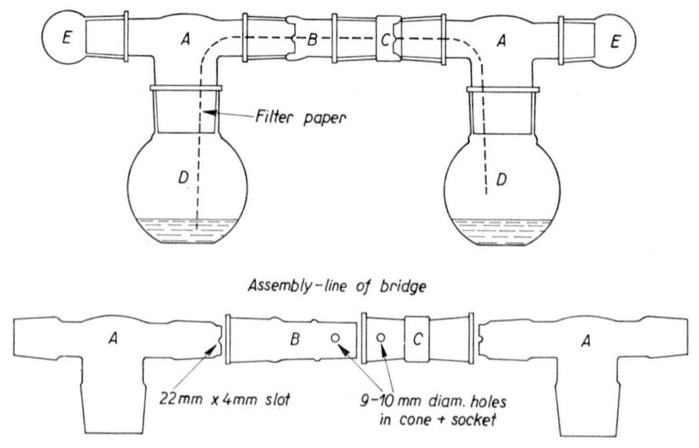

Fig. 16. Bridge unit for filter paper chromatography (Kawerau[267]).

(Fig. 18). This technique was further elaborated by Rockland *et al.*[273], and by Rockland and Underwood[274]. The test-tube technique was further used by Gorbach *et al.*[275] and Râbek[276]. The latter recommend rather long tubes (paper length 46 cm) for routine examination of many solvents, however, it appears doubtful whether a saturated atmosphere is ever reached in such apparatus.

For a *continuous* ascending technique, see Fischenbachen and Levine[277].

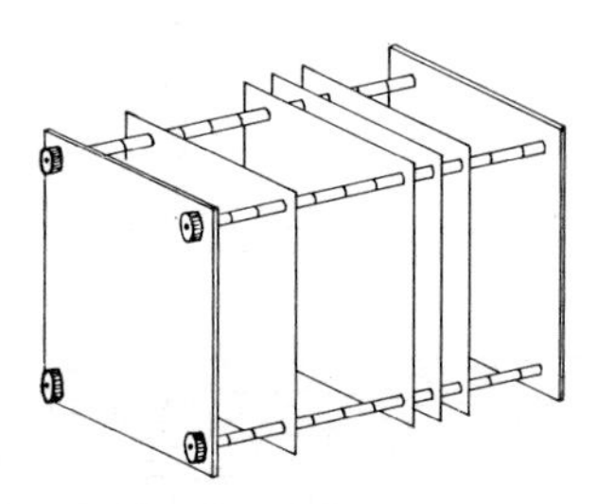

Fig. 17. Apparatus for mass-production of two-way paper chromatograms (Datta *et al.*[268]).

Development of strips in a horizontal apparatus by moving the paper past a wick after suitable movement of the solvent, yields, according to Halbensteiner[278], a better resolution due to longer movement of the spots than is possible with a single development. Development with both phases simultaneously was investigated by Allouf and Macheboeuf[279] who could not find any advantage in this over ordinary development.

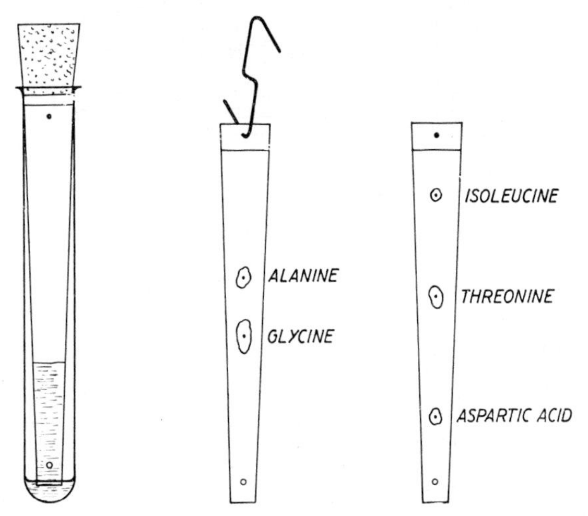

Fig. 18. Chromatography in a test tube (Rockland and Dunn[272]).

References p. 208

(iv) Improvement of uni-dimensional separations by modifications of the shape of the paper strip

It was pointed out by numerous authors that when a round spot is placed on a strip of paper the edges are affected in a different way by the developing solvent than the centre since on both sides of the spot only pure solvent is running over the paper. This results in distorted ovoid spots. If it is desired to obtain maximum resolution of close lying spots a shape of paper or spot should be used so that the solvent cannot travel around the substances to be separated but only over them. A very successful shape of paper is shown on the right side of Fig. 19 from the work of Matthias[280,281]. Similar designs have also been employed by Reindel and Hoppe[282], Ganguli[283] and Schwerdtfeger[284].

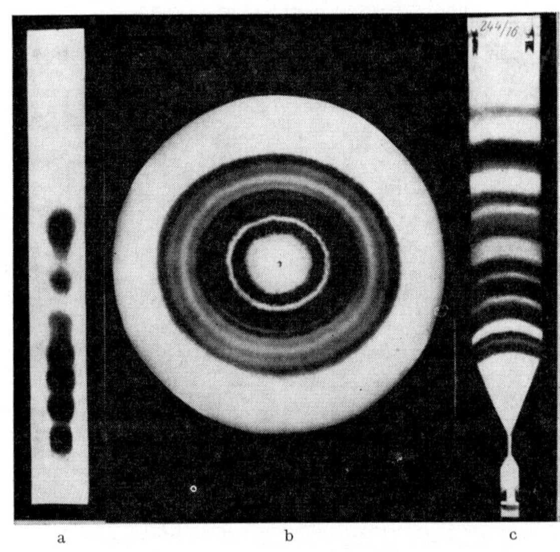

Fig. 19. Amino acids from a protein hydrolysate; (a) normal ascending chromatogram, (b) circular chromatogram, (c) special strip chromatogram; the mixture to be separated is placed at the lower entrance of the narrow part of the strip. Solvent, butanol–acetic acid–water (4:1:1) (Matthias[280]).

(v) Two-dimensional development

If one solvent is unable to resolve the mixture of substances to be analysed it is often possible to effect a separation by running one spot on a sheet of filter paper first with one solvent in one direction, then after drying off the first solvent, with a second solvent at right angles to the first. This method was first described by Consden, Gordon and Martin[4] for the separation of twenty amino acids (Fig. 20). Two-dimensional separations have been utilised in most cases where a different sequence can be obtained with two different solvents. However, all constituents of the first solvent have to be volatile or inert for a successful application of another solvent in the second dimension.

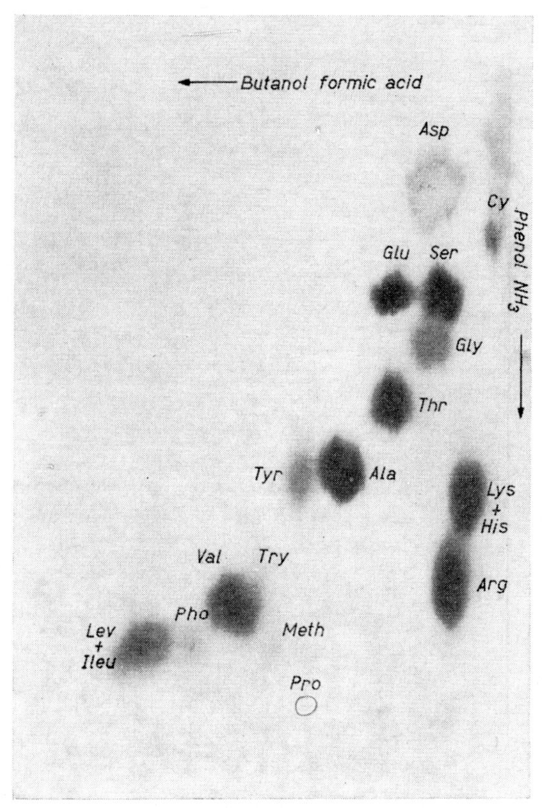

Fig. 20. Two-dimensional chromatogram of amino acids after reaction with ninhydrin. (Hydrolysate of lysozyme; Fromageot and Jutisz, unpublished).

(vi) *Multiple development in the same direction*

This technique has been used for separating closely adjacent sugars by Jeanes *et al.*[285], also by Csoban[286]. Development in the same direction with two different solvents can also be employed (see Burstall *et al.*[287], also Decker *et al.*[288]).

(vii) *Two-dimensional development with the same solvent in both directions*

Schwarz and Bitancourt[289] and Decker[290] pointed out that when unstable substances (for example certain indole derivatives) are chromatographed in

References p. 208

both dimensions with the same solvent, the sequence of the decomposition reaction may be interpreted, with respect to both axes, from the position of the products formed.

A typical example is the demonstration of the conversion of caffeic acid to esculetin by Butler and Siegelman[291] when chromatographing with 5% acetic acid as solvent. The method could also find application in radioactive series, providing that the half-lives are of the order, or longer than, the time of development.

(viii) Radial development

Lately many papers have appeared describing radial techniques. As introduction to this topic we shall quote Martin's Nobel Prize lecture on the evolution of paper chromatographic techniques: "I was already familiar with the use of filter paper chromatograms as used by the dyestuff chemist and adopted at first their technique. A ten centimetre circular paper was cut to a semi-circle with a three centimetre tail about one centimetre wide at the centre. *It was found quicker and more convenient to hang strips of paper* from troughs containing the solvents and this method was adopted as a routine."

Rutter[292] employed circular discs of filter paper to which the solvent is admitted by cutting a wick 2 mm wide from the periphery to the centre of the disc. The disc, together with a small dish of solvent is housed in a petri dish. Another type of feed for circular development consisting of a cone of filter paper in contact with the centre of the disc chromatogram is employed by Rosebeek[293]. See also Zimmermann and Nehring[294,295], Berlingozzi and Serchi[296], Bersin and Müller[297] and Fig. 19. Chromatography on arcs of a circle was employed by Marchal and Mittwer[298,299]. In a series of papers, Giri and his coworkers[300-304] describe not only development techniques for single paper discs but also preparative radial techniques. Saifer and Oreskes[305] study the physical factors in circular chromatography claiming this technique advantageous in a *small laboratory*. For further work see Rao[306], Lakshminarayanan[307], Brockmann and Gröne[308], Lüderitz and Westphal[309], Ganguli[310-312], Schwerdtfeger[313], LeStrange and Müller[314] and Chakrabortty and Burma[315,316]. For further modifications of radial techniques see also Ambe *et al.*[317], Ceriotti[318], Carles[319], Erbring and Patt[320], Berlingozzi[321], Chakrabortty and Burma[322], Ganguli[323,324], Krishnamurthy and Swaminathan[325], Philippu[326], Sulser[327] and Weihrauch[328]. *Conical paper chromatography* with the claim that simultaneous concentration may be possible, has been suggested by Osawa[329].

In spite of the opinions expressed by Martin above, which are shared by the authors, a recent review of radial development by Peyron[330] lists 302 references dealing with techniques and their applications.

(ix) Centrifugally accelerated paper chromatography

Caronna[331] and McDonald *et al.*[332-334] introduced centrifugally accelerated development, which reduces the time of development to a fraction of the usual. A circular disc chromatogram is rotated on a gramophone-like apparatus* with a central feed of solvent. As the solvent flow is faster in the machine direction the solvent distributes itself in the form of an ellipse with the major axis in the machine direction. Dyes were separated by adsorption chromatography on paper in a matter of minutes. Amino acids still produced compact zones with 975 rev./min and separations with reproducible R_F values were again possible in as little as 15 minutes.

To avoid the problems due to the elliptical form of the developed disc (corrections in calculations of R_F values) Tata and Hemmings[335] develop on discrete paper strips placed in a circle. The advantages of the method when separating radioactive materials of short half-lives were demonstrated by these authors in the separation of brominated thyronines labelled with ^{82}Br.

(x) Paper chromatography with gradient development

Solvent gradients. A simple ascending apparatus may be assembled with a magnetic stirrer on which the development chamber is placed and into which the second solvent is run from a burette at a rate proportional to the solvent ascent[336]. For descending development mixing chambers similar to those employed for columns have been described by Franks[337].

pH gradients on the paper. The separation of alkaloids and barbiturates was described by Schmall *et al.*[338,339] with papers on which buffers of increasing pH were placed along lines at right angles to the solvent flow. Depending on their pH value, bases moving with the solvent are fixed once a certain pH value is reached.

Paper impregnated with varying pH buffers in lines in the direction of the solvent flow were investigated by Bitancourt and Nogueira[340]. When the mixture to be examined is applied as a line along the paper each zone gives characteristic maxima and minima on the zones impregnated with buffers and the nature of the separated zones may thus be examined.

(xi) Preparative scale development

On a preparative scale, a stack of filter paper discs may be clamped together. This is called the *chromatopile*[341,342] (Fig. 21); after development the discs are separated and the constituents tested for and extracted from the paper. A pack of vertically orientated strips of paper compressed between two steel

* The apparatus of McDonald *et al.* is being manufactured by A. S. LaPine and Company (Chicago).

plates has also been used to separate large quantities of material on paper (the *chromatopack*[343]). Zechmeister[344] discusses the difficulties entailed in the use of stacks of filter paper inside a glass tube. The paper in such a tube must be cut with high precision to fit exactly the diameter of the tube.

The *cellulose sheets* used by Cuendet *et al.*[345] are paper sheets $^1/_8$ inch thick.

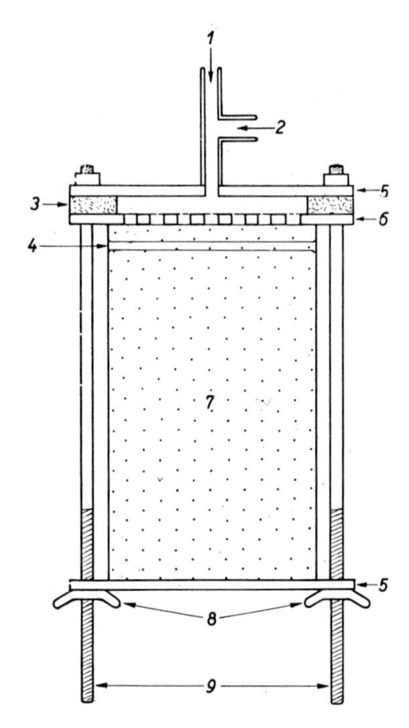

Fig. 21. Diagram of the chromatopile. (1) Connection for a rubber tube for filling the siphon; (2) connection for the siphon tube; (3) rubber gasket; (4) filter paper discs containing the sample; (5) stainless steel plates; (6) perforated stainless steel plates; (7) filter paper disc pile; (8) wing nuts; (9) bolts at four corners of steel plates (Mitchell and Haskins[342]).

Hedén[346] separates 5 mg or more of amino acids by running a row of spots on an ordinary sheet, washing the row towards one end after the first development and then separating in the second dimension on the same paper. See also Fritz and Bauer[347] and Fischer and Behrens[348]. Danielson[349] and Hagdahl and Danielson[350] described a new way of rolling paper sheets into a column which now is commercially available as the *Grycksbo chromatographic filter paper column*. It consists of a roll of filter paper closely wound around a central cylindrical rod of inert material and placed in a polyethylene cylinder, which is closed at both ends with polyethylene covers.

Liquid inlets and outlets are provided in the covers. Gram quantities of amino acids can be separated on this column.

(*f*) *Conditions necessary to obtain reproducible R_F values*

Bate-Smith[351] has studied the conditions necessary to obtain *reproducible* R_F values. The following recommendations are made: (*a*) the temperature should be controlled to $\pm$ 0.5°; (*b*) the time of running should be constant; (*c*) the paper should be equilibrated with the atmosphere in the chamber for 24 h prior to irrigation with solvent[352]; (*d*) one batch of paper should be used for all determinations; (*e*) a control substance should be run on every chromatogram. If the R_F differs from the standard by more than $\pm$ 0.02, that run should be discarded and fresh solvents used; (*f*) when solvents are used which undergo reactions, *e.g.* esterification, they should be allowed to stand for three days at the working temperature prior to use. Both Kowkabany and Cassidy[353] and Zimmermann[354] also point out that the R_F value may vary with the height of the spot above the level of the developing solvent. Zimmermann considers also machine direction of the paper, concentration of substance and the presence of other substances for the reproducibility of R_F values. See also Beck and Ébrey[355,356].

(*g*) *General techniques for spraying with reagents and detecting spots on the paper*

Solutions of reagents are added to the filter paper with atomisers or painted on with a brush. Numerous designs of atomisers are recorded in the literature and marketed by various firms (for examples see Wingo[357]). The general shortcomings of such atomisers is the production of a relatively thin jet which makes uniform spraying over a large chromatogram difficult. Thus when quantitative reactions are desired a mosquito spray gun or atomiser of similar jet size is required.

Zweig[358] and Wegmann[359] drew attention to the advantages in keeping chromatographic sprays in aerosol bottles. This idea has already been taken up commercially and ninhydrin reagent can be obtained in aerosol bottles.

Gases such as H_2S are passed directly over the paper and solids such as Zn dust are dusted on as a fine powder. If possible, the reactions are carried out so as not to diffuse the spots on the paper. For example, ninhydrin is sprayed on in butanol in which the amino acids are insoluble. Dipping the paper into the reagent is sometimes feasible when a stable insoluble product is formed. See for example Smith[360].

A rather useful tray for dipping chromatograms was designed by Morris *et al.*[361].

References p. 208

Reagents

Reagents and their sensitivity must be discussed in relation to the compounds and the problem involved. We shall deal here solely with several reagents having rather general applications.

Iodine vapours or spray were shown by Brante[362], Marini-Bettolo and Guarino[363], Bush[364], Whitehouse *et al.*[365] to yield spots darker or paler than the background with almost all organic compounds. This reaction appears to be often physical, a solution of iodine in the spots being formed. For the sensitivity of this reaction with a large range of lipid substances see Whitehouse *et al.*[365] and Table VI. Pan[366] recommends spraying the paper with aluminium sulphate before exposure to iodine vapours and subsequent spraying with starch, for increasing the sensitivity of this reaction.

Compounds containing iodine may be detected by reaction with ceric sulphate and arsenious acid[367]. This reaction may be enhanced by darkening the background with brucine or sulphanilic acid[368] or with phenol vapours[369].

$KMnO_4$ in dilute H_2SO_4 is a reagent which gives white or light yellow spots on a brown background with most organic compounds (Procházka[370]).

Mitchell[371] uses silver nitrate together with suitable background treatment or light exposure as reagent for reducing agents, halogenated pesticides, halides, phosphates, sulphates, higher fatty acids and some amino acids.

For detection of amphoteric substances, bases or acids, indicators may be sprayed on the paper. By then holding the paper over a volatile acid (CH_3COOH) or base (NH_3), a difference in pH between the background and the spots can be achieved. Tropeolin OO was used in this manner by Sluyterman and Veenendaal[372], universal indicator by Long *et al.*[373], bromocresol purple by Reid and Lederer[374] and methyl red by Walker[375].

Fluorescence or dark spots under ultraviolet light can be used as an almost universal detection method (purines, pyrimidines, alkaloids etc.). See for example Tennent *et al.*[376] and Paladini and Leloir[377]; for enhanced light absorption, Price *et al.*[378]. However, special filters or fluorescent background sprays (*e.g.* fluorescein) are often necessary for revealing certain spots.

Blueprint paper or contact printing is often used with ultraviolet light detection (see Gordon[379] and Kinnory and Greco[380]). An ultraviolet scanner camera was constructed by Drake *et al.*[381].

Szent-Györgyi[382] found that fluorescence is often obtained from non-fluorescing substances when the paper is cooled to low temperatures with dry ice.

For the application of luminol in paper chromatography see Moučka and Pařízek[383].

Differential charring on heating was obtained with some phosphate esters by Caldwell[384] and with mineral acids by Coch-Frugoni[385] and Baas Becking *et al.*[386].

TABLE VI

SENSITIVITY OF LIPIDS TO IODINE VAPOUR (24-h EXPOSURE) ON WHATMAN No. I PAPER (WHITEHOUSE *et al.*[365])

Compound	*Quantity in μg*		
	50	*100*	*200*
Triolein	++	+++	+++
Tristearin	±	±	+
Monomyristin	—	±	±
Phrenosine	+	+	++
Sphingomyelin	++	+++	+++
Phosphatidyl choline	++	+++	+++
Phosphatidyl ethanolamine	+	+++	+++
Lipositol	+	+	++
Cholic acid	+	+	+
Deoxycholic acid*	+	+	+
Lithocholic acid	+	+	+
Trihydroxycoprostane	+	+	+
Cholesterol	++	++	++
Lanosterol	+	+	+
Ergosterol	+++	+++	+++
β-Sitosterol	+	++	++
Progesterone	+++	+++	+++
Testosterone	+++	+++	+++
Estradiol	+	+	+
Androstenedione	+	+	+
Cortisone	+	+	+
Hydrocortisone	++	++	++
Corticosterone	+	++	++
Deoxycorticosterone	++	++	++
Kryptogenin	++	++	++
Diosgenin	++	++	++
Pimaric acid	+	++	++
Abietic acid	++	++	++
β-Carotene	+	++	++
Lycopene	±	+	+
Squalene	+	+	+
Vitamin A	+++	+++	+++

* Deoxycholic acid required a long period of time (48 hours) in the iodine before a reaction was noticeable.

For amperometric detection see De Vries and Van Dalen[387] and De Vries[388]; for detection by an impedance method see Blake[389].

(*h*) *Measurement of* R_F *values*

R_F values are usually measured with reference to the liquid front. When two liquid fronts are formed, either may be taken, but it is important to state to which it refers. Lacourt *et al.*[390] record the band front and band end rather than referring to the centre of gravity of a band.

References p. 208

For sugars[391], the R_G value is usually measured where

$$R_G = \frac{\text{Distance travelled by substance}}{\text{Distance travelled by glucose}}$$

Evans and coworkers[392] use the R'_F value for phenols, where

$$R'_F = \frac{\text{Distance travelled by spot front}}{\text{Distance travelled by solvent front}}$$

An instrument for rapid R_F measurements was constructed by Phillips[393], consisting of a graduated elastic band from which the R_F values can be read off directly; a transparent scale for the same purpose is described by Rockland and Dunn[394] (the *partogrid*), others by Nettleton and Mefferd[395] and Glazko and Dill[396]. Savoia[397] proposes two rulers joined with a hinge which permit direct reading of R_F values. See also Houston[398].

9. Quantitative methods

(*a*) *Evaluation of spots*

Generally, quantitative estimation of substances separated on paper can be performed either by examination of the spots on the paper, or by elution of the substances and subsequent determination in the eluate.

Fisher *et al.*[399,400] showed that the spot area of round and ovoid spots increases as the logarithm of the spot content. This relationship holds well for a wide range of concentrations. To obtain quantitative results, the spot area of an unknown substance must be compared with spots obtained from the same volume of a known concentration of the same substance developed on the same sheet of paper.

The increase of the spot area with time and with length of development was theoretically treated first by Brimley[401], Fisher and Holmes[402], Kauman and Bak[403] and further elaborated by Giddings and Keller[404].

Two independent factors can be recognised which tend to increase the surface of a spot, (1) diffusion, which occurs even when the chromatogram is stationary (without movement of the solvent, for some results see ref.[405]) and depends on time and the concentration of the substance in the original spots, and (2) the spread due to the partitioning during the development, which gives the spot a Gaussian curve type of distribution in the direction of the development (see p. 154).

As diffusion occurs in all dimensions and the partitioning effect in only one, usually ovoid spots are obtained.

Mathematical treatments of spot area-spot concentration relationship were given in a number of papers[399,401,404,406].

The uniformity of the paper used is important and Reid and Lederer[374] found that of a number of Whatman papers only Whatman No. 1 *for chromatography* gave satisfactory results for volatile fatty acids.

The techniques employed to evaluate spots are:

Measurement of spot length: for ovoid regular spots the length of the spot is proportional to the logarithm of the spot content[400]. Fowler[407] has used this relationship for sugars.

Planimetric measurement: Fisher *et al.*[400] obtained an accuracy of $\pm$ 2%.

Counting squares: The area of the spots can be traced out with a sharp pencil and copied with carbon paper onto graph paper and the number of squares counted. The accuracy of this technique[374] is about $\pm$ 5%.

Weighing excised spots: The spots can be cut out and the piece of paper weighed, giving results equal to the method of counting squares (Overell, private communication).

Approximate analysis by visual comparison: This method was used by Arden *et al.*[408] for estimation of UO_2^{++} and gives an accuracy of about 30%.

For some applications of the spot area methods see: Block[409-411], Åkerfeldt[412], who determined amino acids; Blumer[413] who determined porphyrins; Fowler[407] for sugars; Miyaki *et al.*[414,415] for thiamine and Manganelli and Brofazi[416] for fatty acids.

(b) *Combination of paper chromatography with standard quantitative methods*

Numerous methods have been described for the application of the usual quantitative methods to substances chromatographically separated on paper.

For sugars, amino acids etc., the spots are usually cut out and eluted with water (Fig. 22). It is also possible to extract the spots by merely leaving the

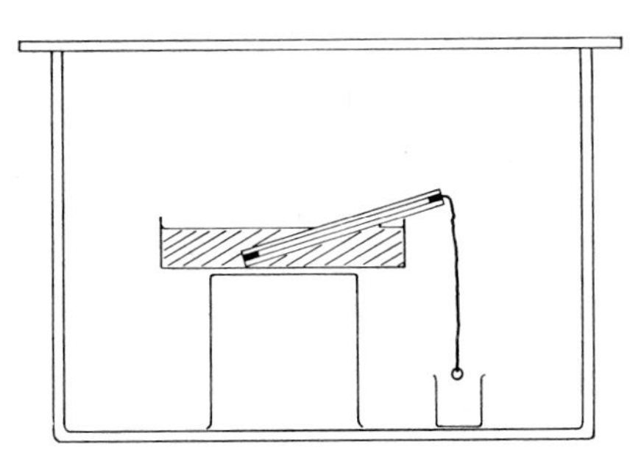

Fig. 22. Washing out of spots. The piece of filter paper containing the required substance is pinched between two pieces of glass resting in a Petri dish. The water in the dish rises between the plates by capillary attraction and is thus supplied to the filter paper. The wash liquor eventually drops off the end of the paper into the little beaker. Evaporation must be prevented by the large outer vessel (Dent[417]).

paper in contact with water for half an hour, or by the use of a micro-soxhlet extractor. Dumazert and Bozzi-Tichadou[418] describe a simple apparatus for the elution of spots.

(c) *Use of instruments for measurement of spot intensity*

(i) *Photoelectric cells*

The measurement of spot intensity is required not only in paper chromatographic but also in paper electrophoretic methods as well as in spot colorimetry, diffusion measurements inside filter paper etc. The number of commercial instruments available is considerable. Most consist of a photoelectric cell arrangement with direct reading and a device for moving paper strips past a light beam at regular intervals. Direct recording instruments have also been designed. Müller and Clegg[419-421] carried out extensive work on the instrumental possibilities. See also Fosdick and Blackwell[422], Block[423,424], Bull *et al.*[425], Crook *et al.*[426], Eberle[427], Bassir[428], Kutáček and Koloušek[429], Gorbach[430], Miettinen and Moisio[431], De Wael and Cadavieco[432], Röttger[433], Silver and Bookman[434], Kronmueller[435], Barrollier *et al.*[436].

Of the commercial instruments we shall only mention the recording photodensitometer of Joyce, Loebl and Co. Ltd. (England), the Shandon densitometer, the Elphor photometer (Bender and Hobein, Munich), the transmission densitometer of Baldwin Scientific Instruments (Dartford, Kent), the photometer of Jouan (Paris), the densitometer of the Photovolt Corp., the microphotometer of Dr. B. Lange (Berlin) and the recording photometer of Lerès (Paris).

Wieme[437] drew attention to the error introduced when irregular spots are scanned at a certain width only. He constructed an apparatus in which a very thin slit is moved over the entire spot and which integrates the total amount of absorbing material.

Supports for the paper strip to be used in the Beckman-photometer were described by Treiber and Koren[438] and Ehrmantraut and Weinstock[439]. For an instrument measuring reflected radiation see refs. [440-442].

Hashimoto[443,444] designed an instrument for the measurement of *ultraviolet absorption* of colourless substances on the paper strip. Examples cited are the separation of luteolin, acacetin and rutin (at 2600 Å) and methyl and ethyl xanthates (at 3000 Å). Mori[445-448] describes a new technique for use with photometry in which the spot is made to travel into a narrow channel formed on the paper, the length of the spot being then measured with greater accuracy than a round spot. It is not quite clear how this could be applied to a large number of spots as in amino acid separations.

Fluorescence was measured by Semand and Fried[449] and Brown and

Marsh[450]. See also Kaiser and Wildemann[451]. For infrared absorption measurements see Goulden[452] and Kalkwarf and Frost[453].

Some authors consider it advisable to decrease the absorption of filter paper in transmission photometry. This problem was mainly dealt with for paper electrophoresis by Grassmann[454,455], also by Barrollier[456].

For the *spectrophotometry* of spots on the paper see Campbell and Simpson[457], Neuhaus and Richartz[458] and Eger[459].

(ii) Photographic methods

Fisher *et al.*[400] obtained photographs with sharp spot edges with copy cat (Miles Aircraft), which were measured with a Hilger photomicrometer giving a linear relationship between extinction and the amounts present, over a limited range. Pokrovskiĭ[460] confirms these results. See also Mykolajewycz[461]. The use of negatives and their photometric evaluation is extensively used for estimations of purines, pyrimidines and related substances.

(d) Retention analysis

This method of quantitative estimation was developed by Wieland *et al.*[462,463]. A strip chromatogram about 6 cm wide is developed in the second dimension, with a reagent for the separated spots. Wherever a spot reacts with the ascending reagent, a V-shaped notch is formed due to the retardation of the flow of reagent in this zone (Fig. 23).

For example, for Cu^{++} ions ascending through spots of amino acids, let α be the adsorption of Cu^{++} in the paper and β the absorption of Cu^{++} by the

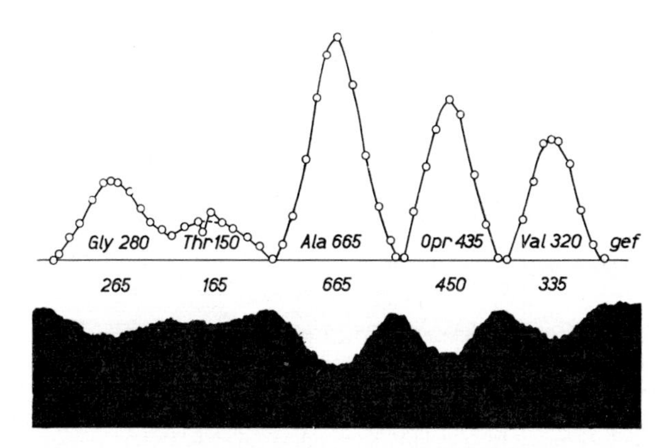

Fig. 23. Retention analysis. Separation of a mixture of glycine, threonine, alanine, hydroxyproline and valine (Wieland and Wirth[463]). The upper row of figures represents the values found; theoretical figures are given underneath.

References p. 208

amino acid; the distance travelled by Cu^{++} in the free paper is then $1/\alpha = h$ and the distance travelled in the amino acid spot

$$\frac{1}{(\alpha + \beta)} = \gamma$$

The relation of the two is

$$\frac{\alpha + \beta}{\alpha} = 1 + \frac{\beta}{\alpha} = \frac{h}{\gamma} \qquad (1)$$

The concentration of the amino acid in each point of the V-shaped notch is proportional to β/α, which according to equation (1) is $h/\gamma - 1$.

By plotting $h/\gamma - 1$ against distance on the paper strip, one obtains curves whose area is directly proportional to the concentration of the spot. This method has yielded very good results in many cases, but suffers from the fact that the paper is usually not sufficiently uniform, thus yielding curves with serrated edges. These serrations lower the accuracy as well as reducing the ability to distinguish between closely adjacent bands.

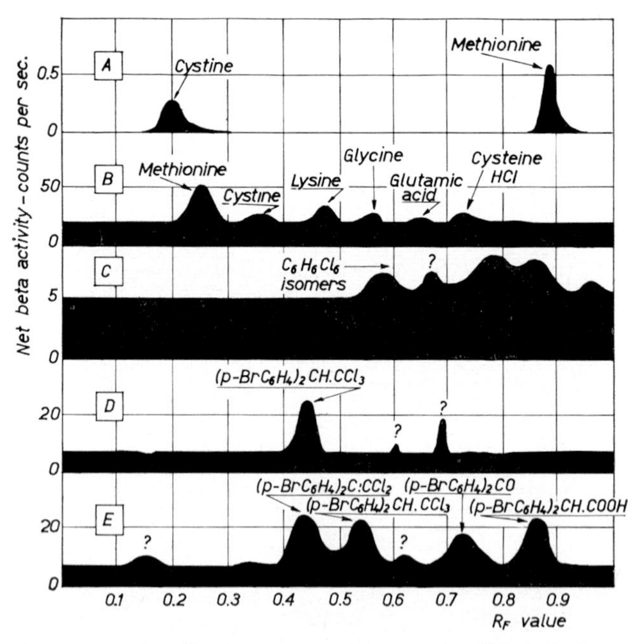

Fig. 24. Experimental radio-chromatograms on paper (Winteringham *et al.* [467]). *A*, chromatogram of protein hydrolysate from wheat grown on ^{35}S; *B*, strip spotted with known amino acids and exposed to ^{131}I-labelled CH_3I; *C*, neutron-activated chromatogram of $C_6H_6Cl_6$ isomers; *D*, neutron-activated chromatogram of a bromine analogue of DDT; *E*, neutron-activated chromatogram of bromine analogues of DDT derivatives.

Retention analysis was employed for hydroxy acids (Wieland and Feld[464]), amino acids (Wieland and Wirth[463]) and for glycine, sarcosine and dimethylglycine (Kuhn and Ruelius[465]).

(e) *Direct polarographic scanning*

Langer[466] constructed a polarograph with a circular rotating gold amalgam electrode over which the paper strip is passed, while being over a certain area in contact with a calomel half-cell. The results with inorganic ions look very promising.

10. The application of radioactivity in paper chromatography

The use of radioactive tracers in biochemical reactions and their elucidation by means of paper chromatography is beyond the scope of this chapter. The reader is referred to treatises such as *Radioactive Isotopes in Biochemistry*, by E. Broda (Elsevier, Amsterdam, 1960) or *La chimie nucléaire et ses applications*, by M. Haissinsky (Masson, Paris, 1957). However, there are some techniques which concern general paper chromatography.

(a) *Reaction of chromatograms with radioactive substances*

Winteringham *et al.*[467] reacted a developed chromatogram of amino acids with ^{131}I-labelled CH_3I. As shown in Fig. 24 the amino acids may then be detected by their radioactivity but a rather strong background activity is also formed. Radioactive $H_2{}^{35}S$ is used by Van Erkelens[468] to detect micro-grams of metals on developed paper chromatograms. Both techniques seem unsuitable for general practice as special equipment is necessary when dealing with radioactive gases.

(b) *Neutron activation of chromatograms*

This method was also employed by Winteringham *et al.*[467] for hexachlorcyclohexanes and bromine analogues of DDT and as shown in Fig. 24 a rather high background is produced.

(c) *Paper chromatography with labelled derivatives*

Copper complexes of amino acids with radioactive Cu were separated by Wieland *et al.*[469]. The pipsyl method of Keston, Udenfriend *et al.*[470–473] with either ^{131}I pipsyl or ^{35}S pipsyl derivatives should be mentioned here. An ingenious test for identity is also possible by preparing mixed chromatograms where each constituent is labelled with another isotope. This is illustrated in Fig. 25.

References p. 208

(d) *The measurement of radioactivity on paper chromatograms*

The methods of measurement of radioactivity were reviewed recently by Pocchiari and Rossi[474]; for an earlier review see also Lissitzky and Michel[475].

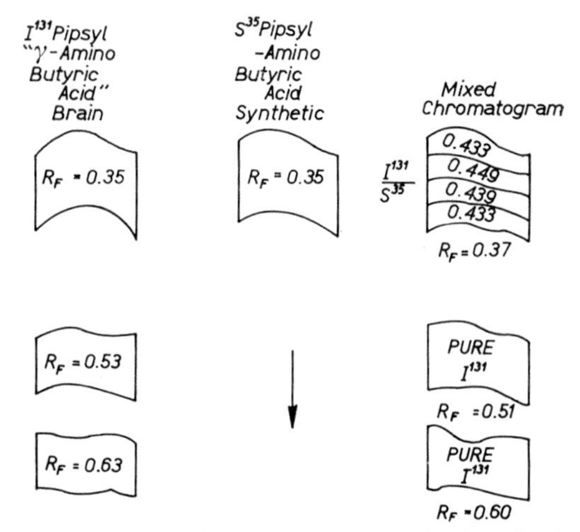

Fig. 25a. Chromatograms of the ^{131}I-labelled pipsyl derivative obtained from extracts of mouse brain and the ^{35}S-labelled pipsyl derivative of an authentic sample of γ-aminobutyric acid (Udenfriend[471]).

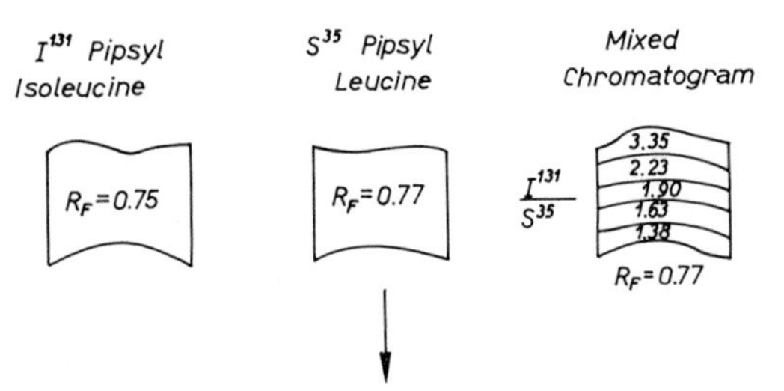

Fig. 25b. Chromatograms of ^{131}I-labelled pipsyl isoleucine and ^{35}S-labelled pipsyl leucine.

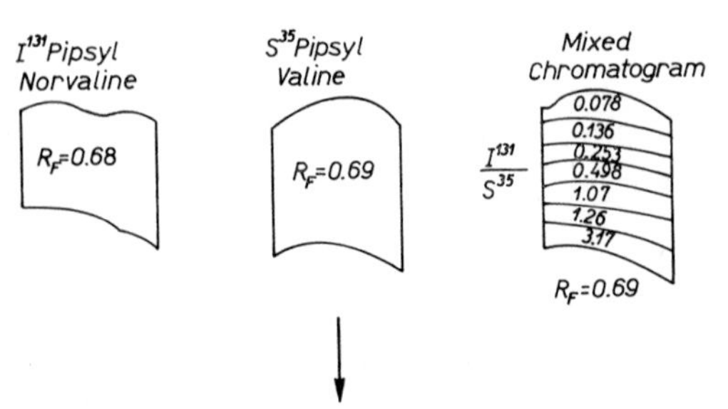

Fig. 25c. Chromatograms of ^{131}I-labelled pipsyl norvaline and ^{35}S-labelled pipsyl valine.

(i) The use of photographic plates (radioautography)

The developed chromatogram is left in contact with an undeveloped photographic plate or film and then developed in the usual way. This method is mainly qualitative or semi-quantitative but has great advantages, due to its simplicity, in the detection of radioactivity on two-dimensional chromatograms. It was used in the work on photosynthesis by Benson *et al.*[476]. Absorbers may of course be placed between the paper and the photographic plate and thus for example ^{14}C and ^{32}P be distinguished. A scintillating liquid may also be interposed as is necessary in the radioautography of tritium (scintillation autograph)[477].

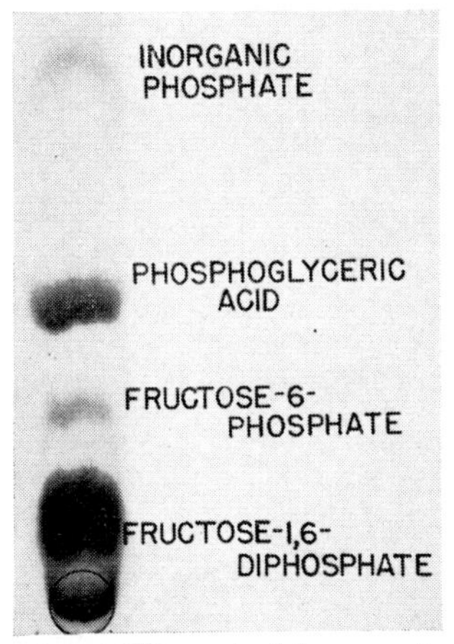

Fig. 26. Paper chromatography of ^{32}P-marked hexose phosphates (Benson *et al.*[476]).

A typical uni-dimensional radioautograph is shown in Fig. 26. Errors are possible in this technique due to constituents of the solvent interfering with the photographic plate (*e.g.* HCl or HBr in solvent (author's observation)) or due to pressure or pencil marks which transfer themselves onto the plate[65]. Against the latter a cellophane sheet may be interposed.

A photographic emulsion may also be poured directly around and over the chromatogram and after the necessary time, developed and examined microscopically. This technique (evolved by E. Picciotto) is especially suited to micro-chromatograms on thin bands or threads and can also be used for simultaneous quantitative measurements of several activities by observing the differences of their paths.

(ii) Counting techniques

Direct counting methods. The chromatogram may be cut into sections and each placed under the counter, observing the same geometry for all and

References p. 208

counted for the same time. From the activities measured a histogram can be graphically constructed. The only error of this method is due to self-absorption due to the density variation of the paper, which of course is never completely uniform. Some values indicating the magnitude of this error are shown in Table VII.

TABLE VII

EFFECT OF PAPER DENSITY VARIATION ON SELF-ABSORPTION

(Winteringham *et al.*[467])

Isotope	*Proportion of beta particles unabsorbed by paper of mean density 8.785 mg/cm²*	*Variation of self-absorption correction factor corresponding to a variation of ± 10% in paper density*
^{14}C	0.366	± 7.4 %
^{35}S	0.431	± 6.5 %
^{82}Br	0.787	± 2.4 %
^{131}I	0.828	± 1.9 %
^{36}Cl	0.843	± 1.7 %
^{32}P	0.957	± 0.5 %

Usually, however, the chromatogram is drawn past a counter tube which is shielded by lead, except for a window (2–5 mm wide). The paper is wrapped in cellophane when possible, and distances either marked on the cellophane or on a rule to which the chromatogram is attached. A measurement is then made with the paper in a certain position and then the paper moved a given distance (usually 5 mm or 1 cm) and again the activity measured. This method although faster than the previous, introduces an error due to inefficient shielding by the lead protection of the counting tube, which makes the activity curves appear wider than they actually are. However, this error depends on the type of radiation measured and is considerable with hard gamma rays, such as from ^{65}Zn, but very small from weak β rays as from ^{35}S. (See Götte and Pätze[478].) Numerous simple devices for this technique have been proposed in the literature: Atkinson[479], Bourne[480], Boursnell[481], Tomarelli and Florey[482], Fosdick and Blackwell[483], Gray *et al.*[484], Jones[485], Katz and Chaikoff[486] and Linskens[487]. The above techniques permit the scanning of a uni-dimensional chromatogram in less than half an hour but are extremely time consuming when two-dimensional chromatograms are to be measured.

Automatic counting devices. Several automatic instruments have been constructed in which the paper strip is moved automatically past a shielded counter tube and the activity recorded on a synchronously moving pen-recorder. For some designs see Rockland *et al.*[488], Williams and Smith[489], Bradley[490], Berthet[491], Bonet-Maury[492], Wingo[493], Lerch and Neukomm[494] and Vigne and Lissitzky[495]. These instruments have the disadvantage of inadequate shielding of the chromatogram and also of the error due to the response of the recording instrument.

In the laboratory of E. B. Chain (Istituto Superiore di Sanità) a fully automatic instrument was constructed, which uses scanning at regular intervals instead of a continuously moving paper. The activity is automatically typed onto a chart by a typewriter. Some models, using this principle, permit the automatic scanning in two dimensions, resulting in a chart which shows the activity per area in figures. This instrument seems to be the most suitable of those so far proposed for general biochemical work (see E. B. Chain, *Methods of quantitative radiochromatography as applied to the study of intermediate metabolism*, Blackwell, Oxford, 1956).

References p. 208

REFERENCES

[1] A. J. P. Martin and R. L. M. Synge, *Biochem. J.*, 35 (1941) 91.
[2] L. C. Craig, *Anal. Chem.*, 22 (1950) 1346.
[3] A. J. P. Martin and R. L. M. Synge, *Biochem. J.*, 35 (1941) 1358.
[4] R. Consden, A. H. Gordon and A. J. P. Martin, *Biochem. J.*, 38 (1944) 224.
[5] C. E. Dent, *Biochem. J.*, 43 (1948) 169.
[6] L. B. Rockland and M. S. Dunn, *Science*, 111 (1950) 332.
[7] J. Boldingh, *Experientia*, 4 (1948) 270.
[8] J. Boldingh, *Rec. trav. chim.*, 69 (1950) 247.
[9] M. W. Partridge and J. Chilton, *Nature*, 167 (1951) 79.
[10] G. A. Howard and A. J. P. Martin, *Biochem. J.*, 46 (1950) 532.
[11] F. P. W. Winteringham, A. Harrison and R. G. Bridges, *Nature*, 166 (1950) 999.
[12] A. J. P. Martin, *Biochem. Soc. Symposia (Cambridge)*, No. 3 (1949) 4.
[13] M. Verzele, private communication.
[14] R. Lindner, *Z. Elektrochem.*, 54 (1950) 421.
[15] F. C. Nachod, *Ion Exchange*, Academic Press, New York, 1949, p. 411.
[16] E. Cremer and R. Müller, *Mikrochemie ver. Mikrochim. Acta*, 36/37 (1951) 553.
[17] S. W. Mayer and E. R. Tompkins, *J. Am. Chem. Soc.*, 69 (1947) 2866.
[18] J. Beukenkamp, W. Rieman III and S. Lindenbaum, *Anal. Chem.*, 26 (1954) 505.
[19] H. van Duin, *Biochim. Biophys. Acta*, 10 (1953) 198, 343; 12 (1953) 489.
[20] H. van Duin, *Rec. trav. chim.*, 73 (1954) 68.
[21] A. H. Gordon, A. J. P. Martin and R. L. M. Synge, *Biochem. J.*, 37 (1943) 79.
[22] A. J. P. Martin, *Ann. N.Y. Acad. Sci.*, 49 (1948) 249.
[23] C. Fromageot, M. Jutisz and E. Lederer, *Biochim. Biophys. Acta*, 2 (1948) 487.
[24] E Lester Smith, *Nature*, 169 (1952) 60.
[25] T. C. J. Ovenston, *Nature*, 169 (1952) 924.
[26] L. M. Kay and K. N. Trueblood, *Anal. Chem.*, 26 (1954) 1566.
[27] G. R. Tristram, *Biochem. J.*, 40 (1946) 721.
[28] F. A. Isherwood, *Biochem. J.*, 40 (1946) 688.
[29] R. Harris and A. N. Wick, *Ind. Eng. Chem., Anal. Ed.*, 18 (1946) 276.
[30] H. F. Liddell and H. N. Rydon, *Biochem. J.*, 38 (1944) 68.
[31] F. E. Resnik, L. A. Lee and W. A. Powell, *Anal. Chem.*, 27 (1955) 928.
[32] M. Morrison and E. Stotz, *J. Biol. Chem.*, 213 (1955) 373.
[33] A. A. Levi and S. G. Terjesen and I.C.I., *Brit. Pat.*, (1945) 569,844: *C.A.*, 41 (1947) 6026-h.
[34] L. L. Ramsey and W. I. Patterson, *J. Assoc. Offic. Agr. Chemists*, 29 (1946) 337.
[35] L. L. Ramsey and W. I. Patterson, *J. Assoc. Offic. Agr. Chemists*, 31 (1948) 441.
[36] F. A. Vandenheuvel and E. R. Hayes, *Anal. Chem.*, 24 (1952) 960.
[37] V. Zbinovsky, *Anal. Chem.*, 27 (1955) 764.
[38] M. H. Peterson and M. I. Johnson, *J. Biol. Chem.*, 174 (1948) 775.
[39] E. F. Phares, E. H. Mosbach and F. W. Denison Jr., *Anal. Chem.*, 24 (1952) 660.
[40] A. J. P. Martin and R. R. Porter, *Biochem. J.*, 49 (1951) 215.
[41] R. R. Porter, *Biochem. J.*, 53 (1953) 320.
[42] R. R. Porter, in *The Chemical Structure of Proteins*, Ciba Foundation Symposium, 1953, p. 31.
[43] R. R. Porter, *Biochem. J.*, 59 (1955) 405.
[44] S. Moore and W. H. Stein, *Ann. N.Y. Acad. Sci.*, 49 (1948) 265.
[45] M. M. Daly and A. E. Mirsky, *J. Biol. Chem.*, 179 (1949) 981.
[46] L. Hough, J. K. N. Jones and W. H. Wadman, *Nature*, 162 (1948) 448; *J. Chem. Soc.*, (1949) 2511.
[47] A. A. Levi, *Discussions Faraday Soc.*, 7 (1949) 124.
[48] H. E. Carter, R. K. Clark Jr., P. Kohn, J. W. Rothrock, W. R. Taylor, C. A. West, G. B. Whitfield and W. G. Jackson, *J. Am. Chem. Soc.*, 76 (1954) 566.
[49] A. Fischer and M. Behrens, *Z. physiol. Chem., Hoppe Seyler's*, 291 (1952) 242.
[50] A. Kuritzkes, J. von Euw and T. Reichstein, *Helv. Chim. Acta*, 42 (1959) 1502.
[51] R. J. Boscott, *Chem. & Ind. (London)*, (1952) 472.
[52] J. Hirsch, *Federation Proc.*, 18 (1959) 972.

[53] J. F. Nyc, D. M. Maron, J. B. Garst and H. B. Friedgood, *Proc. Soc. Exptl. Biol. Med.*, 77 (1951) 466.
[54] L. Bosch, *Biochim. Biophys. Acta*, 11 (1953) 301.
[55] S. M. Partridge and T. Swain, *Nature*, 166 (1950) 272.
[56] O. Wiss and U. Gloor, *Z. physiol. Chem., Hoppe Seyler's*, 310 (1958) 260.
[57] R. A. Morton, U. Gloor, O. Schindler, G. M. Wilson, L. H. Chopard-dit-Jean, F. W. Hemming, O. Isler, W. M. F. Leat, J. F. Pennock, R. Rüegg, U. Schwieter and O. Wiss, *Helv. Chim. Acta*, 41 (1958) 2343.
[58] I. M. Hais and K. Macek, *Handbuch der Papierchromatographie, Band I, Grundlagen und Technik* (German translation of the 2nd Czech ed. by J. Liebster), G. Fischer Verlag, Jena, 1958.
[59] J. Opienska-Blauth, A. Waksmundski and M. Kanski, *Chromatografia*, Panstwowe Wydawnictwe Naukowe, Warsaw, 1957.
[60] E. Lederer and M. Lederer, *Chromatography*, 2nd ed., Elsevier, Amsterdam, 1957.
[61] J. N. Balston and B. E. Talbot, *A Guide to Filter Paper and Cellulose Powder Chromatography*, Reeve Angel, London, 1952, 145 pp.
[62] R. J. Block, E. L. Durrum and G. Zweig, *A Manual of Paper Chromatography and Paper Electrophoresis*, Academic Press, New York, 1955, 484 pp.
[63] F. Cramer, *Papierchromatographie, Monographien zu "Angewandte Chemie" und "Chemie-Ingenieur-Technik"*, No. 64, 3rd ed., Verlag Chemie, Weinheim, 1954, 136 pp.
[64] H. G. Cassidy, *Fundamentals of Chromatography*, Interscience, New York, 1957.
[65] H. F. Linskens, *Papierchromatographie in der Botanik*, 2nd ed., Springer, Berlin, 1959.
[66] I. Smith, *Chromatographic Techniques, clinical and biochemical applications*, Heinemann, London, 1958.
[67] R. Neher, *Chromatographie von Sterinen, Steroiden und verwandten Verbindungen*, Elsevier, Amsterdam, 1958.
[68] M. Lederer, *Progrès récents de la chromatographie*, 2me partie (chimie minérale), Hermann, Paris, 1952.
[69] F. H. Pollard and J. F. W. McOmie, *Chromatographic Methods of Inorganic Analysis*, Butterworth, London, 1953.
[70] E. Blasius, *Chromatographische Methoden in der analytischen und präparativen anorganischen Chemie, mit besonderer Berücksichtigung der Ionenaustauscher*, Ferdinand Enke Verlag, Stuttgart, 1958.
[71] Z. Tamura, *Inorganic Chromatography*, Kyoritsu Publishing Co., Tokyo, 1957.
[72] M. Lederer, Ed., *Chromatographic Reviews*, Vol. I (1959), Vol. II (1960), Vol. III (1961), Vol. IV (1962), Elsevier, Amsterdam.
[73] P. H. Hermans, *Physics and Chemistry of Cellulose Fibres*, Elsevier, Amsterdam, 1949, 543 pp.
[74] F. H. Burstall, G. R. Davies and R. A. Wells, *Discussions Faraday Soc.*, 7 (1949) 179.
[75] L. C. Craig, *Anal. Chem.*, 22 (1950) 1346.
[76] C. S. Hanes and F. A. Isherwood, *Nature*, 164 (1949) 1107.
[77] S. Moore and W. H. Stein, *Ann. N.Y. Acad. Sci.*, 49 (1948) 265.
[78] A. J. P. Martin, *Ann. Rev. Biochem.*, 19 (1950) 517.
[79] H. R. Bentley and J. K. Whitehead, *Biochem. J.*, 46 (1950) 341.
[80] M. Lederer, *Anal. Chim. Acta*, 5 (1951) 185.
[81] B. Milicevic, *Bull. soc. chim. Belgrade*, 16 (1951) 101: *C.A.*, 46 (1952) 4319-g.
[82] R. Munier and M. Macheboeuf, *Bull. soc. chim. biol.*, 32 (1950) 904.
[83] L. Horner, W. Emrich and A. Kirschner, *Z. Elektrochem.*, 56 (1952) 987.
[84] S. Moore and W. H. Stein, *Ann. Rev. Biochem.*, 21 (1952) 521.
[85] D. P. Burma and B. Banerjee, *Science and Culture (Calcutta)*, 15 (1950) 363.
[86] E. Pluchet and M. Lederer, *J. Chromatog.*, 3 (1960) 290.
[87] J. Uri, *Nature*, 183 (1959) 1188.
[88] T. Schönfeld and E. Broda, *Mikrochemie ver. Mikrochim. Acta*, 36/37 (1951) 537.
[89] D. P. Burma, *Anal. Chem.*, 25 (1953) 549.
[90] R. J. Boscott, *Chem. & Ind. (London)*, (1952) 472.
[91] J. B. Schute, *Nature*, 171 (1953) 839.

[92] A. J. Ultee and J. Hartel, *Anal. Chem.*, 27 (1955) 557.
[93] F. Miranda and S. Lissitzky, *J. Chromatog.*, 2 (1959) 354.
[94] R. Tschesche, G. Grimmer and F. Seehofer, *Chem. Ber.*, 86 (1953) 1235.
[95] C. Levine and E. Chargaff, *J. Biol. Chem.*, 192 (1951) 481.
[96] E. C. Bate-Smith and R. G. Westall, *Biochim. Biophys. Acta*, 4 (1950) 427.
[97] E. R. Reichl, *Monatsh. Chem.*, 86 (1955) 69.
[98] H. K. Schauer and R. Burlisch, *Z. Naturforsch.*, 10b (1955) 683.
[99] J. Franc and J. Jokl, *J. Chromatog.*, 2 (1959) 424.
[100] H. Holness and W. R. Stone, *Analyst*, 83 (1958) 71.
[101] J. Franc and J. Latinák, *Chem. listy*, 49 (1955) 317; 49 (1955) 325; 49 (1955) 328: *C.A.*, 49 (1955) 9352-e.
[102] J. Franc and J. Jokl, *Chem. listy*, 50 (1956) 373: *C.A.*, 50 (1956) 8288-i.
[103] J. Franc and J. Jokl, *Collection Czechoslov. Chem. Communs.*, 21 (1956) 1161; 24 (1959) 250.
[104] J. Franc and J. Jokl, *Z. Elektrochem.*, 61 (1957) 1069.
[105] J. Franc, *Collection Czechoslov. Chem. Communs.*, 22 (1957) 995.
[106] J. M. Calvo, *Euclides (Madrid)*, 15 (1955) 208.
[107] S. Dikstein, *J. Chromatog.*, 2 (1959) 204.
[108] F. Sanger, *Advances in Protein Chem.*, 7 (1952) 1.
[109] A. B. Pardee, *J. Biol. Chem.*, 190 (1951) 757.
[110] T. B. Moore and C. G. Baker, *J. Chromatog.*, 1 (1958) 513.
[111] D. G. Roux and S. R. Evelyn, *J. Chromatog.*, 1 (1958) 537.
[112] E. R. Reichl, *Mikrochim. Acta*, (1956) 958.
[113] K. Macek and Z. J. Vejdelek, *Nature*, 176 (1955) 1173.
[114] A. Polson, *Biochim. Biophys. Acta*, 3 (1949) 205.
[115] K. Satake and T. Seki, *J. Japan. Chem.*, 4 (1950) 557: *C.A.*, 45 (1951) 4604-f.
[116] O. J. Draper and A. L. Pollard, *Science*, 109 (1949) 448.
[117] P. H. Mars, *Pharm. Weekblad*, 88 (1953) 319: *C.A.*, 47 (1953) 8585-f.
[118] H. R. Bentley and J. K. Whitehead, *Biochem. J.*, 46 (1950) 341.
[119] A. Lacourt, G. Sommereyns, E. DeGeyndt, J. Baruh and J. Gillard, *Mikrochemie ver. Mikrochim. Acta*, 34 (1949) 215.
[120] W. R. Walker and M. Lederer, *Anal. Chim. Acta*, 5 (1951) 191.
[121] F. A. Isherwood and M. A. Jermyn, *Biochem. J.*, 48 (1951) 515.
[122] G. P. Briner, *Ph. D. Thesis*, University of Melbourne, 1959.
[123] R. Osteux, J. Guillaume and J. Laturaze, *J. Chromatog.*, 1 (1958) 70.
[124] M. Lederer, *Proc. Surface Chem. Congress*, London, 1957.
[125] J. A. Thoma and D. French, *Anal. Chem.*, 29 (1957) 1645.
[126] A. J. Landua, R. Fuerst and J. Awapara, *Anal. Chem.*, 23 (1951) 162.
[127] E. F. McFarren, *Anal. Chem.*, 23 (1951) 168.
[128] A. Waksmundski and E. Soczewinski, *J. Chromatog.*, 3 (1960) 252.
[129] W. Debska, *Nature*, 182 (1958) 666.
[130] J. W. H. Lugg and B. T. Overell, *Nature*, 160 (1947) 87.
[131] J. W. H. Lugg and B. T. Overell, *Australian J. Sci. Research*, 1 (1948) 98.
[132] R. Munier and M. Macheboeuf, *Bull. soc. chim. biol.*, 33 (1951) 846.
[133] R. Munier, *Bull. soc. chim. France*, (1952) 852.
[134] C. S. Hanes and F. A. Isherwood, *Nature*, 164 (1949) 1107.
[135] F. A. Isherwood and C. S. Hanes, *Biochem. J.*, 55 (1953) 824.
[136] M. Lederer, *Anal. Chim. Acta*, 4 (1950) 629.
[137] H. Zahn, *Textil-Praxis*, 6 (1951) 127.
[138] R. A. Keller and J. C. Giddings, *J. Chromatog.*, 3 (1960) 205.
[139] A. S. Curry, *Nature*, 71 (1953) 71.
[140] B. Erdem and H. Erlenmeyer, *Helv. Chim. Acta*, 37 (1954) 2220.
[141] C. H. Hassall and K. E. Magnus, *Experientia*, 10 (1954) 425.
[142] D. M. Waldron-Edward, *Chem. & Ind. (London)*, (1954) 104.
[143] I. W. Wark, *Proc. Roy. Soc. N.S.W.*, 63 (1929) 47.
[144] J. N. Counsell, L. Hough and W. H. Wadman, *Research (London)*, 4 (1951) 143.
[145] D. P. Burma, *Nature*, 168 (1951) 565.
[146] S. N. Tewari, *Kolloid-Z.*, 138 (1954) 178.

[147] F. A. Isherwood and M. A. Jermyn, *Biochem. J.*, 48 (1951) 515.
[148] M. Alcock and J. S. Cannell, *Analyst*, 79 (1954) 389.
[149] M. Alcock and J. S. Cannell, *Nature*, 177 (1956) 327.
[150] E. C. Bate-Smith, *Partition Chromatography, Biochem. Soc. Symposia*, No. 3, 1950, p. 62.
[151] H. R. Roberts and M. G. Koler, *Nature*, 183 (1959) 460.
[152] H. R. Roberts, *Anal. Chem.*, 29 (1957) 1443.
[153] H. R. Roberts and W. Bucek, *Anal. Chem.*, 29 (1957) 1447.
[154] G. N. Kowkabany and H. G. Cassidy, *Anal. Chem.*, 22 (1950) 817.
[155] D. P. Burma, *J. Indian Chem. Soc.*, 29 (1952) 567.
[156] E. Lederer, *Bull. soc. chim. France*, (1952) 815.
[157] I. E. Bush, *Recent Progr. in Hormone Research*, 9 (1954) 321.
[158] V. Wynn, *Nature*, 164 (1949) 445.
[159] F. Bryant and B. T. Overell, *Nature*, 168 (1951) 167.
[160] F. Micheel and H. Schweppe, *Mikrochim. Acta*, (1954) 53.
[161] F. Micheel and P. Albers, *Chem. Ber.*, 89 (1956) 140.
[162] E. M. Buras Jr. and S. R. Hobart, *Anal. Chem.*, 27 (1955) 1507.
[163] J. W. H. Zijp, *Chem. Weekblad*, 51 (1955) 547.
[164] F. Micheel and P. Albers, *Mikrochim. Acta*, (1954) 489.
[165] T. M. Spotswood, *J. Chromatog.*, 2 (1959) 90.
[166] E. Kovacz, *Naturwiss.*, 44 (1957) 181.
[167] G. A. Morin, A. Cheutin, O. Costerousse and M. Fouquet, *Bull. soc. chim. biol.*, 34 (1952) 193.
[168] M. Ezrin and H. G. Cassidy, *Ann. N.Y. Acad. Sci.*, 57 (1953) 79.
[169] B. Sansoni, *Naturwiss.*, 41 (1954) 213.
[170] R. H. Müller and D. L. Clegg, *Anal. Chem.*, 21 (1949) 1123.
[171] R. H. Müller and D. L. Clegg, *Anal. Chem.*, 21 (1949) 1429.
[172] R. H. Müller and D. L. Clegg, *Anal. Chem.*, 23 (1951) 396.
[173] F. Goppelsroeder, *Mitt. k.k.Technol. Gewerbe-Museums, Wien*, II (1888) Nos. 3 and 4; III (1889) Nos. 1–4.
[174] F. Goppelsroeder, *Verhandl. naturforsch. Ges. Basel*, 14 (1901); 17 (1904); 19 (1907) Heft 2.
[175] M. A. Jermyn and F. A. Isherwood, *Biochem. J.*, 44 (1949) 402.
[176] M. L. Karnovsky and M. J. Johnson, *Anal. Chem.*, 21 (1949) 1125.
[177] B.-J. Ackerman and H. G. Cassidy, *Anal. Chem.*, 26 (1954) 1874.
[178] H. G. Cassidy, *Anal. Chem.*, 24 (1952) 1415.
[179] E. Erdos and I. Vavruch, *Chem. listy*, 50 (1956) 29: *C.A.*, 50 (1956) 4584-d.
[180] J. Dixmier, P. Dupuis and M. Nortz, *Chim. Anal.*, 38 (1956) 129: *C.A.*, 50 (1956) 16531-e.
[181] J. C. Giddings, G. H. Stewart and A. L. Ruoff, *J. Chromatog.*, 3 (1960) 239.
[182] J. C. Giddings, *J. Chromatog.*, 3 (1960) 443.
[183] R. Munier and M. Macheboeuf, *Bull. soc. chim. biol.*, 32 (1950) 192.
[184] R. Consden and A. H. Gordon, *Nature*, 162 (1948) 180.
[185] R. Consden, A. H. Gordon and A. J. P. Martin, *Biochem. J.*, 41 (1947) 590.
[186] R. Acher, M. Jutisz and C. Fromageot, *Biochim. Biophys. Acta*, 8 (1952) 442.
[187] N. R. Joseph, *J. Biol. Chem.*, 126 (1938) 403.
[188] T. Astrup, A. Stage and E. Olsen, *Acta Chem. Scand.*, 5 (1951) 1343.
[189] J. Katz and I. L. Chaikoff, *J. Biol. Chem.*, 206 (1954) 887.
[190] W. H. Stein and S. Moore, *J. Biol. Chem.*, 190 (1951) 103.
[191] M. Brenner and R. Frey, *Helv. Chim. Acta*, 34 (1951) 1701.
[192] K. A. Piez, E. B. Tooper and L. S. Fosdick, *J. Biol. Chem.*, 194 (1952) 669.
[193] A. Drèze and A. de Boeck, *Arch. intern. physiol.*, 60 (1952) 201.
[194] A. Drèze, S. Moore and E. J. Bigwood, *Anal. Chim. Acta*, 11 (1954) 554.
[195] P. Boulanger and G. Biserte, *Bull. soc. chim. biol.*, 33 (1951) 1930.
[196] P. Boulanger and G. Biserte, *Bull. soc. chim. biol.*, 31 (1949) 696.
[197] F. H. Malpress and A. B. Morrison, *Nature*, 164 (1949) 963.
[198] H. K. Berry and L. Cain, *Arch. Biochem.*, 24 (1949) 179.
[199] S. Ishii and T. Andô, *Science (Tokyo)*, 20 (1950) 24: *C.A.*, 45 (1951) 10,141-c.

[200] B. R. BALIGA, K. KRISHNAMURTHY, R. RAJAGOPALAN AND K. V. GIRI, *J. Indian Inst. Sci.*, 37 (1955) 18.
[201] G. ZWEIG AND S. L. HOOD, *Anal. Chem.*, 29 (1957) 438.
[202] E. WATZKE, *Naturwiss.*, 43 (1956) 83.
[203] M. H. ZIMMERMANN, *Science*, 122 (1956) 766.
[204] D. I. FRENCH AND M. R. GIBSON, *Anal. Chem.*, 29 (1957) 1166.
[205] P. H. LIST, *Naturwiss.*, 44 (1957) 280.
[206] R. ANTOSZEWSKI, *J. Chromatog.*, 2 (1959) 222.
[207] R. N. GREENSHIELDS, *Nature*, 181 (1958) 280.
[208] H. BOSER, *Z. physiol. Chem., Hoppe Seyler's*, 296 (1954) 10.
[209] A. TAUROG, W. TONG AND I. L. CHAIKOFF, *J. Biol. Chem.*, 184 (1950) 83.
[210] K. HOLZER, *Mikrochim. Acta*, (1956) 1434.
[211] K. F. URBACH, *Science*, 109 (1949) 259.
[212] A. J. GLAZKO, W. A. DILL AND M. C. REBSTOCK, *J. Biol. Chem.*, 183 (1950) 679.
[213] W. G. DUNCOMBE AND B. W. E. PEAPLE, *Analyst*, 82 (1957) 212.
[214] L. LEVENBOOK, *Anal. Chem.*, 29 (1957) 1719.
[215] W. MERZ, *Mikrochim. Acta*, (1957) 474.
[216] C. YANOVSKY, E. WASSERMANN AND D. M. BONNER, *Science*, 111 (1950) 61.
[217] L. NOVELLIE, *Nature*, 169 (1952) 672.
[218] U. S. VON EULER AND R. ELIASSON, *Nature*, 170 (1952) 664.
[219] C. J. BARKER AND R. H. PERRY, *Chem. & Ind. (London)*, (1955) 588.
[220] J. W. PORTEOUS, *J. Chromatog.*, 2 (1959) 58.
[221] J.-P. DURUISSEAU, *Anal. Chem.*, 30 (1958) 3; 455.
[222] W. J. VAN GULIK, *Nature*, 178 (1956) 994.
[223] D. VAN DER SIJDE AND J. DE FLINES, *J. Chromatog.*, 2 (1959) 436.
[224] O. F. WIEGAND AND H. R. SCHRANK, *Anal. Chem.*, 28 (1956) 259.
[225] A. M. MOORE AND J. B. BOYLEN, *Science*, 118 (1953) 19.
[226] W. S. REITH, *Nature*, 179 (1956) 580.
[227] D. I. FRENCH AND M. R. GIBSON, *Anal. Chem.*, 29 (1957) 1166.
[228] A. STÖCKLI, *Helv. Chim. Acta*, 37 (1954) 1581.
[229] L. A. BOGGS, *Anal. Chem.*, 24 (1952) 1673.
[230] G. B. MARINI-BETTOLO, M. LEDERER, M. A. JORIO AND A. PIMENTA, *Gazz. chim. ital.*, 84 (1954) 1155.
[231] G. F. GREGORY, *Science*, 121 (1955) 169.
[232] E. CHARGAFF AND J. KREAM, *J. Am. Chem. Soc.*, 74 (1952) 4274; 5157.
[233] K. T. WILLIAMS AND A. BEVENUE, *Science*, 113 (1951) 582.
[234] V. PREY, A. KABIL AND H. BERBALK, *Mikrochim. Acta*, 1 (1959) 68.
[235] V. PREY AND A. KABIL, *Mikrochim. Acta*, 1 (1959) 79.
[236] P. B. BAKER, F. DOBSON AND A. J. P. MARTIN, *Analyst*, 75 (1950) 651.
[237] T. MÜNZ, *Naturwiss.*, 41 (1954) 553.
[238] M. J. HEAD AND R. J. CANAWAY, *Chem. & Ind. (London)*, (1955) 1472; 1473.
[239] A. ENSGRABER, *Naturwiss.*, 44 (1957) 281.
[240] J. A. COCH-FRUGONI, *J. Chromatog.*, 2 (1959) 69.
[241] K. N. F. SHAW AND J. TREVARTHEN, *Nature*, 182 (1958) 664.
[242] R. J. BLOCK AND D. BOLLING, *The Amino Acid Composition of Proteins and Foods*, Charles C. Thomas, Springfield, Ill., 1951.
[243] G. TOENNIES AND J. J. KOLB, *Anal. Chem.*, 23 (1951) 823.
[244] K. HEYNS AND G. ANDERS, *Z. physiol. Chem., Hoppe Seyler's*, 287 (1951) 8.
[245] M. YAMAGUCHI AND F. D. HOWARD, *Anal. Chem.*, 27 (1955) 332.
[246] M. ALCOCK AND J. S. CANNELL, *Analyst*, 79 (1954) 389; *Nature*, 177 (1956) 327.
[247] F. IRREVERRE AND W. MARTIN, *Anal. Chem.*, 26 (1954) 257.
[248] L. C. MITCHELL, *J. Assoc. Offic. Agr. Chemists*, 37 (1954) 216: *C.A.*, 48 (1954) 14088-f.
[249] K. FINK, R. B. HENDERSON AND R. M. FINK, *J. Biol. Chem.*, 197 (1952) 441.
[250] I. R. HUNTER, D. F. HOUSTON AND H. S. OWENS, *Anal. Chem.*, 28 (1956) 283; 284.
[251] C. KOWALA, *Chem. & Ind. (London)*, (1957) 1234.
[252] W. A. WINSTEN, *Science*, 107 (1948) 605.
[253] J. K. MIETTINEN AND A. I. VIRTANEN, *Acta Chem. Scand.*, 3 (1949) 459.
[254] F. J. R. HIRD, *Australian J. Sci.*, 11 (1949) 170: *C.A.*, 43 (1949) 7092-a.

[255] H. F. Atkinson, *Nature*, 162 (1948) 858.
[256] W. H. Longenecker, *Science*, 107 (1948) 23.
[257] F. S. Steward, W. Stepka and J. F. Thompson, *Science*, 107 (1948) 451.
[258] W. L. Porter, *Anal. Chem.*, 26 (1954) 439.
[259] Ch. Wunderly, *Nature*, 173 (1954) 267.
[260] J. F. Thompson and M. V. Marion, *Anal. Chem.*, 28 (1956) 288.
[261] R. J. Williams and H. Kirby, *Science*, 107 (1948) 481.
[262] R. Ma and T. D. Fontaine, *Science*, 110 (1949) 232.
[263] J. Simek, *Chem. Przemysl*, 4 (1954) (29), 56: *C.A.*, 49 (1955) 4439-h.
[264] J. Barrollier, *Naturwiss.*, 42 (1955) 486.
[265] W. Q. Wolfson, C. Cohn and W. A. Devaney, *Science*, 109 (1949) 541.
[266] A. J. Singer and L. Kenner, *Anal. Chem.*, 23 (1951) 387.
[267] E. Kawerau, *Biochem. J.*, 48 (1951) 281.
[268] S. P. Datta, C. E. Dent and H. Harris, *Biochem. J.*, 46 (1950) xlii.
[269] H. Brockmann, N. Grubhofer, W. Kass and H. Kalbe, *Chem. Ber.*, 84 (1951) 260.
[270] T. Borkowski and S. Trojnar, *J. Chromatog.*, 1 (1958) 552.
[271] W. H. Longenecker, *Anal. Chem.*, 21 (1949) 1502.
[272] L. B. Rockland and M. S. Dunn, *Science*, 109 (1949) 539.
[273] L. B. Rockland, J. L. Blatt and M. S. Dunn, *Anal. Chem.*, 23 (1951) 1142.
[274] L. B. Rockland and J. C. Underwood, *Anal. Chem.*, 26 (1954) 1557.
[275] G. Gorbach, H. Demmel and S. Gräsböll, *Mikrochim. Acta*, (1955) 1037; *C.A.*, 50 (1956) 3943-c.
[276] V. Râbek, *Naturwiss.*, 42 (1955) 581; 582.
[277] H. Fischenbach and J. Levine, *Science*, 121 (1955) 602.
[278] H. Halbensteiner, *J. Chromatog.*, 2 (1959) 113.
[279] R. Allouf and M. Macheboeuf, *Bull. soc. chim. biol.*, 34 (1952) 215.
[280] W. Matthias, *Naturwiss.*, 41 (1954) 17.
[281] W. Matthias, *Der Züchter*, 24 (1954) 313.
[282] F. Reindel and W. Hoppe, *Naturwiss.*, 40 (1953) 245.
[283] N. C. Ganguli, *Naturwiss.*, 41 (1954) 282.
[284] E. Schwerdtfeger, *Naturwiss.*, 41 (1954) 18.
[285] A. Jeanes, C. S. Wise and R. J. Dimler, *Anal. Chem.*, 23 (1951) 415.
[286] G. Csoban, *Magyar Kem. Folyóirat*, 56 (1950) 449: *C.A.*, 46 (1952) 1384-g.
[287] F. H. Burstall, P. Swain, A. F. Williams and G. A. Wood, *J. Chem. Soc.*, (1952) 1497.
[288] P. Decker, W. Riffart and G. Oberneder, *Naturwiss.*, 38 (1951) 288.
[289] K. Schwarz and A. A. Bitancourt, *Science*, 126 (1957) 607.
[290] P. Decker, *Naturwiss.*, 10 (1957) 305.
[291] W. L. Butler and H. W. Siegelman, *Nature*, 183 (1959) 1813.
[292] L. Rutter, *Nature*, 163 (1949) 487; *Analyst*, 75 (1950) 37.
[293] S. Rosebeek, *Chem. Weekblad*, 46 (1950) 813: *C.A.*, 45 (1951) 4298-d.
[294] G. Zimmermann, *Naturwiss.*, 42 (1955) 257.
[295] G. Zimmermann and K. Nehring, *Angew. Chem.*, 63 (1951) 556.
[296] S. Berlingozzi and G. Serchi, *Sperimentale, Sez. chim. biol.*, 3 (1952) 1.
[297] T. Bersin and A. Müller, *Helv. Chim. Acta*, 35 (1952) 475.
[298] J. G. Marchal and T. Mittwer, *Compt. rend. soc. biol.*, 145 (1951) 417.
[299] J. G. Marchal and T. Mittwer, *Koninkl. Ned. Akad. Wetenschapp., Proc., Ser. C*, 54 (1951) 391: *C.A.*, 46 (1952) 2442-e.
[300] K. V. Giri, *Nature*, 171 (1953) 1159.
[301] K. V. Giri, *Nature*, 173 (1954) 1194.
[302] K. V. Giri, *J. Indian Inst. Sci.*, 37 (1955) 1.
[303] K. V. Giri and D. B. Parihar, *Nature*, 175 (1955) 304.
[304] K. V. Giri, A. N. Radhakrishnan and C. S. Vaidyanathan, *Nature*, 170 (1952) 1025.
[305] A. Saifer and I. Oreskes, *Anal. Chem.*, 25 (1953) 1539.
[306] V. K. Mohan Rao, *Experientia*, 9 (1953) 151.
[307] K. Lakshminaryanan, *Arch. Biochem. Biophys.*, 49 (1954) 396.
[308] H. Brockmann and H. Gröne, *Naturwiss.*, 40 (1953) 22.

[309] O. LÜDERITZ AND O. WESTPHAL, *Z. Naturforsch.*, 7b (1952) 136.
[310] N. C. GANGULI, *Naturwiss.*, 40 (1953) 624.
[311] N. C. GANGULI, *Nature*, 174 (1953) 189.
[312] N. C. GANGULI, *Anal. Chim. Acta*, 12 (1955) 335.
[313] E. SCHWERDTFEGER, *Naturwiss.*, 40 (1953) 201.
[314] R. J. LESTRANGE AND R. H. MÜLLER, *Anal. Chem.*, 26 (1954) 953.
[315] H. C. CHAKRABORTTY AND D. P. BURMA, *Current Sci. (India)*, 22 (1953) 238: *C.A.*, 48 (1954) 3438-b.
[316] H. C. CHAKRABORTTY AND D. P. BURMA, *Science and Culture (Calcutta)*, 19 (1954) 467: *C.A.*, 48 (1954) 9869-f.
[317] K. S. AMBE, L. KULKARNI AND K. SOHONIE, *J. Sci. Ind. Research (India)*, 13B (1954) 380: *C.A.*, 48 (1954) 13519-g.
[318] G. CERIOTTI, *Nature*, 175 (1955) 897.
[319] J. CARLES, *Bull. soc. chim. biol.*, 37 (1955) 521.
[320] H. ERBRING AND P. PATT, *Naturwiss.*, 41 (1954) 216.
[321] DI S. BERLINGOZZI, *Stoll Festschr.*, (1957) 98.
[322] H. C. CHAKRABORTTY AND D. P. BURMA, *Anal. Chim. Acta*, 15 (1956) 451.
[323] N. C. GANGULI, *Experientia*, 12 (1956) 38; 39.
[324] N. C. GANGULI, *Naturwiss.*, 42 (1955) 486.
[325] K. KRISHNAMURTHY AND M. SWAMINATHAN, *Current Sci. (India)*, 23 (1954) 223; 224: *C.A.*, 49 (1955) 10886-a.
[326] A. J. PHILIPPU, *Nature*, 182 (1958) 1159.
[327] H. SULSER, *Mitt. Gebiete Lebensm. u. Hyg.*, 47 (1956) 149: *C.A.*, 50 (1956) 12725-a.
[328] H. WEIHRAUCH, *Chemiker Ztg.*, 80 (1956) 415: *C.A.*, 51 (1957) 3193-g.
[329] Y. OSAWA, *Nature*, 180 (1957) 705.
[330] LOUIS PEYRON, *Bull. soc. chim. France*, (1958) 889.
[331] G. CARONNA, *Chim., e ind. (Milan)*, 37 (1955) 113.
[332] H. J. MCDONALD, E. W. BERMES AND H. G. SHEPHERD, *Naturwiss.*, 44 (1956) 9.
[333] H. J. MCDONALD AND L. V. MCKENDELL, *Naturwiss.*, 44 (1957) 616.
[334] HUGH J. MCDONALD, L. V. MCKENDELL AND E. W. BERMES JR., *J. Chromatog.*, 1 (1958) 259.
[335] J. R. TATA AND A. W. HEMMINGS, *J. Chromatog.*, 3 (1960) 225.
[336] M. LEDERER, *Nature*, 172 (1953) 727.
[337] F. FRANKS, *Analyst*, 81 (1956) 384; 390.
[338] M. SCHMALL, E. G. WOLLISH AND E. G. E. SHAFER, *Anal. Chem.*, 28 (1956) 1373.
[339] M. SCHMALL, E. G. WOLLISH, R. COLARUSSO, C. W. KELLER AND E. G. E. SHAFER, *Anal. Chem.*, 29 (1957) 791.
[340] A. A. BITANCOURT AND A. P. NOGUEIRA, *Science*, 129 (1958) 99.
[341] H. K. MITSCHELL, M. GORDON AND F. A. HASKINS, *J. Biol. Chem.*, 180 (1949) 1071.
[342] H. K. MITSCHELL AND F. A. HASKINS, *Science*, 110 (1949) 278.
[343] W. L. PORTER, *Anal. Chem.*, 23 (1951) 412.
[344] L. ZECHMEISTER, *Science*, 113 (1951) 35.
[345] L. S. CUENDET, R. MONTGOMERY AND F. SMITH, *J. Am. Chem. Soc.*, 75 (1953) 2764.
[346] C. G. HEDÉN, *Nature*, 166 (1950) 999.
[347] H. FRITZ AND A. BAUER, *Chem.-Ing.-Tech.*, 26 (1954) 609.
[348] A. FISCHER AND M. BEHRENS, *Z. physiol. Chem., Hoppe Seyler's*, 291 (1952) 14.
[349] C. E. DANIELSON, *Arkiv Kemi*, 5 (1952) 173.
[350] L. HAGDAHL AND C. E. DANIELSON, *Nature*, 174 (1954) 1062.
[351] E. C. BATE-SMITH, *Partition Chromatography, Biochem. Soc. Symposia*, No. 3, 1950, p. 62.
[352] M. A. JERMYN AND F. A. ISHERWOOD, *Biochem. J.*, 44 (1949) 402.
[353] G. N. KOWKABANY AND H. G. CASSIDY, *Anal. Chem.*, 24 (1952) 643.
[354] G. ZIMMERMANN, *Z. anal. Chem.*, 138 (1953) 321.
[355] M. T. BECK AND P. ÉBREY, *Acta Chim. Acad. Sci. Hung.*, 4 (1954) 231: *C.A.*, 49 (1955) 4458-g.
[356] M. T. BECK AND P. ÉBREY, *Biochim. Biophys. Acta*, 20 (1956) 393.
[357] W. J. WINGO, *Anal. Chem.*, 25 (1953) 1939.
[358] G. ZWEIG, *Anal. Chem.*, 28 (1956) 428.

[359] K. WEGMANN, *J. Chromatog.*, 2 (1959) 321.
[360] I. SMITH, *Nature*, 171 (1953) 43.
[361] N. J. MORRIS AND A. C. F. MASON, *Anal. Chem.*, 28 (1956) 2038.
[362] G. BRANTE, *Nature*, 163 (1949) 651.
[363] G. B. MARINI-BETTOLO-MARCONI AND S. GUARINO, *Experientia*, 3 (1950) 309.
[364] I. E. BUSH, *Nature*, 166 (1950) 445.
[365] M. W. WHITEHOUSE, A. E. BRESLER AND E. STAPLE, *J. Chromatog.*, 1 (1958) 385.
[366] S. C. PAN, *J. Chromatog.*, 2 (1959) 433.
[367] C. H. BOWDEN, N. F. MACLAGAN AND J. H. WILKINSON, *Biochem. J.*, 59 (1955) 93.
[368] A. M. GAWIENOWSKI, *Analyst*, 82 (1957) 452.
[369] W. HÜLSEN, *J. Chromatog.*, 1 (1958) 91.
[370] Z. PROCHÁZKA, *Chem. listy*, 44 (1950) 43: *C.A.*, 45 (1951) 5561-c.
[371] L. C. MITCHELL, *J. Assoc. Offic. Agr. Chemists*, 37 (1954) 1021: *C.A.*, 49 (1955) 2248-f.
[372] L. A. Æ. SLUYTERMAN AND H. J. VEENENDAAL, *Rec. trav. chim.*, 68 (1949) 717.
[373] A. G. LONG, J. R. QUAYLE AND R. J. STEDMAN, *J. Chem. Soc.*, (1951) 2197.
[374] R. L. REID AND M. LEDERER, *Biochem. J.*, 50 (1951) 60.
[375] W. R. WALKER, *Australian J. Sci.*, 13 (1950) 26: *C.A.*, 45 (1951) 1912-g.
[376] D. M. TENNENT, J. B. WHITLA AND K. FLOREY, *Anal. Chem.*, 23 (1951) 1748.
[377] A. C. PALADINI AND L. F. LELOIR, *Anal. Chem.*, 24 (1952) 1024.
[378] T. D. PRICE, P. B. HUDSON AND D. F. ASHMAN, *Nature*, 175 (1955) 45.
[379] H. T. GORDON, *Science*, 128 (1958) 3321.
[380] D. S. KINNORY AND J. GRECO, *Anal. Chem.*, 29 (1957) 1562.
[381] N. A. DRAKE, J. HAINES, R. E. KNAUFF AND E. D. NIELSON, *Anal. Chem.*, 28 (1956) 2036.
[382] A. SZENT-GYÖRGYI, *Science*, 126 (1957) 751.
[383] V. MOUČKA AND R. PAŘÍZEK, *Collection Czechoslov. Chem. Communs.*, 21 (1956) 1356.
[384] P. C. CALDWELL, *Biochem. J.*, 60 (1955) xii.
[385] J. A. COCH-FRUGONI, *J. Chromatog.*, 1 (1958) 90.
[386] L. G. M. BAAS BECKING, A. D. HALDANE AND D. IZARD, *Nature*, 182 (1958) 645.
[387] G. DE VRIES AND E. VAN DALEN, *Rec. trav. chim.*, 73 (1954) 1028.
[388] G. DE VRIES, *Nature*, 173 (1954) 735.
[389] G. G. BLAKE, *Anal. Chim. Acta*, 15 (1956) 232; 542.
[390] A. LACOURT, G. SOMMEREYNS, E. DEGEYNDT, J. BARUH AND J. GILLARD, *Mikrochemie ver. Mikrochim. Acta*, 34 (1949) 215.
[391] E. L. HIRST AND J. K. N. JONES, *Discussions Faraday Soc.*, 7 (1949) 268.
[392] R. A. EVANS, W. H. PARR AND W. C. EVANS, *Nature*, 164 (1949) 674.
[393] D. M. P. PHILLIPS, *Nature*, 162 (1948) 29.
[394] L. B. ROCKLAND AND M. S. DUNN, *Science*, 111 (1950) 332.
[395] R. M. NETTLETON JR. AND R. B. MEFFERD JR., *Anal. Chem.*, 24 (1952) 1687.
[396] A. J. GLAZKO AND W. A. DILL, *Anal. Chem.*, 25 (1953) 1782.
[397] S. SAVOIA, *Chimica (Milan)*, 9 (1954) 223.
[398] D. F. HOUSTON, *J. Chem. Educ.*, 32 (1955) 411: *C.A.*, 49 (1955) 15362-b.
[399] R. B. FISHER AND R. HOLMES, *Biochem. J.*, 44 (1949) liv.
[400] R. B. FISHER, D. S. PARSONS AND G. A. MORRISON, *Nature*, 161 (1948) 764.
[401] R. C. BRIMLEY, *Nature*, 163 (1949) 215.
[402] R. B. FISHER AND R. HOLMES, *Biochem. J.*, 44 (1949) liv.
[403] W. G. KAUMAN AND T. A. BAK, *Nature*, 182 (1958) 743.
[404] J. C. GIDDINGS AND R. A. KELLER, *J. Chromatog.*, 3 (1960) 205.
[405] M. LEDERER, *Anal. Chim. Acta*, 6 (1952) 521.
[406] R. B. FISHER, D. S. PARSONS AND R. HOLMES, *Nature*, 164 (1949) 183.
[407] H. D. FOWLER, *Nature*, 168 (1951) 1123.
[408] T. V. ARDEN, F. H. BURSTALL AND R. P. LINSTEAD, *J. Chem. Soc.*, (1949) S311.
[409] R. J. BLOCK, *Anal. Chem.*, 22 (1950) 1327.
[410] R. J. BLOCK, *J. Dairy Sci.*, 34 (1951) 1.
[411] R. J. BLOCK, *Arch. Biochem. Biophys.*, 31 (1951) 266.
[412] S. ÅKERFELDT, *Acta Chem. Scand.*, 8 (1954) 521.
[413] M. BLUMER, *Anal. Chem.*, 28 (1956) 1640.
[414] K. MIYAKI, H. MOIYAMA AND M. HAYASAKI, *J. Pharm. Soc. Japan*, 72 (1952) 688.

[415] K. Miyaki and H. Moiyama, *J. Pharm. Soc. Japan*, 72 (1952) 1061.
[416] R. M. Manganelli and F. R. Brofazi, *Anal. Chem.*, 29 (1957) 1441.
[417] C. E. Dent, *Biochem. J.*, 41 (1947) 240.
[418] C. Dumazert and M. Bozzi-Tichadou, *Bull. soc. chim. biol.*, 37 (1955) 169.
[419] R. H. Müller, *Anal. Chem.*, 22 (1950) 72.
[420] R. H. Müller and D. L. Clegg, *Anal. Chem.*, 21 (1949) 1123.
[421] R. H. Müller and E. N. Wise, *Anal. Chem.*, 23 (1951) 207.
[422] L. S. Fosdick and R. O. Blackwell, *Science*, 109 (1949) 314.
[423] R. J. Block, *Anal. Chem.*, 22 (1950) 1327.
[424] R. J. Block, *Anal. Chem.*, 23 (1951) 298.
[425] H. B. Bull, J. W. Hahn and V. H. Baptist, *J. Am. Chem. Soc.*, 71 (1949) 550.
[426] E. M. Crook, H. Harris, F. Hassan and F. L. Warren, *Biochem. J.*, 56 (1954) 434.
[427] H. Eberle, *Naturwiss.*, 41 (1954) 479.
[428] O. Bassir, *Chem. & Ind. (London)*, (1954) 709.
[429] M. Kutàček and J. Kaloušek, *Sborník Českoslov. akad. zemědělkých věd*, 26A (1953) 575: *C.A.*, 48 (1954) 5259-c.
[430] G. Gorbach, *Mikrcchemie ver. Mikrcchim. Acta*, 39 (1952) 204.
[431] J. K. Miettinen and T. Moisio, *Acta Chem. Scand.*, 7 (1953) 1225.
[432] J. De Wael and R. Diaz Cadavieco, *Rec. trav. chim.*, 73 (1954) 333.
[433] H. Röttger, *Experientia*, 9 (1953) 150.
[434] D. Z. Silver and R. Bookman, *Anal. Chem.*, 28 (1956) 558.
[435] G. Kronmueller, *J. Chromatcg.*, 2 (1959) 429.
[436] J. Barrollier, J. Heilmann and E. Watzke, *J. Chromatog.*, 1 (1958) 434.
[437] R. J. Wieme, *J. Chromatog.*, 1 (1958) 166.
[438] E. Treiber and H. Kőren, *Monatsh. Chem.*, 84 (1953) 478: *C.A.*, 48 (1954) 1078-c.
[439] H. C. Ehrmantraut and A. Weinstock, *Biochim. Biophys. Acta*, 15 (1954) 589.
[440] R. Grüttner, *Klin. Wochschr.*, 32 (1954) 263: *C.A.*, 48 (1954) 6900-i.
[441] S. V. Vaeck, *Nature*, 172 (1953) 213.
[442] S. V. Vaeck, *Anal. Chim. Acta*, 10 (1954) 48.
[443] Y. Hashimoto, *Pharm. Bull. (Tokyo)*, 1 (1953) 176: *C.A.*, 48 (1954) 7433h.
[444] Y. Hashimoto and I. Mori, *Nature*, 170 (1952) 1024.
[445] I. Mori, *J. Pharm. Soc. Japan*, 73 (1953) 958: *C.A.*, 48 (1954) 702-a.
[446] I. Mori, *J. Pharm. Soc. Japan*, 74 (1954) 213: *C.A.*, 48 (1954) 5709-d.
[447] I. Mori, *J. Pharm. Soc. Japan*, 74 (1954) 525: *C.A.*, 48 (1954) 9857-h.
[448] I. Mori, *Science*, 119 (1954) 653.
[449] K. Semand and R. Fried, *Naturwiss.*, 39 (1952) 326.
[450] J. A. Brown and M. M. Marsh, *Anal. Chem.*, 25 (1953) 1865.
[451] H. Kaiser and L. Wildemann, *Prods. pharm.*, 12 (1957) 247: *C.A.*, 51 (1957) 11156-e.
[452] J. D. S. Goulden, *Nature*, 173 (1954) 646.
[453] D. R. Kalkwarf and A. A. Frost, *Anal. Chem.* 26, (1954) 191.
[454] W. Grassmann and K. Hannig, *Z. physiol. Chem., Hoppe Seyler's*, 290 (1952) 1.
[455] W. Grassmann and K. Hannig, *Klin. Wochschr.*, 32 (1954) 838: *C.A.*, 48 (1954) 13780-b.
[456] J. Barrollier, *Naturwiss.*, 42 (1955) 126.
[457] H. Campbell and J. A. Simpson, *Chem. & Ind. (London)*, (1953) 342.
[458] A. Neuhaus and W. Richartz, *Angew. Chem.*, 70 (1958) 434.
[459] Ch. Eger, *Experientia*, 12 (1956) 37; 38.
[460] A. A. Pokrovskiĭ, *Byull. Eksptl. Biol. Med.*, 38 (1954) No. 12, 69: *C.A.*, 49 (1955) 6358-i.
[461] R. Mykolajewycz, *Anal. Chem.*, 29 (1957) 1300.
[462] T. Wieland, *Angew. Chem.*, 60 (1948) 313.
[463] T. Wieland and L. Wirth, *Angew. Chem.*, 63 (1951) 171.
[464] T. Wieland and U. Feld, *Angew. Chem.*, 63 (1951) 258.
[465] R. Kuhn and H. W. Ruelius, *Chem. Ber.*, 83 (1950) 420.
[466] A. Langer, *Anal. Chem.*, 28 (1956) 426; 427.
[467] F. P. W. Winteringham, A. Harrison and R. G. Bridges, *Analyst*, 77 (1952) 19.
[468] P. C. van Erkelens, *Nature*, 172 (1953) 357.

[469] T. Wieland, K. Schmeiser, E. Fischer and G. Maier-Leibnitz, *Naturwiss.*, 36 (1949) 280.
[470] A. S. Keston, S. Udenfriend and M. Levy, *J. Am. Chem. Soc.*, 69 (1947) 315; 72 (1950) 748.
[471] S. Udenfriend, *J. Biol. Chem.*, 187 (1950) 65.
[472] S. Udenfriend and M. Gibbs, *Science*, 110 (1949) 708.
[473] S. Udenfriend and S. F. Velick, *J. Biol. Chem.*, 190 (1951) 733.
[474] F. Pocchiari and C. Rossi, *J. Chromatog.*, 5 (1961) 377.
[475] S. Lissitzky and R. Michel, *Bull. soc. chim. France*, (1952) 891.
[476] A. A. Benson, J. A. Bassham, M. Calvin, T. C. Goodale, V. A. Haas and W. Stepka, *J. Am. Chem. Soc.*, 72 (1950) 1710.
[477] A. T. Wilson, *Nature*, 182 (1958) 524.
[478] H. Götte and D. Pätze, *Z. Elektrochem.*, 58 (1954) 636.
[479] H. F. Atkinson, *Nature*, 164 (1949) 541.
[480] G. H. Bourne, *Nature*, 163 (1949) 923.
[481] J. C. Boursnell, *Nature*, 165 (1950) 399.
[482] R. M. Tomarelli and K. Florey, *Science*, 107 (1948) 630.
[483] L. S. Fosdick and R. Q. Blackwell, *Science*, 109 (1949) 314.
[484] I. Gray, S. Ikeda, A. A. Benson and D. Kritchevsky, *Rev. Sci. Instr.*, 21 (1950) 1022.
[485] A. R. Jones, *Anal. Chem.*, 24 (1952) 1055.
[486] J. Katz and I. L. Chaikoff, *J. Biol. Chem.*, 206 (1954) 887.
[487] H. F. Linskens, *J. Chromatog.*, 1 (1958) 472.
[488] L. B. Rockland, J. Lieberman and M. S. Dunn, *Anal. Chem.*, 24 (1952) 778.
[489] R. R. Williams and R. E. Smith, *Proc. Soc. Exptl. Biol. Med.*, 77 (1951) 169.
[490] J. E. S. Bradley, *Biochem. J.*, 56 (1954) xlviii.
[491] J. Berthet, *Biochim. Biophys. Acta*, 15 (1954) 1.
[492] P. Bonet-Maury, *Bull. soc. chim. France*, (1953) 1066.
[493] W. J. Wingo, *Anal. Chem.*, 26 (1954) 1527.
[494] P. Lerch and S. Neukomm, *Schweiz. med. Wochschr.*, 84 (1954) 515.
[495] J. Vigne and S. Lissitzky, *J. Chromatog.*, 1 (1958) 309.
[496] E. Demole, *J. Chromatog.*, 6 (1961) 2.
[497] E. Stahl, *Angew. Chem.*, 73 (1961) 646.
[498] E. G. Wollish, M. Schmall and M. Hawrylyshyn, *Anal. Chem.*, 33 (1961) 1138.
[499] E. Stahl and U. Kaltenbach, *J. Chromatog.*, 5 (1961) 351.

Chapter III

Gas Chromatography

P. CHOVIN

Town laboratory for Explosives, Radioactivity, Electricity, Chemistry, Public and Industrial Health, Scientific Research, Paris (France)

LIST OF SYMBOLS EMPLOYED

c_f Concentration of the solute in the stationary (fixed) phase ($g \cdot ml^{-1}$).

c_m Concentration of the solute in the mobile phase ($g \cdot ml^{-1}$).

C_f Molecular concentration of the solute in the stationary (fixed) phase ($gmol \cdot ml^{-1}$).

C_m Molecular concentration of the solute in the mobile phase ($gmol \cdot ml^{-1}$).

d Distance measured on the chart.

d_m True retention distance for air on the chart from an ideal chromatographic apparatus.

d_p Diameter of the particles of the support.

d_r True retention distance for an ideal chromatographic apparatus without dead volume except in the column.

d_M Retention distance for air on the chart from an actual chromatographic apparatus.

d_R Retention distance of a solute.

d'_R Adjusted retention distance, measured from the air peak.

D_f Molecular coefficient of diffusion of the solute in the stationary (fixed) phase.

D_m Molecular coefficient of diffusion of the solute in the mobile phase.

e_f Thickness of the film of stationary phase surrounding the particles of support.

$(\ )_f$ The subscript f denotes a magnitude of the fixed (stationary) phase.

f Fugacity of a solute above its solution in the stationary phase.

f^0 Fugacity of a solute above its own pure liquid.

F_F Flow rate of the carrier gas measured in the flowmeter.

F_0 Flow rate of the carrier gas measured at the column outlet under the conditions prevailing in this part of the chromatograph.

h	Height equivalent to a theoretical plate (HETP).
$(\ )_i$	The subscript i refers to a magnitude measured at the column inlet, or to the "i-th" constituent of a mixture.
j	Correction factor for the loss in pressure along the column; $$j = \frac{3[(p_i/p_0)^2 - 1]}{2[(p_i/p_0)^3 - 1]}$$
k'	$k' = KV_f/V_m$
K	Partition coefficient of a solute between the stationary and mobile phases.
K_B	Bunsen's partition coefficient; $K_B = 273\ K/T_c$
L	Length of the column.
$(\ )_m$	The subscript m denotes a magnitude of the mobile phase.
M	Molecular weight of the solute.
M_f	Molecular weight of the stationary phase.
N_f	Number of molecules of stationary phase per unit of volume.
$(\ )_0$	The subscript o denotes magnitudes measured at the column outlet.
p	Vapour pressure of the solute above its solution in the stationary phase.
$\bar{p}$	Average operating pressure of the column.
p_F	Pressure of the carrier gas in the flowmeter.
p_i	Pressure of the carrier gas at the column inlet.
p_0	Pressure of the carrier gas at the column outlet.
p^0	Saturated vapour pressure of the solute in equilibrium with its pure liquid at the column temperature.
P	Resolution between two peaks; percentage of stationary phase with respect to the support.
Q_1	Quantity of solute introduced into the first plate.
Q_{p+1}	Quantity of solute present in a plate of serial number p.
r	Serial number of the last plate; efficiency of the column, expressed in the number of theoretical plates.
r_{AB}	Relative retention of two substances A and B.
R_F	Retardation factor.
t_M	Retention time of air.
t_R	Retention time of a given substance.
t_R'	Adjusted retention time of a given substance.
T_c	Column temperature.
T_{Bp}	Boiling point of a solute.
T_F	Temperature of the flowmeter.
u_m	Linear velocity of the mobile phase in the column.
u_p	Speed of the paper in the recorder.

References p. 263

v_f Volume of stationary phase present in a plate.
v_m Volume of mobile phase present in a plate.
V Effective volume of a plate; $V = v_m + Kv_f$
V_f Volume of stationary phase present in the column at the prevailing temperature.
V_d Dead volume of the detector.
V_g Specific retention volume.
V_i Dead volume of the sample introduction chamber.
V_m True retention volume of air.
V_r True retention volume of a given substance.
V_M Retention volume of air.
V_N Net retention volume of a given substance.
V_R Retention volume of a given substance.
V_{mol} Net retention volume of a given substance per molecule of stationary phase present in the column.
V'_R Adjusted retention volume.
V^0_m Corrected retention volume of air; it is equal to the interstitial volume of the column.
V^0_R Corrected retention volume of a given substance.
$( )'$ An accent denotes "adjusted" magnitudes, measured from the air peak.
$( )^0$ The superscript ^{0} denotes magnitudes that have undergone the correction for pressure loss of James and Martin; indicates a limiting value, in a general sense.
w_f Mass of stationary phase present in the column.
ΔG_s Free energy of solution.
ΔH_s Heat of solution.
ΔS_s Entropy of solution.
Δt_R Peak width, in time units.
ΔV_R Peak width, in volume units.
γ Coefficient of tortuosity of the path travelled by the carrier gas in the column; activity coefficient.
γ^0_p Activity coefficient at infinite dilution, referred to the vapour pressure.
γ^0_f Activity coefficient at infinite dilution, referred to the fugacity.
ω Peak width, expressed in units of distance.
λ Coefficient of irregularity of the column packing.
ρ_f Density of the stationary phase at the column temperature.

1. Introduction

Chromatography, a procedure dealt with in the Chapter II, has been excellently defined by Strain and Sato[1] as: "... a widely applicable, differential migration technique, in which flow of solvent or gas causes the components of mixtures to migrate differentially from a narrow initial zone in a ... sorptive medium."

This definition covers the case in which the mixture to be separated is gaseous or volatile and in which its entrainment is effected by means of a current of gas—the so-called *carrier gas*. This brings us into the field of chromatography in the gas phase, known for short as gas chromatography. As in the case of liquid-phase chromatography, the stationary sorptive medium (generally referred to as the *stationary* or *fixed phase*) may be either an adsorbent (we then speak of adsorption chromatography or *gas–solid chromatography*, G.S.C.) or a liquid absorbent with a negligible vapour pressure at the working temperature (when the method is known as partition chromatography or *gas–liquid chromatography*, G.L.C.).

In G.S.C., separation is obviously governed by differences in adsorbability. In the case of G.L.C., the "differential migration" mentioned in the above definition is due to the greater of lesser extent to which exchanges take place between the stationary and mobile phases. The substances (known as *solutes*) transported by the latter dissolve in the stationary phase (the *solvent*), remain there for a short or longer period, evaporate again into the mobile phase, dissolve once more in the stationary phase, and so on, until they appear at the end of the column, classified according to the total time they have resided in the stationary phase, those having resided the shortest time obviously appearing first. In order to promote these exchanges, the liquid stationary phase is distributed either over the surface of numerous very fine porous grains of an inert solid, or on the inner wall of an extremely fine-bored tube of considerable length. Tubes packed with the granular charge first mentioned constitute the conventional type of chromatographic column; tubes prepared in the second manner are known as the capillary type of column.

At the outlet of the column, both in G.S.C. and G.L.C., a *detector* is placed; this is an instrument capable of indicating at an instant t either the concentration of each of the substances present in the gaseous effluent (differential detection), or the total of some property related to the mass of the substances that have passed through the outlet of the column (integral detectors). In general an arrangement is present for registering the signal. When a carrier gas is used that is less strongly sorbed by the stationary phase than the components to be separated*, the traces obtained from

* The reverse case will not be considered here.

References p. 263

differential detectors are in the form of peaks, whilst those from integral detectors take the shape of steps. The first type gives the second by integration; the second gives the first by differentiation.

On the charts so recorded the abscissa of the point corresponding to the maximum concentration of a certain substance (top of a peak or inflexion point of a step) provides an important piece of information. It allows one to calculate the *retention time*, or time of residence of the substance concerned in the apparatus, from the moment of its introduction into the head of the column until the time of its passage through the detector. Since the retention time depends, among other factors, on the flow rate of the carrier gas, it is preferable to employ the product of these two quantities – the *retention volume*. At a definite temperature and with a definite apparatus the retention volume is characteristic of the substance in question, just as is its boiling point. In principle, retention volumes can therefore be used for identifying the constituents of a mixture. Furthermore – and subject to certain corrections – the area of a peak, or the difference in height of two steps, is proportional to the mass of the component present. These facts constitute the qualitative and quantitative foundations of chromatography.

Gas–solid chromatography is, generally speaking, employed only for the permanent gases and the very lowest members of the hydrocarbon series. Hardy and Pollard[2], in a excellent review, trace its history back to 1905, when Ramsay[3] used a method of selective adsorption and desorption for separating gaseous mixtures. More recently, the investigations of Claesson[4] and Janák[5] gave the method its present status.

Gas–liquid chromatography is much younger. In a now classic paper on the theory of partition chromatography in the liquid phase, published in 1941, Martin and Synge[6] used the following words:

"The mobile phase need not be a liquid but may be a vapour. Very refined separations of volatile substances should therefore be possible in a column in which permanent gas is made to flow over gel impregnated with a non-volatile solvent in which the substances to be separated approximately obey Raoult's law . . ."

These prophetic words nevertheless passed completely unnoticed. It remained for Martin himself, with another collaborator, James, to show – eleven years later – what profit could be derived from them[7,8]. His discovery claimed the immediate attention of theoreticians, analysts and . . . constructors. In six years' time the method has developed to an unparalleled extent and has given rise to a multitude of investigations; it has led to the creation of panels and associations of specialized workers, to the organisation of symposia, meetings and exhibitions of apparatus – in short it has everywhere aroused a vivid interest which shows no signs of abating.

References p. 263

What is it that has given the method this remarkable popularity? The answer is that the new technique possesses certain properties rendering it one of the most powerful and versatile now known: its relative simplicity, its high sensitivity, the fact that the analysis simultaneously provides qualitative and quantitative data, the versatility of the technique, its speed, its automatic character, the possibility of preserving a record, the existence of a sound theoretical base, the possibility of attacking problems other than strictly analytical ones, and so on. It will be admitted that these advantages, against which only the fairly high cost of the apparatus must be noted as a slight drawback, are enough to claim the attention of technologists and scientists.

2. Theoretical Aspects of Gas Chromatography

It will not be attempted here to give a detailed account of all the efforts that have been made to arrive at a clear understanding of the mechanism by which a substance passes through the chromatographic column. We shall restrict ourselves on the one hand to a representation on the fundamental principles on which calculations are based (the reader is referred for their development to the original publications), and on the other hand to a deduction from these theories of such results as can be used directly by the experimental worker for the judicious utilisation of the phenomena involved.

From this point of view the theories can at present be classified in various ways (see, in particular, Martin[9]). We shall divide them here into two large groups according to whether they are concerned with adsorption or partition chromatography. In the theories of partition chromatography we must again distinguish between those of the so-called conventional columns and those of capillary colums. Finally the theories of the conventional columns can be subdivided into those related to the theory of distillation columns ("plate theories") and those taking into account the true phenomena governing the exchanges occurring between the stationary and the mobile phases ("rate theories").

(a) *Preliminary definition of the principal magnitudes encountered in gas chromatography*

The majority of the magnitudes defined below have not been given the names used here by the authors who have introduced them. The nomenclature employed in the present article is in agreement with the resolutions passed by a standardizing committee under the chairmanship of D. Ambrose and appointed by the Section for Analytical Chemistry of the International Union of Pure and Applied Chemistry; this committee used the recommendations of Ambrose, Keulemans and Purnell[10] and of Johnson and Stross[11]

References p. 263

as a starting point. As a result of direct contact, the suggestions made by a group of French investigators[12] could largely be taken into account. It is to be expected that the definite nomenclature of gas chromatography will in the future not depart much from that given here.

(*i*) *True retention volume*, V_r

The true retention volume, V_r, is the volume of carrier gas, measured at the outlet pressure, p_0 and the temperature of the column, T_c, that has passed through an ideal chromatographic apparatus (reduced to its column only, that is to say having a sample chamber and a detector of zero dead volume) between the injection of the substance and the appearance at the outlet of the maximum in the concentration.

This definition applies to the carrier gas itself, and it would be possible (at all events in partition chromatography) to confuse the true retention volume of the carrier gas, V_m, with that of a gas such as air, which is not appreciably retained by the stationary phase (see Fig. 1a).

(*ii*) *Retention volume*, V_R

If unqualified, the term "retention volume" denotes the volume of carrier gas, measured at the outlet pressure, p_0, and the temperature of the column, T_c, that has passed through an actual chromatographic apparatus, between the injection of the substance and the appearance of the maximum in concentration in the detector.

This definition applies to the carrier gas itself, and it would be possible (at all events in partition chromatography) to confuse the retention volume of the carrier gas, V_M, with that of a gas such as air, which is not appreciably retained by the stationary phase (see Fig. 1b).

The difference between "retention volumes" and "true retention volumes" lies in the contribution to the first of the dead volumes of the sample chamber, V_i, and of the detector, V_d. Since a pressure p_i prevails in the sample chamber and a pressure p_0 in the detector, Ambrose proposed the formula

$$V_M = V_i \cdot p_i / p_0 + V_d + V_m \tag{1}$$

and similarly

$$V_R = V_i \cdot p_i / p_0 + V_d + V_r \tag{2}$$

(*iii*) *Adjusted retention volume*, V'_R

While the retention volume is calculated from the chart by starting from the time $t = 0$, the adjusted retention volume is taken to start from the "air peak", at least in partition chromatography (see Fig. 1). Subtraction of (1) from (2) gives

$$V'_R = V_R - V_M = V_r - V_m \tag{3}$$

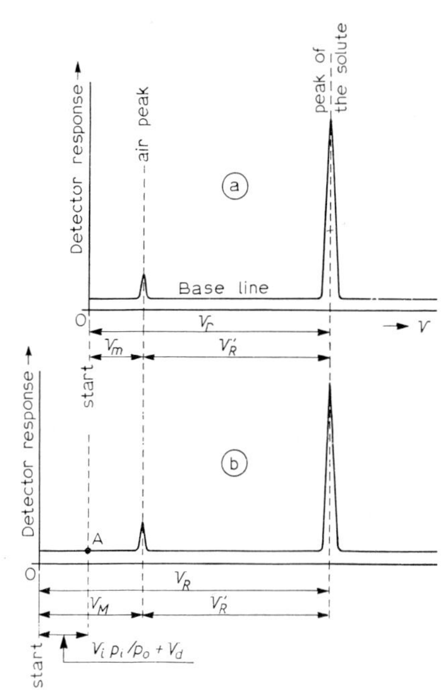

Fig. 1. Retention values (distances, times, volumes). (a) Registration by an ideal chromatographic apparatus without dead volume. (b) Registration by an actual chromatographic apparatus.

It has been agreed to distinguish all adjusted retention volumes by the addition of the "prime" ('). In French, the adjusted retention volume is termed "le volume de rétention réduit".

(*iv*) *Corrected retention volume*, V_R^0

As the mobile phase is compressible, the true retention volume depends on the ratio between the pressures at the inlet and the outlet. The corrected retention volume, V_R^0, is the limit approached by the true retention volume when the ratio between the inlet and outlet pressures, p_i/p_0, approaches unity.

James and Martin have shown that the corrected retention volume is obtained by multiplying the true retention volume by a factor j, smaller than unity, termed the "factor correcting for pressure drop along the column" (see p. 232), which depends on the ratio p_i/p_0 and approaches unity as p_i approaches p_0*.

$$V_R^0 = jV_r \tag{4}$$

* A table giving values of j against values of the ratio p_i/p_0 from 1 to 3 in thousandths has been published in the *Journal of Chromatography*[13].

It may be remarked that the corrected retention volume of air

$$V_m^0 = jV_m \tag{5}$$

is identical, in partition chromatography, to the interstitial volume of the column, namely to the part of the volume of the latter not occupied by the particles of support impregnated with stationary phase. It has been agreed to attach the superfix zero (°) to all retention values that have been corrected for pressure drop. In French, the corrected retention volume is termed "le volume de rétention limite".

(v) Net retention volume, V_N

This is a completely corrected retention volume, *i.e.* one that has been both "adjusted" and "corrected" as described above.

$$V_N = jV'_R = j(V_R - V_M) = j(V_r - V_m) = V_R^0 - V_m^0 \tag{6}$$

It is equivalent to the volume of carrier gas, measured at the outlet pressure p_0 and the column temperature T_c, that has passed through an ideal column (having zero interstitial volume and operating without pressure drop from inlet to outlet), between the injection of the substance in the column head and the appearance at its outlet of the maximum in concentration.

The net retention volume of air is obviously zero. In French, the net retention volume is termed "le volume de rétention absolu".

(vi) Specific retention volume, V_g

This is the net retention volume referred to unit mass of stationary phase and converted to 0° C. If T_c is the temperature of the column and w_f the mass of the stationary phase that it contains, we can formulate V_g as

$$V_g = 273\, V_N/w_f T_c \tag{7}$$

The specific retention volume is hence equivalent to the volume of carrier gas, converted to 0° C, that has passed through an ideal column (having an interstitial volume of zero, operating without pressure drop from the inlet to the outlet and containing 1 gram of stationary phase) between the injection of the substance in the head of the column and the appearance at its outlet of the maximum in the concentration.

(vii) Relative retention, r_{AB}

For two substances A and B this is the ratio between those retention values (V'_R, V_g or V_N) which are independent of the dimensions of the apparatus:

$$r_{AB} = (V'_R)_A/(V'_R)_B = (V_g)_A/(V_g)_B = (V_N)_A/(V_N)_B \tag{8}$$

This ratio is also called the separation factor. Frequently component B is one employed as internal standard (see p. 248). The advantage of this procedure is that the ratio r_{AB} is less susceptible to small variations in certain experimental conditions—such as the column temperature T_c and the gas flow rate F_0— than the retention values themselves. It is therefore preferable to refer the identification of a solute to an internal standard than to work without reference points, using the absolute values of the chromatographic constants.

(viii) Peak resolution, P

Let d_A and d_B be the distances of two peaks from the origin and let ω_A and ω_B be their widths, defined as the portion of the baseline intercepted by the tangents at the points of inflexion of the peak flanks (see Fig. 2). Then the resolution P of the two peaks can be defined by the formula:

$$P = 2(d_B - d_A)/(\omega_A + \omega_B) \tag{9}$$

which has been so chosen that P varies from $P = 0$ (no resolution) in the case of two overlying peaks to $P = 1$ (total resolution) for two entirely separated peaks. If the peaks are still further apart, P becomes greater than 1.

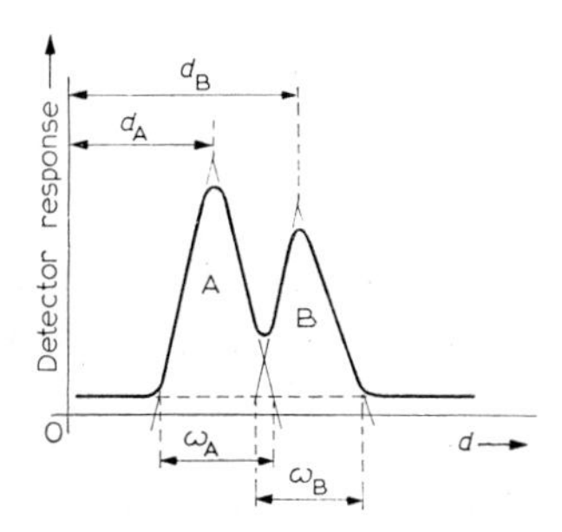

Fig. 2. Resolution of two peaks A and B.

(ix) Column efficiency, r

In one of the groups of gas-chromatographic theories to be discussed later (p. 231) the chromatographic column is compared to a distillation column. James and Martin[7,8] define the *height equivalent to a theoretical plate* (HETP) as the length of column (assumed to be of constant magnitude h)

having such a value that the gas emerging from it is in distribution equilibrium with the liquid which it contains. A column of length L contains r theoretical plates if

$$r = L/h \tag{10}$$

This number r of theoretical plates, which can be determined experimentally, is used to express the efficiency of a column. The efficiency varies with the column packing and, for a certain column, with the substance employed for determining the efficiency. The substance used should therefore be stated.

While the relative retention r_{AB} characterizes the capability of a certain solvent of separating the peak maxima of two solutes A and B, the column efficiency r indicates the greater or lesser tendency of a column of given construction to broaden the peak of a certain solute (see p. 236).

(*x*) *Adsorption isotherm*

Suppose that a gaseous substance is in equilibrium at a temperature T_c with an adsorbent. The equilibrium can be characterized by the curve representing the amount q of substance adsorbed (in grams per gram of adsorbent) as a function of the concentration c_m of this substance in the gas phase (in grams per milliliter). In most cases the curve in question—known as the adsorption isotherm—is concave with respect to the c_m-axis, a fact signifying that the adsorbent finally becomes saturated at a sufficiently high concentration c_m. A curved isotherm is generally speaking characteristic of *non-linear chromatography*.

(*xi*) *Distribution isotherm and partition coefficient, K*

If the solutes and solvents encountered in gas–liquid chromatography obeyed Raoult's law, the partial pressure p of the solute dissolved in the stationary phase at a certain temperature would be given, over the whole range of concentration, by the expression $p = p^0 x$, in which p^0 is the vapour pressure of the pure solute at the same temperature, and x its concentration in moles per mole of solution. Without exception, the solute–solvent pairs with which we have to deal in G.L.C. show wide departures from Raoult's law. We can then, however, express p in terms of Henry's law, an adaptation of Raoult's law, modified by the addition of a correction factor γ, known as the activity coefficient. This coefficient is not a constant, but since the concentrations occurring in G.L.C. are usually very low, we may frequently assume its constancy in the range considered. In many cases we can, without excessive error, take γ to be equal to the limiting values to which it approaches with dimishing concentration, the so-called *activity coefficient at infinite dilution* γ_p^0. Henry's law is then expressed by

$$p = p^0 x \gamma_p^0$$

Assuming the foregoing and taking the gas law to be valid at the low dilutions involved, one can easily show that the *partition coefficient* K (the ratio between the concentrations C_f and C_m of the solute in the stationary and mobile phases respectively, expressed in moles per unit of volume, or the identical ratio between c_f and c_m, the corresponding concentrations expressed in grams per unit of volume) is a constant in the range concerned. This will appear from the following developments of K

$$K = C_f/C_m = c_f/c_m \fallingdotseq C_f RT_c/p = c_f RT_c/Mp = xN_f RT_c/p \qquad (11)$$

(in which M = molecular weight of the solute and N_f = number of moles per unit volume of stationary phase). By introducing the value of p given by Henry's law into the last equation we obtain

$$K = N_f RT_c/p^0\gamma_p^0$$

which is a constant for a given solute–solvent pair at the temperature T_c in a given column. Instead of the expression $p = p^0 x\gamma_p^0$ for the partial pressure, a corresponding expression for the fugacity f (a thermodynamic magnitude) is sometimes adopted, *viz.* $f = f^0 x\gamma_f^0$, in which f^0 is the fugacity of the saturated vapour over the pure liquid and γ_f^0 is an equivalent "activity coefficient" for fugacity. At the high dilutions in question f and p are almost the same, so that we can write

$$K = N_f RT_c/p^0\gamma_p^0 \approx N_f RT_c/f^0\gamma_f^0 \qquad (12)$$

It thus follows—at least in certain cases and in the range of dilutions considered—that the graph connecting C_f (or c_f) and C_m (or c_m), known as the *distribution isotherm,* is a straight line. The condition of *linear chromatography* is then said to prevail. However, there are cases in G.L.C. where, even at the high dilutions present, noticeable departures from constancy occur in the coefficient K, as the result of variations in γ. This is observed, for instance, when the solute has a strong tendency to association (examples: organic acids and alcohols) or when it forms transient adducts with the stationary phase.

(*xii*) *Net retention volume per molecule,* V_{mol}

This is the net retention volume referred to one gram-molecule of stationary phase. If N_f is the number of gram-molecules of stationary phase per unit of volume and V_f the volume of stationary phase present in the column, we get, by definition

$$V_{\text{mol}} = V_N/N_f V_f$$

References p. 263

It is equivalent to the volume of carrier gas, measured at the outlet pressure p_0 and the column temperature T_c, which has passed through an ideal column (having zero interstitial volume, operating without pressure drop from inlet to outlet and containing one gram-molecule of stationary phase) between the injection of the substance in the head of the column and the appearance at the outlet of the maximum in the concentration[14]. It will be seen later (p. 233) that V_N is related to the partition coefficient K by the simple expression

$$V_N = KV_f \tag{21}$$

from which

$$V_{\text{mol}} = K/N_f$$

and hence, together with eqn. (12)

$$V_{\text{mol}} = RT_c/f^0\gamma_f^0 = RT_c/p^0\gamma_p^0 \tag{13}$$

When written in the forms

$$\gamma_f^0 V_{\text{mol}} = RT_c/f^0 \quad \text{and} \quad \gamma_p^0 V_{\text{mol}} = RT_c/p^0$$

the preceding relationship shows that the product of the activity coefficient at infinite dilution and the net retention volume per molecule (two values which are both characteristic of the pair solute–stationary phase) depends only on the nature of the solute and on the temperature, and in no way on the stationary phase. For several stationary phases 1, 2, . . . n and one solute we can hence write

$$\begin{cases} (\gamma_f^0 V_{\text{mol}})_1 = (\gamma_f^0 V_{\text{mol}})_2 = \ldots (\gamma_f^0 V_{\text{mol}})_n = \varphi_f(T_c) \\ (\gamma_p^0 V_{\text{mol}})_1 = (\gamma_p^0 V_{\text{mol}})_2 = \ldots (\gamma_p^0 V_{\text{mol}})_n = \varphi_p(T_c) \end{cases}$$

in which expressions the functions $\varphi_f(T_c)$ and $\varphi_p(T_c)$ depend only on the temperature.

Finally, if M_f is the molecular weight of the stationary phase, V_{mol} is related to V_g by

$$V_{\text{mol}} = V_g M_f T_c/273$$

(b) Theories of gas–solid (or adsorption) chromatography

The essentials of the theory of adsorption chromatography in the liquid phase, established by numerous investigators (Wilson[15], Weiss[16], De

Vault[17], Thomas[18], Roubaud-Valette[19], Glueckauf[20], etc.) have been reconsidered and adapted to the theory of adsorption chromatography in the gas phase (Wicke[21], Klinkenberg and Sjenitzer[22]). It was here necessary to take into account the compressibility of the mobile phase, a phenomenon not playing a part in liquid-phase chromatography. This complication does not, however, alter a result found for an incompressible stationary phase, namely that the curvature of the adsorption isotherm (see p. 228) causes an asymmetry of the peaks unfavourable to the resolution of the components of a mixture. An isotherm which is concave towards the c_m-axis results in the tailing of the rear end of a peak, so that this end will tend to encroach on the front of the following peak. In practice it has been found possible to reduce this effect by coating the adsorbent with a small amount of a liquid of low volatility; this liquid does not act as a partitioning agent, but immobilizes the most active centres of the adsorbent which are responsible for the curvature of the isotherm[58,230].

(c) *Theories of gas–liquid (or partition) chromatography*

(i) *The plate theories*

The earliest, very successful treatment of the problem consisted in comparing the chromatographic column to a distillation column. The first steps in this direction were taken by James and Martin[7,8], who reconsidered and adapted the theory of partition chromatography in the liquid phase, established a few years previously by Martin and Synge[6]. Various other authors (Van Deemter, Zuiderweg and Klinkenberg[23], Klinkenberg and Sjenitzer[22], Glueckauf[24], Jaulmes[25], etc.) have also published important contributions.

A theoretical plate, defined as was done before (see p. 227), contains a volume v_f of stationary phase and leaves a volume v_m vacant between its grains for the mobile phase. If an amount Q_1 of substance is introduced into the first plate, it divides itself between the stationary and mobile phases according to the distribution equilibrium previously mentioned (p. 228). The passage through the column of a volume element ∂v of mobile phase causes the transport of a computable quantity of the substance into the second plate, where an equilibrium will become established. At the same time the equilibrium of the first plate is upset, and can be recalculated. A second passage of a volume ∂v of mobile phase results in an analogous transfer into the third plate, coupled with a perturbation of the equilibria in the first and second plates, and so on. Finally, after a certain number of transfers, say n, corresponding to the passage of a volume $v = n \cdot \partial v$ of mobile phase, we can examine what is taking place in the $(p + 1)$th plate.

We find that the quantity of substance present in it, with respect to that introduced into the first plate, takes the form

$$Q_{p+1}/Q_1 = f(p, v/V) \tag{14}$$

an expression in which V represents the "effective volume of a theoretical plate", given by the relationship

$$V = v_m + Kv_f \tag{15}$$

where K has the usual meaning of the partition coefficient.

Calculation of the true retention volume. The variations of the ratio Q_{p+1}/Q_1 may be examined either as a function of the serial number p of the plate, after a given volume v of the mobile phase has been passed through the column, or, in a plate of given serial number p, as a function of the volume v of the carrier gas. Only the latter case will be considered here. Eqn. (14) then takes on the form $(Q_{p+1}/Q_1)_p = f(v/V)$, and its derivative $f'(v/V)$ becomes zero when

$$v = pV \tag{16}$$

At this special value of the variable v the function $f(v/V)$, which corresponds with a good approximation to a Gaussian curve, passes through a maximum. Let us examine what takes place in the last plate, of serial number r. When the maximum traverses it, a quantity of gas equal to the true retention volume V_r has by definition flowed through. With $p = r$ and $v = V_r$ eqn. (16) becomes

$$V_r = rV = r(v_m + Kv_f) = V_m + KV_f \tag{17}$$

In this expression $V_f = rv_f$ is the total volume of stationary phase in the whole column and $V_m = rv_m$ is the true retention volume of the carrier gas, since when $K = 0$ we get $V_r = V_m$.

Correction for pressure drop. Calculation of the corrected retention volume. Actually relationship (eqn. 17) was established for liquid–liquid chromatography, in which the mobile phase is incompressible, and cannot be applied without adjustment to gas–liquid chromatography, where the mobile phase expands from one plate to the next because of the existence of a pressure drop along the column. By attacking the problem in another manner, and calculating the true retention time t_r and the gas flow rate F_0 at the column outlet (the product of which two factors is the true retention volume V_r), James and Martin[7,8] obtained the expression

$$V_r = \frac{V_m}{R_F} \cdot \frac{2}{3} \cdot \frac{(p_i/p_0)^3 - 1}{(p_i/p_0)^2 - 1}$$

in which R_F stands for the "retardation factor", the ratio between the linear rates of propagation of the substance and the carrier gas in the column. Conversely we can write

$$V_m/R_F = jV_r \tag{18}$$

where

$$j = 3\,[(p_i/p_0)^2 - 1] : 2\,[(p_i/p_0)^3 - 1] \tag{19}$$

As p_i approaches p_0, j approaches unity, so that the limit of V_r is V_m/R_F. But, by definition, this limit is the corrected retention volume V_R^0 (see p. 225). We thus obtain

$$V_R^0 = V_m/R_F$$

or, in accordance with eqn. (18)

$$V_R^0 = jV_r \tag{4}$$

Calculation of the net retention volume. We can now reconsider relationship (17). Strictly speaking it is applicable only under conditions in which the mobile phase can be considered as incompressible. This, now, is precisely the case when $p_i = p_0$, because the column then operates without loss in pressure. We must then replace V_r by V_R^0 and V_m by V_m^0, which gives us

$$V_R^0 = V_m^0 + KV_f \tag{20}$$

This is a fundamental relationship, as it allows us to calculate the net retention volume. Taking into account eqn. (20), we can complete relationships (6) as follows

$$V_N = jV'_R = j(V_R - V_M) = j(V_r - V_m) = V_R^0 - V_m^0 = KV_f \tag{21}$$

For a given column (with a fixed value of V_f), the net retention volume is directly proportional to the partition coefficient K.

Calculation of the specific retention volume. Finally, we can express the specific retention volume (see p. 226):

$$V_g = 273 \cdot V_N/w_f T_c = 273 \cdot KV_f/w_f T_c = 273 \cdot K/\rho_f T_c = K_B/\rho_f \tag{22}$$

in which ρ_f denotes the density of the stationary phase at the temperature T_c and $K_B = 273 \cdot K/T_c$ is the Bunsen partition coefficient.

Calculation of the efficiency of a column. On the other hand, James and Martin were able to calculate the width of a peak (see p. 227). If we denote it as ΔV_r when measured as a volume and as ω when measured as a distance on the chart, we arrive at the following expressions:

$$\Delta V_r = 4V_r/\sqrt{r} \quad \text{and} \quad \omega = 4d_r/\sqrt{r}$$

Conversely we can obtain r by an expression which approaches that given hereunder all the more closely as d_r approximates to d_R, the distance separating the top of a peak on the chart from the origin*:

$$r = 16\,(d_R/\omega)^2 \tag{23}$$

By a simple geometrical construction and a measurement of lengths, it is hence possible to determine the efficiency of the column, expressed as a number of theoretical plates, and from this to calculate the height equivalent to a theoretical plate (HETP), h, given the length L of the column, by using formula (10).

Calculation of the length of column required for a given separation. Suppose that two substances A and B are to be separated with a certain degree of resolution P (see p. 227). By means of a preliminary experiment carried out in a trial column of length L', operating at the same temperature T_c and charged with the same packing per unit of length as the column to be made finally, both the relative retention r_{AB} and the efficiency r' are determined. (In the case of substances that are very adjacent chromatographically, the efficiency for each of them is practically identical.) From r_{AB} we can deduce, with the aid of eqns. (9), (10), and (23), the required efficiency r:

$$r = [2P(r_{AB} + 1)/(r_{AB} - 1)]^2 \tag{24}$$

and, assuming as a first approximation that the HETP's of the two columns are equal, we can write

$$L/r = L'/r'$$

from which we can obtain L.

(*ii*) *The "Rate Theories"*

While the preceding theories are to some extent static and are founded as a whole on the notion of equilibrium, a considerable number of publications have appeared in which the accent has, on the other hand, been laid on the real physical phenomena governing the exchanges between the stationary

---

* Logically, when using this relationship, one should not measure the distances of the peaks on the chart from the origin but from point A in Fig. 1, where the true retention volumes start. The error is small if d_R is large with respect to ω and if V_i and V_d are small with respect to V_M.

and mobile phases. Because the rates of diffusion of the solute molecules, as well as the linear displacement speed of the mobile phase, have been taken into account in these theories, they have been termed "rate theories".

The credit for giving a clear representation of the phenomena and expressing them mathematically is undoubtedly due to Van Deemter, Zuiderweg and Klinkenberg[23], who based their work on that of predecessors (Ketelle and Boyd[26], Boyd, Myers and Adamson[27], Lapidus and Amundson[28], Glueckauf[29], etc.).

The passage of a molecule of solute through a column is subject to the following influences.

(*a*) It is transported by the current of carrier gas and after a certain time dissolves in the stationary phase, from which it again evaporates and is transported by the carrier gas, and so on.

(*b*) In the mobile phase the molecules of solute are subject to diffusion, resolving into two factors: a molecular diffusion that would occur even if the gas rate were nil, and a turbulent diffusion associated with the fact that the gas is in motion.

(*c*) In the stationary phase, diffusion (only of the molecular type) also takes place.

(*d*) The phenomena of exchange between the stationary and mobile phases are characterized by a "resistance to mass transport" due to the fact that the stationary phase by no means constitutes a homogeneous film spread over perfectly smooth grains of support. On the contrary, it is present in the pores of the grains, at the end of channels of varying length and varying sinuosity, through which the solute molecules have to pass in two directions: from the flowing carrier gas to the stationary phase in order to dissolve in the latter, and from the stationary phase to the carrier gas after the inverse process of evaporation. The equilibrium between the mobile and stationary phases on which the plate theory is founded assumes that at every point the relationship $K = c_f/c_m$ is satisfied. Here, on the other hand, the resistance to mass transfer is the greater, the larger the discrepancy from equilibrium, that is to say the more the quantity $|Kc_m - c_f|$ departs from zero.

The solution of the differential equation established by Van Deemter, Zuiderweg and Klinkenberg is again a Gaussian curve, as in the plate theory, a fact justifying to some extent the two deductions. Another and even more essential feature is that the authors, in identifying the corresponding terms provided by the two theories, have set up a fundamental relationship expressing the height equivalent to a theoretical plate, h, as a function of a number of variables*:

$$h = 2\lambda d_p + 2\gamma D_m/u_m + \frac{8}{\pi^2} \cdot \frac{k'}{(1 + k')^2} \cdot \frac{e_f^2}{D_f} \cdot u_m$$

* For recent developments concerning the theory of packed columns, see ref.[267] (p. 760).

References p. 263

The letters in this formula have the following meanings:

λ and γ	Parameters denoting respectively the irregularity in the packing and the sinuosity of the path followed by the gas in the column.
d_p	Diameter of the particles of the support.
D_m	Coefficient of diffusion of the solute molecules in the mobile phase.
D_f	Coefficient of diffusion of the solute molecules in the stationary phase.
e_f	Effective thickness of the "film" of stationary phase surrounding the particles of support.
u_m	Linear velocity of the mobile phase at a certain point in the column.
k'	Constant related to the partition coefficient by $k' = KV_f/V_m$.

As might be expected there has been no lack of experiments designed to check the validity of the "Van Deemter" equation[23,30–37]. Below we give a short summary of the principal influences that have been studied (see also ref. [38]); in all cases the object has been to find the conditions of highest efficiency, *i.e.* those under which h is a minimum and r a maximum.

Particle size of the support. This dimension occurs in the Van Deemter equation as d_p. But d_p is connected to the correction factor λ in such a manner that when d_p is reduced, for obtaining a better efficiency, λ increases and the product λd_p tends to remain constant. There is hence no incentive for choosing a very fine-grained support. On the contrary, excessively fine grains resist the passage of the carrier gas and produce a large pressure drop between the inlet and outlet of the column. According to Keulemans and Kwantes[31] the optimum dimensions for ground refractory brick lie between 175 and 590 μ. A point of even greater importance, not directly indicated by the Van Deemter equation, is that the particles should as far as possible be of the same size. The range in particle diameter should in other words be very small; Scott[34,37] suggests a range of 110–120 mesh, or if necessary 120–160 mesh.

Amount of the stationary phase. De Wet and Pretorius[33] have pointed out that the amount of the stationary phase enters into the Van Deemter equation both in the thickness of the film e_f and through V_f in $k' = KV_f/V_m$. If the percentage of stationary phase is denoted by P, it can be shown that the relationship $h = f(P)$ passes through a minimum, a fact confirmed experimentally. The above-mentioned authors place this minimum at 30%, but Keulemans and Kwantes[31] found a value of 15% by experiment. At present there exists a tendency to reduce P to 10% and even 5% (Scott[34]).

Nature of the carrier gas. The nature of the carrier gas plays a part in the Van Deemter equation through the factor D_m, the coefficient of diffusion of the solute in this gas. For a given solute, D_m is smaller the higher the molecular weight of the carrier gas. By employing the formula of Gilliland[40] for D_m, De Wet and Pretorius[33] have been able to express h in the form

$$h = A + Bd^{-\frac{1}{2}} + C$$

in which d is the density of the carrier gas, and they have shown experimentally that it is actually of importance to employ a carrier gas of as high a density as possible. If no other considerations need be taken into account, the use of carbon dioxide or argon is therefore preferable to that of helium or hydrogen.

Linear velocity of the gas flow. The factor u_m is actually the most important one (Golay[39], Keulemans[32], etc.). Taking all the others as constants, we can express the Van Deemter equation for the HETP in the form

$$h = A + B/u_m + Cu_m$$

The curve for this function of u_m is a hyperbola (Fig. 3), which passes through a minimum at a certain value u_{opt}, given by $u_{opt} = \sqrt{B/C}$. With values of u_m smaller than this optimum the term B/u_m, corresponding to the molecular diffusion, becomes of importance. On the other side of the optimum, at high linear velocities, the term Cu_m, corresponding to mass transfer, has an

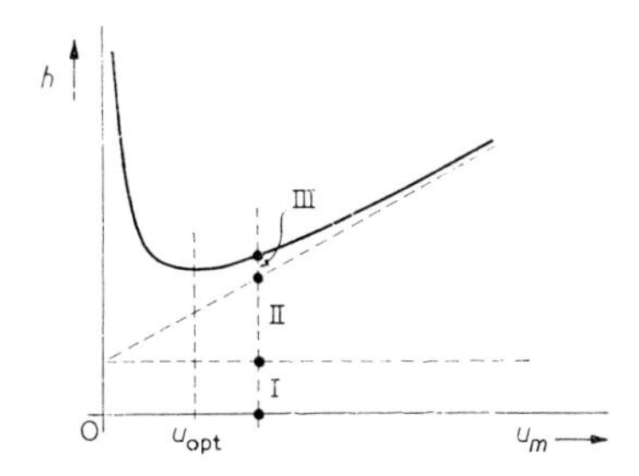

Fig. 3. Influence of the linear velocity of the carrier gas on the HETP. (I) Region of turbulent diffusion corresponding to term A of the Van DEEMTER equation. (II) Resistance to mass transfer, Cu_m. (III) Molecular diffusion, B/u_m.

increasing influence. There is hence an optimum flow rate, which can easily be found by establishing the curve $r = f(F_F)$ for the column efficiency, expressed as the number of theoretical plates calculated according to eqn. (23), as a function of the gas rate measured in the flowmeter. This curve should have a maximum, and this is the most favourable point for operation[41].

Pressure of the carrier gas. Scott and Cheshire[34, 37], see also ref. [42], have demonstrated that an increase in the average pressure of the column has a

References p. 263

favourable influence on the efficiency. This can be explained as being partly due to a reduction in the diffusibility of the solute molecules, *viz.* to a diminution in D_m. Furthermore, since the pressure (and consequently the linear velocity) of the carrier gas vary along the length of the column, only a portion of the latter operates at maximum efficiency. In order to obtain a p_i/p_0 ratio that is as small as possible[38], the same authors place a very narrow constriction at the column outlet, which takes up practically all the pressure drop. In this way they obtained, with an inlet pressure $p_i = 150$ p.s.i. and a p_i/p_0 ratio of approximately 2, an efficiency r of 15,000 to 18,000 theoretical plates, using a column length L of 9′6″.

Temperature of the column. By a consideration of the temperature-dependent terms of the Van Deemter equation, De Wet and Pretorius[33] were able to express the HETP in the form

$$h = A + BT + C/T$$

This is again a hyperbola, a fact signifying that there exists an optimum temperature for operating the column. We must interpret this result as follows. At the temperature concerned the *particular* solute with which the experiment was done gives the narrowest peak that it is possible to obtain, all other factors remaining constant. This fact, however, in no way determines the possibility of separating mixtures containing the solute in question. This matter will be gone into later (p. 240).

Other factors on which the efficiency of the column depends. Besides those entering into the Van Deemter equation, a number of other factors have been examined for their influence on the efficiency of the column.

The size of the sample, for instance, plays a part. An "overloading" of the column becomes evident by a broadening of the peaks, in other words by a reduction of the efficiency. Keulemans[32] has introduced the concept of an HETP for zero sample size, this being the limit to which the HETP approaches on reducing the amount of the sample, and thus corresponding to the maximum efficiency. It may be pointed out that the use of continually smaller samples makes it necessary to employ continually more sensitive detectors.

The way in which the sample is introduced is also very important, the obtainable efficiency of a column being often lowered by a faulty method of introduction. Gaseous mixtures should be introduced without previous dilution by carrier gas, "as a plug"[43]. In the case of liquids, the efficiency depends on the speed of evaporation of the sample, and hence on the temperature of the sample chamber. Pollard and Hardy[44] have shown that when the syringe technique is followed, the maximum efficiency is obtained by inserting the needle to such a depth that its end is level with the top of the column packing.

Variation of column efficiency as a function of retention volume. As has been said, the efficiency r, given by eqn. (23), is valid only for the solute with which it has been determined (see p. 228). An experiment with another solute gives a different value for r, so that one can think of finding a relationship between r and V_r. Littlewood, Phillips and Price[45] were the first to show that in general the efficiency increases with the retention volume (see also ref. [46]). Pollard and Hardy[47] established the following empirical relationship:

$$\log r = A + \tfrac{1}{2} \log V_R$$

which is of value in some cases, for instance when dealing with the members of a homologous series. The effect mentioned may be due in part to the reduction in diffusibility of the solutes resulting from their increase in molecular weight.

(*iii*) *Theory of the capillary columns*

The theory of these very interesting columns, which were first employed almost simultaneously by Dijkstra and De Goey[48] and by Golay[49,50], was developed by the last-named author. The mathematical treatment is too lengthy to be dealt with here, and only the line that was followed can be indicated.

To begin with, the distribution of the velocities of a flowing gas in a narrow-bored cylindrical tube, or in a tube having a flattened rectangular cross-section, is parabolic, the speed being zero at the wall and a maximum in the axis or the axial plane. A first effect, called dynamic diffusion, results from the fact that a foreign molecule, even if not retained by the stationary phase on the walls, will proceed to occupy surface elements of a cross-section owing to transverse diffusion. The durations of occupancy are, however, not necessarily the same: molecules with an extra high occupancy of the tube centre will leave their position faster than those with an extra high occupancy of the portions near the wall. A second effect, which occurs whether the gas be in motion or not, corresponds to static diffusion. Finally in the case of those molecules having an affinity for the stationary phase, there is the additional effect of retention, as the result of which identical molecules on an average spend the same fraction of the time in this stationary phase.

The mathematical treatment previously established by other authors for uncoated round tubes has been extended by Golay to coated tubes of circular and rectangular cross-section. Accepting as a hypothesis that diffusion inside the stationary phase is instantaneous, he succeeded in finding an expression for the HETP. Further he deduced, for the case in which the column is operating at the optimum flow rate, another magnitude, which he termed the *specific performance index,* SPI. In the ideal case the latter

References p. 263

should be equal to unity, but in reality it is considerably higher. Since the mathematical form of the SPI is complicated, Golay simplified it to a so-called *performance index*, PI, which is expressed as a function of the pressure difference Δp between column inlet and outlet, of the retention times t_R and t_M of the solute in question and "air", and of the peak width Δt_R, also expressed in time units:

$$\mathrm{PI} = \left(\frac{\Delta t_R}{t_R - t_M}\right)^4 \cdot \frac{(t_R - t_M)^4 \cdot t_M}{t_R^4(t_R - 15t_M/16)} \cdot t_R \cdot \Delta p$$

In this formula the first factor in brackets is the relative width of the peak; the last factor, the product of the time one has to wait before the substance emerges from the column and the pressure head that has to be applied to the latter, constitutes what Golay calls "the price paid for a given resolution".

The performance index, thus defined, is lower for capillary than for conventional columns, and is proposed as a measure of the intrinsic qualities* of a column, since it can be used by investigators as a basis for comparison.

(*d*) *The temperature factor*

Littlewood, Phillips and Price[45] established the following empirical relationship:

$$\log V_g = a/T_c + b \tag{25}$$

in which a is a constant characteristic of the solute–solvent pair. The graph for $\log V_g = f(1/T)$ is hence a straight line for a given solute. The straight lines for members of one and the same homologous series all pass through one point (Fig. 4). At a certain temperature, the difference between the ordinates of two straight lines corresponds to the separation factor. It is immediately evident that the separation is easier, the lower the column

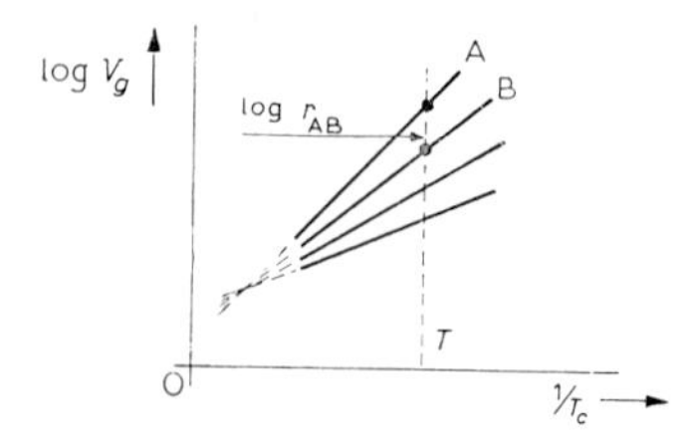

Fig. 4. Plots of $\log V_g$ against $1/T_c$. For the members of homologous series, a pencil of straight lines is obtained.

---

* For recent developments concerning the theory of capillary columns, see ref.[267] (p. 761).

temperature. The proper course is hence to choose the lowest temperature compatible with a residence time of the solutes that is still acceptable. If the solutes do not belong to the same homologous series, it is only by examining the graph showing all the lines for every solute that one can judge the optimum column temperature to be chosen for obtaining the best resolution.

The foregoing illustrates the difference between the "resolution" of two compounds and the "efficiency" of the column. We have seen that the efficiency (*i.e.* the aptitude of the column for giving narrow peaks) passes through a maximum with a progression in temperature (p. 238). The resolution characterizing the separability of two solutes obeys no rule of this kind: the best resolution is not necessarily obtained at the temperature of optimum efficiency.

It has been possible to show that the coefficient a in eqn. (25) has a definite meaning. Actually it is coupled to the heat of solution, ΔH_s, of the solute in the stationary phase constituting the solvent by the relationship

$$\Delta H_s = -2.3\, Ra + RT^2 \frac{\mathrm{d}}{\mathrm{d}T} \log \rho_f$$

of which the second term can be calculated from a knowledge of the coefficient of expansion. If the density of the stationary phase does not vary appreciably with temperature, the preceding relationship reduces to

$$\Delta H_s = -2.3\, Ra$$

and eqn. (25) can be written in the form

$$^{10}\log V_g = -\Delta H_s / 2.3\, RT_c + b$$

Actually, a plot of $^{10}\log V_g$ against $1/T$ does not always give a straight line. Ambrose, Keulemans and Purnell[10] recommend that an Antoine equation should then be used, of the type

$$\log V_g = A/(t + C) + B$$

which permits the curve to be straightened by using a value of C not equal to 273. Other relationships connecting the temperature, or other chromatographic parameters, to thermodynamic magnitudes have been established. Thus the free energy of solution, ΔG_s, is given by the simple formula[51]:

$$\Delta G_s = -RT \ln K_B$$

References p. 263

in which K_B has the significance of Bunsen's partition coefficient as previously defined (p. 233). Furthermore, by applying the general relationship

$$\Delta G_s = \Delta H_s - T\Delta S_s$$

it is possible to arrive at the entropy of solution[52], ΔS_s. These brief indications show that gas chromatography is not only an analytical technique, but that by an interesting extention of its possibilities it is also capable of supplying data that are obtainable only with far more difficulty by classical methods (see also pp. 244 and 247).

(e) *Choice of the stationary phase*

If a solute A is separated from a solute B, this fact is due to its having spent a different time in the stationary phase S; if, for instance, it emerges later, it has remained there longer than B. We can explain this by saying that the forces drawing an isolated molecule of A into the environment of numerous molecules of S are greater than those acting on an isolated molecule of B. In current language we express this by saying that the "affinity" of A for S is greater than that of B for S. The reader can with profit consult the discussion of the nature and relative intensity of the forces in question, as given in a publication by Keulemans, Kwantes and Zaal[52].

The matter can be simplified by stating that the whole problem of the separability of two solutes—which is equivalent to that of the *power of resolution* of a given column—is contained in a new expression that can be formulated for the separation factor r_{AB} (see p. 226) by taking into account its defining relationship (8) and eqns. (12) and (21) or (22). This is:

$$r_{\mathrm{AB}} = K_{\mathrm{A}}/K_{\mathrm{B}} = (f^0_{\mathrm{B}}/f^0_{\mathrm{A}})\,(\gamma^0_{f\mathrm{B\,S}}/\gamma^0_{f\mathrm{A\,S}}) = (p^0_{\mathrm{B}}/p^0_{\mathrm{A}})\,(\gamma^0_{p\mathrm{B\,S}}/\gamma^0_{p\mathrm{A\,S}}) \qquad (26)$$

Regardless of whether the one or the other of these two equalities is employed, it will be observed that the possibility of separating A from B depends on:

(*i*) components A and B themselves, through the ratio between the fugacities or vapour pressures of the pure liquids at the operating temperature of the column. These ratios are inherent in the nature of the solutes to be separated, and are therefore not subject to the experimenter's influence. The data in question can be found, if available, in physical tables.

(*ii*) the stationary phases employed, which makes itself felt in the ratio of the activity coefficients at infinite dilution, a direct result of the relative degrees of interaction between solutes and solvent.

The term *selective solvent*, in its relation to the two solutes A and B, is used for every stationary phase with which the ratio of the activity coefficients at infinite dilution, $\gamma^0_{BS}/\gamma^0_{AS}$, differs from unity. Eqn. (26) shows that a selective phase can not only separate two solutes inseparable by distillation, when $f^0_B/f^0_A \simeq p^0_B/p^0_A \simeq 1$, but also, in the converse case where the solutes can be split by distillation, to make them emerge from a chromatographic column in an order opposite to that in which they would be obtained by distilling them. This order depends on the numerical values of the two ratios whose product is the separation factor.

The term *unselective phase*, with respect to the two solutes A and B, is used for every stationary phase with which the ratio of the activity coefficients at infinite dilution, $\gamma^0_{BS}/\gamma^0_{AS}$, is equal or very close to unity. Eqn. (26) shows that the separation of the two solutes is then entirely governed by their own physical properties, that is to say by the ratios f^0_B/f^0_A or p^0_B/p^0_A. Two solutes inseparable by distillation, for which these ratios are practically equal to unity, can also not be separated by gas chromatography over an unselective stationary phase. Conversely, an unselective stationary phase causes the solutes to emerge in the same order as by distillation.

The curves given in Fig. 5, showing the variation in the vapour pressures of solutes A and B as a function of temperature, prove the above statement.

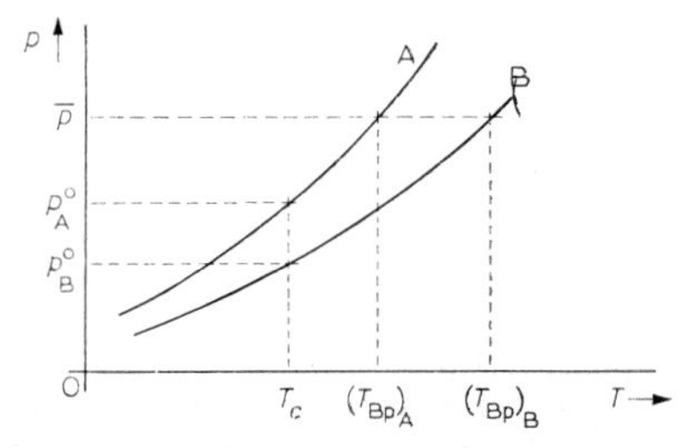

Fig. 5. Relationship between the saturated vapour pressures of two solutes A and B at the operating temperature of the column, T_c, and their boiling points under the average operating pressure of the column, $\bar{p}$.

If we call the boiling points of these solutes at the average pressure $\bar{p}$ of the column $(T_{Bp})_A$ and $(T_{Bp})_B$ respectively, it will be seen that if $(T_{Bp})_B/(T_{Bp})_A > 1$ it follows that $p^0_B/p^0_A < 1$. Since, by hypothesis, $\gamma^0_{BS}/\gamma^0_{AS} = 1$, the separation factor r_{AB} will also be less than unity, so that A emerges before B, as in distillation.

It would be an ideal aid in the selection of a stationary phase for a given separation if it were possible to calculate the activity coefficient at infinite dilution, at every temperature, for every solute–solvent pair. An interesting attempt in this direction has been made by Pierotti and co-workers[53,43]; their method is as yet, however, confined to special cases and is fairly complicated. In the absence of such a procedure it is desirable that tables of

References p. 263

activity coefficients should become available, obtained from accurate and specially-designed chromatographic experiments by means of eqn. (12). The latter has been rewritten below in other forms by conversion with eqns. (13) and (21):

$$\gamma_p^0 = N_f RT_c/p^0 K = V_f N_f RT_c/p^0 V_N = RT_c/p^0 V_{mol}$$

$$\gamma_f^0 = N_f RT_c/f^0 K = V_f N_f RT_c/f^0 V_N = RT_c/f^0 V_{mol}$$

Numerous investigators have undertaken this task (see, in particular, Kwantes and Rijnders[54], Knight[55], Hardy[56], and for a review of the precautions to be taken in order to reduce the errors to a minimum: Keulemans[32]). The principle of a method of comparison has also been given (Chovin and Lebbe[14]). However, it is unfortunately true at present that the number of values of γ_p^0 or γ_f^0 that are known and published in tables is far too small; until they become more numerous, it is necessary to resort to other considerations.

In the majority of cases one of the following possibilities will apply.

(*i*) The solutes A and B have the same polarity. If the stationary phase S also possesses the polarity of A and B it is clear that the forces drawing an isolated molecule of A or an isolated molecule of B into the environment of the molecules of S will not be essentially different from those existing in the pure liquids A and B. In this case the ratio γ_{BS}/γ_{AS} remains close to unity and the stationary phase behaves unselectively. As has already been said, the solutes then emerge approximately in the order of their boiling points.

For example squalane, a saturated, non-polar hydrocarbon, is unselective with respect to all hydrocarbons, whatever their structure (aliphatic, cycloparaffinic or aromatic). Similarly, a polyethyleneglycol of high molecular weight—a polar substance—is unselective towards a mixture of alcohols, also polar.

If A and B on the one hand, and S on the other, have an inverse polarity, the foregoing conclusions as a whole remains true; the forces exerted by surrounding molecules of S on isolated molecules of A and B are either greater than in the pure liquids (A and B being non-polar, S polar), or lower (A and B polar, S non-polar). The ratio γ_{BS}/γ_{AS}, however, can still be approximately unity, and the stationary phase will, generally speaking, be unselective. Nevertheless, structural peculiarities can here exert an influence and modify this rule, which is strictly true only if A and B are close chemical neighbours.

From the foregoing it follows that an arbitrary stationary phase will be unselective with respect to the successive members of an homologous series, regardless of whether the stationary phase is chemically closely related to the series or not. From one member to the next the ratio $\gamma_i^0/\gamma_{i+1}^0$ varies but little, and the variation always occurs in the same direction. The members will therefore emerge in the order of their boiling points, T_{Bp}, or, what is practically the same, in the order of their vapour pressures p^0 at the operating temperature of the column, or again in the order of their molecular weights (or of the number n of carbon atoms that they contain).

Thus, for the members of a homologous series, the graphs of the following expressions

$$\log V_N \text{ (or } V_g) = f(T_{Bp}) \qquad \text{(refs. 57, 58)}$$

$$= f(\log p^0) \qquad \text{(refs. 59, 60)}$$

$$= f(n) \qquad \text{(refs. 7, 61, 62)}$$

are straight lines; they are largely used in qualitative analysis (see p. 247).

(*ii*) The solutes do not have the same polarity. Let us suppose, firstly, that A is non-polar and B polar, and secondly that these two compounds have the same boiling point. They will not be separated by a distillation column. According to the polarity of S, two cases must be considered.

If S is not polar, the forces between A and S, both non-polar, are analogous to those existing in the pure liquid A. But the same does not apply to B, because the powerful forces existing in its own liquid, which restrain the evaporation of a molecule and thus give liquid B an abnormally high boiling point, no longer exist in the environment of S. It follows that B obtains a normal volatility in S and emerges from the column well before A. For instance, over squalane, ethanol emerges before hexane, although the boiling point of the alcohol is even slightly higher than that of the hydrocarbon.

If S is polar and B also polar, the latter will behave as if in the environment of its own liquid. But A will be subject to new forces, due to the permanent dipoles of S, and it will accordingly be retarded with respect to B.

In both cases, A and B, inseparable by distillation, can be separated by gas chromatography. Though the two results are the same, since B emerges before A, the mechanisms are different. Here the phase S, whatever be its polarity, is selective. However, if we take stationary phases of increasing polarity, it becomes possible that the forces acting on the polar solute B are finally superior to those retarding the non-polar compound A; the order of emergence is then reversed, the polar compound being greatly retarded.

An important special case is that in which B, without being polar, is polarizable; new separations then become possible. Thus 2,2′-oxydipropionitrile, a very polar compound, retards aromatic hydrocarbons so powerfully, by induced polarization, with respect to aliphatic hydrocarbons[63] that benzene (Bp. 80° C) emerges later than aliphatic hydrocarbons boiling at 216° C.

(*iii*) Besides the possibilities of separation outlined above, the opportunity sometimes exists for taking advantage of various chemical forces, such as hydrogen bonds, and specific forces of interaction between molecules which are responsible (even outside the field of chromatography) for the formation of adducts and more or less loose complexes. The following are some examples taken from various applications.

The well-known tendency of poly-nitrated derivatives (such as picric acid) to form crystalline additives with aromatic hydrocarbons has been turned to advantage for retaining the latter with respect to aliphatics (Keulemans, Kwantes and Zaal[52], Whitham[64,65]). For the same purpose tetra-chlorophthalic anhydride, and various esters derived from it, have been used[70].

The formation of hydrogen bonds between a stationary phase of poly-ethylenic structure (Lubrol MO) and primary and secondary amines has been utilized by James and Martin[8] for separating the latter from tertiary amines, which do not contain an active hydrogen atom and are therefore but little retained by the stationary phase in question.

Metallic ions have been employed because of their tendency to form complexes. Thus the Ag^+ ion retards olefins (Bradford, Harvey and Chalkley[66,67]). Phillips and co-workers[68] have shown that use can be made of the ions Mn^{++}, Co^{++}, Ni^{++}, Cu^{++} and Zn^{++}, in the form of their molten stearates, which undergo powerful interactions with amines. (See also ref. [69] for the case of esters of amino acids.)

3. Practical and analytical aspects of gas chromatography

(*a*) *Experimental determination of retention values*

(*i*) *Retention times*

The distances d_R and d'_R on the charts (see Fig. 1, p. 225) allow the retention times, t_R, and the adjusted retention times, t'_R, to be determined if the speed of motion of the recorder paper, u_p, is known.

$$t_R = d_R/u_p \quad t'_R = d'_R/u_p = (d_R - d_M)/u_p \tag{27}$$

(*ii*) *Gas flow rate at the outlet of the column*

The gas flow rate is measured in a flowmeter, in which a temperature T_F and a pressure p_F prevail. If F_F is the gas flow rate so determined, corrected if necessary for the vapour pressure of water (as in soap-film flowmeters), the gas flow rate at the column outlet is given by the expression

$$F_0 = F_F(p_F/p_0)\,(T_c/T_F) \tag{28}$$

(iii) Retention values

From eqns. (27) and (28) given above and the various defining relationships we can obtain successively:

$$V_R = t_R F_0 = d_R F_F p_F T_c / p_0 T_F u_p$$

$$V_N = j V'_R = j t'_R F_0 = j F_F d'_R \, p_F T_c / p_0 T_F u_p = K V_f \qquad (29)$$

$$V_g = 273 \cdot j d'_R F_F p_F / p_0 T_F u_p w_f \qquad (30)$$

Formulae (29) and (30) are particularly important. The first, inversely, allows the partition coefficient K to be derived from chromatographic measurements; this method, according to specialists, is the best available for determining the fundamental value in question. The second is widely used in qualitative analysis.

(iv) Relative retentions

If, of two substances A and B, one, say B, is an internal standard, that is to say a substance added in known quantity to the sample and so chosen that it does not interfere chromatographically with any of the constituents of the sample, we have, by eqns. (29) and (30)

$$r_{\mathrm{A,St}} = (V_N)_{\mathrm{A}}/(V_N)_{\mathrm{St}} = (V_g)_{\mathrm{A}}/(V_g)_{\mathrm{St}} = (d'_R)_{\mathrm{A}}/(d'_R)_{\mathrm{St}} \qquad (31)$$

Thus the relative retentions are simply equal to the ratios of the adjusted retention distances on the chart. This fact will often be used later.

(b) Qualitative analysis

(i) Absolute measurements

In principle a knowledge of the specific retention volume, V_g, should be sufficient for identifying an unknown substance. This presupposes that the analyst has at his disposal a catalogue of these values for various solute–solvent pairs, and that he preferably also knows the variation of V_g with temperature, for instance in the form of graphs for $\log V_g = f(1/T_c)$ or of Antoine equations $\log V_g = A/(t + C) + B$ (see p. 241).

There is, however, always a risk of confusion, since several solute–solvent pairs can have the same value of V_g at a given temperature.

The uncertainty in identification is reduced if the compound is passed over a second stationary phase and use is made of graphs[53,77] for

$$\log (V_g \text{ or } V_N)_{\text{st. phase 1}} = f \{ \log (V_g \text{ or } V_N)_{\text{st. phase 2}} \}$$

Finally, if the investigator knows the chemical series to which the compound to be identified belongs, he can with advantage employ the linear graphs representing log $V_g = f$ (number of carbon atoms). The experimentally determined point should correspond to an integral number n of carbon atoms on such a graph.

*(ii) The use of an internal standard**

Actually, there is always an uncertainty due to experimental errors, which can be as much as ± 5% in absolute determinations. The method using an internal standard can then be of great value. All that has been said previously is also valid for relative retention values, which can be determined by means of eqn. (31) with a precision easily attaining ± 1%.

Nevertheless, it is frequently impossible to identify an unknown substance by chromatographic methods. A potent alternative is, however, still available: that of trapping the substance at the column outlet (see p. 259) and then submitting it to chemical or physico-chemical tests, for instance to spectral determinations in the ultraviolet[71] and infrared[72-76], or to mass spectrometry[66,78].

(c) Quantitative analysis

(i) Absolute measurements

In this respect the integral detectors are the most favourably placed, because the difference in level between two steps is directly proportional to the amount of the substance corresponding to the gradient in question.

With the more usually employed differential detectors, the interpretation is more complex. It is based either on the height of the peaks or upon their areas over the base-line. Dimbat, Porter and Stross[79] have shown that the peak heights are more sensitive to the temperature of the column than to the flow rate of carrier gas, whilst the opposite holds for the areas of the peaks.

Various methods are available for measuring peak areas. Use may be made of integrators[80], or planimeters[81-83]; the area may be found by multiplying the height of the peak by its width at half-height[84] or by cutting out the peak from the chart and weighing it[85-87].

Generally speaking, the coefficient of proportionality between the mass of the solute and the peak area varies with the detector and the solute itself; a calibration is therefore necessary and numerous methods have been proposed for carrying this out. With certain detectors, such as the katharometer using hydrogen or helium as carrier gas, calibration is not considered necessary by some workers, though others continue to recommend it[41,79,88]. At all events the absolute methods are liable to relatively high experimental errors.

* For the introduction of the "retention index" by Kovats, see ref.[268].

(ii) The use of an internal standard

Here again the use of an internal standard improves the accuracy. In this method a graph is employed, showing the variations of the ratios between the heights (or areas) of the peaks and that of the internal standard, as a function of the mass ratios[89]. Here, however, the assumption is made that at a given mass, the ratio of the heights or areas is independent of operating conditions, an assumption that is not always justified[44]. Rosie and co-workers[90], on the other hand, have shown that the calibration is independent of the katharometer used and have given a long list of relative coefficients for peak areas (taking benzene as 100), which can be generally employed.

(iii) The method of internal normalisation

Finally there is a method, termed internal normalisation, which consists in finding the ratio between the area of the peak for the compound to be determined and the sum of the areas of all the peaks in the chromatogram. As such, this requires the response of the detector to be independent of the nature of the components present in the sample. If this supposition is not true, it is again necessary to apply suitable correction factors to each of the constituents of the sample. These factors also depend on the detector employed[87,88,90,91].

(d) *Apparatus*

General arrangement

Except for a few variations, an apparatus for chromatography is generally built up of the components shown in Fig. 6. In special cases this set-up may require modification. Thus the flowmeters can be placed in the gas circuit before the column, while a vacuum pump may have to be connected to the outlet of the column if one prefers to work at a reduced pressure.

The detector depicted in Fig. 6 has two channels; its response depends on the difference between the physical property in question of the carrier gas charged with components, as it emerges from the column, and that of the pure carrier gas entering into the column. The difference in pressure existing between these two channels (corresponding to the pressure drop in the column) may, however, have an unfavourable influence, and it will then be desirable to reduce it. In this case an absorber is placed after the traps—for instance an absorber containing chilled active charcoal—and the carrier gas so freed from transported components is passed through the reference channel of the detector. There are, however, detectors that do not require such a reference channel. The arrangement then becomes simpler.

On the other hand it is sometimes necessary to use a more complicated set-up for special purposes. For example, an arrangement has been de-

References p. 263

scribed having two columns in parallel, a single sample being introduced for both; this allows the properties of two stationary phases with respect to one and the same solute to be compared directly, or it can be used to give two separate records simultaneously for the same sample[14], so as to double the collected data. Finally, among many such special cases, that may be

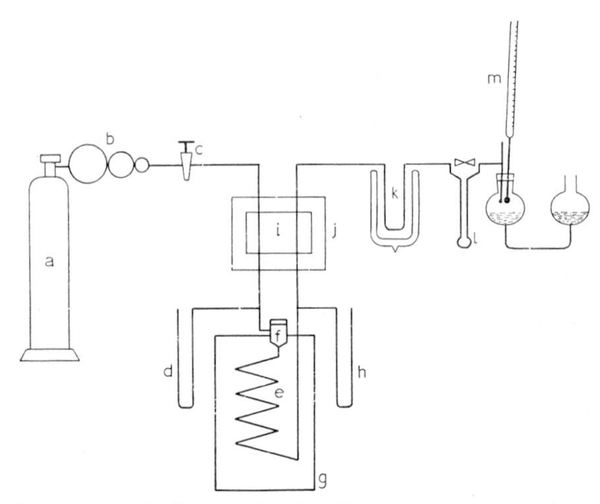

Fig. 6. General arrangement of apparatus for chromatography (a) stock of carrier gas; (b) pressure reduction valve in stages; (c) needle valve; (d) manometer for measuring inlet pressure; (e) column; (f) device for sample introduction; (g) column thermostat; (h) manometer for measuring outlet pressure; (i) detector (here with two channels); (j) thermostat for detector; (k) liquid air trap; (l) flowmeter; (m) soap-film flowmeter.

mentioned in which two columns are placed in series, with a provision for switching over the flow without altering its rate, whereby it is possible to pass a cut of the components issuing from the first column into the second[92]. In this case the stationary liquid of the first column is frequently chosen so as to be unselective towards the components to be separated, while that in the second column is highly selective.

(e) *The carrier gas*

As previously noted (p. 236), there is an advantage in choosing a carrier gas with as high a density as possible. For GSC, Janák employs carbon dioxide, which he removes behind the column outlet by absorbing it in a nitrometer filled with caustic potash solution[5]. Certain modern detectors based on ionization require the use of argon, also a gas of high density. A very widely employed detector, the katharometer or thermal conductivity cell, on the other hand, has the opposite requirement (see p. 256). With this detector it is preferable to employ helium or hydrogen (or, at worst, nitrogen), since it proves better to sacrifice some efficiency in the column rather than sensitivity in the detector. The use of other carrier gases, for instance the vapour of ethyl alcohol[93] has also been suggested.

The average flow rate of the carrier gas in columns of the usual diameters lies between 10 and 400 ml/min. The flow rate corresponding to maximum efficiency (p. 237) can be found by experiment. Even more important than the absolute flow rate, however, is its constancy, which is an experimental requirement that must be scrupulously observed. It can be realized by using pressure reduction valves and needle valves, and furthermore by means of pressure regulating systems[7,94,95]. For measuring the flow rate, capillary meters and rotameters are generally insufficiently accurate, except in rough trial runs[96]. The most recommended flowmeter is the soap-film type[7,97], which causes no pressure drop. With this flowmeter it is, however, necessary to correct for the saturated vapour pressure of water at its operating temperature.

(f) *The column and its accessories*

(i) *Shapes and dimensions*

The so-called conventional columns are contained in tubes of glass, plastic, metal (copper, stainless steel etc.), having diverse shapes and dimensions. They can be in the form of a U, a W, a spiral or a helix; their inside diameter can range from a few millimeters (generally 4 to 6 mm) for analytical work to several centimeters for the preparation of pure samples in measurable amounts[98], up to 70 g. Their length varies from one to two feet in GSC, and can be as much as 100 feet in GLC. The pressure drop along the column of course increases with the length, so that special measures may have to be taken at the entrance of the column, particularly as regards the introduction of the sample.

A column of the capillary type consists of a tube with an inner diameter of 0.2 to 0.3 mm and a length of up to several hundred meters. It may be either of glass (a machine has been described for drawing out commercial tubes[99]), of nylon[100] or of metal (stainless steel, copper, silver, gold etc.). With a pressure head of but one atmosphere at the inlet, the flow rate at the outlet may be as much as several milliliters per minute and an analysis is performed very rapidly.

(ii) *Devices for introducing the sample*

In the case of gaseous samples, calibrated tubes of small volume are filled with the gas to be analyzed, at a known pressure and temperature, and are connected in the circuit of the carrier gas by means of a suitable switch-over

References p. 263

arrangement not affecting the throughput[103-105], for instance by three-way cocks lubricated with a special grease[101,102], or electromagnetic valves. With such an arrangement the sample introduced into the apparatus can be measured accurately[106,107].

When dealing with a liquid it is by no means so easy to introduce an accurately measured sample, which may be as small as 1 μl. Hypodermic syringes[62] are very frequently used, but in spite of improvements made in their construction[108-111] they are still only moderately accurate. If a greater precision is required, capillary pipettes can be employed[112-114], or better still small sealed tubes, into which the sample is weighed out and which are opened in place by crushing[79,115]. In all cases the evaporation chamber should be as close to the column entrance as possible, and it should be maintained at the column temperature, or preferably somewhat above it[44,66,116,117].

(iii) The column thermostat

Eqn. (25) shows that the specific retention volume varies with an exponential function of the reciprocal column temperature. Hence it is important to maintain the latter at a very constant value, within limits of $\pm$ 0.1° C or less. This is attained by placing the column in a thermostat, which can consist of a jacket containing the vapours of some suitable boiling liquid[81,118-121], of a liquid bath or of an air bath, the latter being if necessary kept in motion by a fan or circulated[64,122]. There are also arrangements incorporating a programmed heating system[123-127].

(g) The column packing

(i) Adsorbants

In GSC the stationary phase consists of one of the standard adsorbing agents such as activated alumina, active charcoal or silica gel; alternatively, one can use various treated zeolites[128,129], which play the part of *molecular sieves* and allow certain specific separations to be performed[112,130].

(ii) Supports for GLC

The solid support and the liquid stationary phase employed in GLC can best be considered separately.

Two types of support have been generally adopted. The first is a diatomaceous earth called Celite, obtainable commercially (Johns Manville Sales Corp., New York), which may sometimes be used as marketed, but in other cases is submitted to various pretreatments[7,131]. It is a somewhat fine-grained material and thus causes an appreciable resistance to the carrier gas in long columns*. The other type of support is silicious firebrick, which is

* Celite fractions with a narrow range of particle size, specially prepared for GLC are now marketed.

crushed, sieved, if necessary washed for the removal of fine material[47,132] and finally dried[148]. Two kinds of firebrick are mentioned in the chromatographic literature: the brick called Sterchamol (Sterchamolwerke GmbH, Dortmund, Germany), utilized by Keulemans and Kwantes[133], and the type C22 (Johns Manville), employed by Dimbat, Porter and Stross[79]. Comparative experiments on the advantages and drawbacks of these two types of support have been carried out (Desty *et al.*[134]).

Firebrick, like Celite, can show a residual adsorption for highly polar compounds, as becomes evident by a more or less pronounced tailing of the peaks. Knight[139] reduces it by admixing the carrier gas with a strongly adsorbed substance, while Scott[140] deals with it by "plating" the brick with a layer of silver.

Other supports have been suggested, for instance glass powder[36,47,135], sand, carbon and carborundum[136], helices of stainless steel[137] or of copper[54] and zeolites[138], but in general they give a much lower column efficiency.

(*iii*) *The stationary liquids*

The liquids forming the actual stationary phase in GLC have to comply with certain general requirements drawn up by Keulemans and Kwantes[133] and by Adlard[132], that can be summarized as follows.

(*a*) The stationary liquid should be a good solvent for at least one of the compounds to be separated.

(*b*) It must not react irreversibly with the compounds passing through the column. But while such a reaction is undesirable in the column proper, it may be turned to advantage when using preliminary columns for removing specific components[106,141,142].

(*c*) It must be thermally stable at the temperature of operation.

(*d*) Its vapour pressure should be as low as possible. If this is not the case, there will result in the course of time a reduction in the capacity of the column, a change in efficiency and above all an instability of the detector, owing to the progressive entrainment of stationary phase by the carrier gas.

TABLE I

STATIONARY LIQUIDS RECOMMENDED FOR THE COMPARISON OF SOLUTES

Stationary liquid	*Temperature range in which it can be used (°C)*
n-Hexadecane	+ 20 to + 50
Squalane	+ 20 to + 150
Benzyldiphenyl	+ 80 to + 150
Dinonyl phthalate	+ 20 to + 100
Dimethylformamide	— 20 to + 20
Diglycerol	+ 20 to + 100

References p. 263

TABLE II

STATIONARY LIQUIDS IN CURRENT USE

Hydrocarbons
- *n*-Decane
- *n*-Dodecane
- *n*-Hexadecane
- Triisobutylene
- Squalane
- Benzyldiphenyl

Alcohols and ethers
- *n*-Undecanol
- *n*-Tetradecanol
- *n*-Octadecanol
- Benzyl oxide

Nitrated compounds
- Nitrobenzene
- *p*-Nitraniline
- Picric acid–fluorene
- Ethyl dinitrodiphenyl-dicarboxylate
- Trinitrobenzoate of polyethylene-glycol 400
- Trinitrofluorene

Amines
- Triethanolamine

Amides
- Dimethylformamide
- Diethylformamide
- Hexamethylphosphoramide

Ketones
- Acetonylacetone

Polyols and derivatives
- Ethylene glycol + silver nitrate
- Diethyleneglycol-monoethylether (Carbitol)
- Tetraethyleneglycol-dimethylether
- Polyethyleneglycols of mol. wt. 400, 600 and 1000
- Diglycerol

Esters
- Ethyl acetoacetate
- *n*-Butyl malate
- Di(ethyl-2-hexyl) sebacate (octoil S)
- Dibutyl phthalate
- Di-*n*-octyl phthalate
- Di(ethyl-2-hexyl) phthalate
- Dinonyl phthalate
- Didecyl phthalate
- Di-tetrahydrofuryl phthalate
- Mellitic esters of C_1 to C_6 alcohols
- Napthalene-2,3,6,7-tetracarboxylates of C_5 and C_6 alcohols
- Tricresyl phosphate

Nitriles
- 2,2′-Oxydipropionitrile

Miscellaneous
- Saturated fatty acids of high molecular weight
- Dimethylsulpholane
- Benzyl cyanide + silver nitrate

Undefined and commercial products
- "Liquid paraffin"
- Paraffin wax
- Lubricating oils
- Transformer oils
- Apiezon greases L, M, and N
- Silicone DC 550
- Silicone DC 702
- Silicone DC 703
- Silicone DC 550 + stearic acid

(*e*) Its viscosity should be low at the column temperature, in order to promote exchange.

Much is to be said for using definite compounds of reproducible purity. Where possible, the use of such indefinable commercial products as lubricating and transformer oils, silicone oils and greases, etc., should be avoided. Nevertheless such materials may occasionally be useful, and succeed where others fail; the same applies to mixtures of compounds[143].

The use of definite compounds as stationary phase has been recommended[96], in order to facilitate the comparison of solutes in quoting retention volumes. They are given in Table I. The principal stationary phases that are employed are collected in Table II.

Descriptions have been published of methods for impregnating the support with the stationary liquid, dissolved in a volatile solvent that is finally removed by evaporation[132]. The retained amount of stationary liquid is determined by weighing the support before and after the impregnation.

Capillary columns are coated by forcing a solution of the stationary liquid in a volatile solvent through them with the aid of compressed inert gas. After the liquid has run through and has left a film of the stationary liquid on the walls, the current of gas is maintained in order to remove the greater part of the solvent. Finally the column so prepared is kept for 24 h at 10 to 20° above the temperature of operation, while a current of carrier gas is passed through it[144].

(*h*) *Detectors*

As we have seen previously (p. 221), detectors may be either of the *integral* type if they give a summation of some property related to the mass of the compounds that have passed through the column, or of the *differential* type if they indicate the instantaneous concentrations. We have also seen (p. 249) that they can be classed into detectors having a single channel and those having two channels (comparative detectors).

The main requirements for a detector, brought forward by various authors[79,145,146], can be summarized in the following points.

(*i*) It should respond to all compounds, whatever their chemical nature.

(*ii*) It should have a sensitivity that is as high as possible, together with a good intrinsic stability.

(*iii*) Its dead volume should be as low as possible.

(*iv*) Its response should be rapid, if possible independent of the pressure and flow rate of the carrier gas and of the chemical nature of the solutes, linear (that is to say proportional to the concentration of the substance in the carrier gas) and, finally, capable of registration.

Needless to say these properties are encountered in different degrees in various detectors. The following are the main types.

(*i*) *Titrating detectors*

This term can be used for all devices in which, after the column effluent has bubbled through a reactive liquid, the change in some physical or chemical property of this reagent is determined.

The standard methods of acidimetry and alkalimetry have been utilized by James and Martin[7,8], who employed a burette manipulated by hand or operated automatically by means of a vessel containing a coloured solution of a pH indicator sensed by a photo-electric cell (see also ref. [147]). Other methods that have been employed consisted in following and registering the variations in the conductivity of a reagent[148], in its redox potential[136], in the quantity of carbon dioxide resulting from the combustion of the substance over copper oxide[149], etc. The methods of coulometry[150-155] and polarography[156,157] have also been applied to gas chromatography.

(ii) Volumetric measurement of gases

According to Janák the volume of gaseous substances is measured directly, after absorption of the carbon dioxide used as carrier gas. The procedure has been rendered automatic[5]. The measurements can be performed at constant pressure (see also refs. [142,158,159]) or at constant volume[101].

(iii) Thermal conductivity cells (katharometers)

Detectors based on the thermal conductivity of gases are at present very widely employed. They are known as thermal conductivity cells or katharometers. They usually contain a fine wire, stretched in the axis of a cylindrical channel maintained at a constant temperature. The wire, when heated electrically, takes on an average temperature depending not only on the electric energy supplied, but also on the thermal energy lost by radiation, convection and conduction. The thermal conductivity of the gas surrounding the wire varies with its nature. In the case of a mixture, such as a column effluent containing a component diluted with carrier gas, the thermal conductivity is generally intermediate between that of the carrier gas and the component (though not necessarily by linear interpolation in accordance with the amount in which each of these is present). Every variation in composition results in a change in the amount of heat removed by conduction, and consequently in the temperature of the wire and its ohmic resistance. As a rule two identical channels are used; through one of these (the comparison channel) the pure carrier gas passes, while the column effluent passes through the other (the measuring channel). The two wires are then so arranged as to form two arms of a Wheatstone bridge circuit. When a substance emerges from the column it gives rise to an out-of-balance voltage in this circuit; this voltage is amplified and recorded.

The thermal conductivities of organic compounds in the gaseous state are relatively low. (The majority range from about 0.5 to 1, relative to air at 100° C.) For a large signal it is hence desirable to employ a carrier gas with a high conductivity, that is to say hydrogen or helium (thermal conductivities relative to air at 100°: 7.1 and 5.5 respectively); the value for nitrogen (0.996) is much closer to that of the organic compounds (and is exceeded by that of methane: 1.45), so that nitrogen gives a very much smaller and more variable response from the katharometer than hydrogen and helium, though it can be employed in some cases. Carbon dioxide and argon are unsuitable, as their conductivities fall in the middle of the range of that of organic compounds.

With helium as carrier gas, the response of katharometers is stated to be independent of the temperature, the concentration and the carrier gas flow rate, a fact facilitating the calibration (see p. 248), which is independent of the katharometer employed[90] (see also refs. [82,160]).

The construction of katharometers has been dealt with by various authors (see, for instance refs. [32,161,162]); their theory and the factors on which their response depends, such as the nature and temperature of the wire, the temperature of the cell walls, and the flow rate of carrier gas are extensively discussed by Keulemans[32] (see also Chovin and Lebbe[163]). Instead of resistance wires, thermistors may be used in thermal conductivity cells[164,165] whereby it is possible to obtain a higher sensitivity, a very low dead volume and rapid response, and constructions within a single cell[111,165,166]. Katharometers intended for high temperatures present special difficulties[167,168]. Thermistors[169] cannot be used above 300° C. A simple solution has been achieved by using model airplane glow plugs[170], but various other techniques have been proposed, which have been summarized by Hardy and Pollard[2].

If the sensitivity appears insufficient in a certain case, such as the detection and measurement of small amounts of an impurity, it can be increased by converting the components at the column outlet either into carbon dioxide[171,172], methane[173] or hydrogen[171]. For calibration, it is then only necessary to take into account the number of carbon or hydrogen atoms in the original molecule.

(iv) Gas density balance

In this ingenious device Martin and James[174] utilize the difference in density existing between the column effluent and the pure carrier gas to cause a minute flow of gas from a channel carrying the denser gas to one carrying the less dense gas. This flow is detected by the disequilibrium of two thermo-junctions, which attain a different temperature as the result of unequal heating.

The gas density balance has a good sensitivity and can operate at a relatively high temperature, though the sensitivity is thereby reduced[119,175].

(v) Flame detectors

Scott[176] has developed a simple detector by using hydrogen as carrier gas, burning it at a small jet behind the column outlet and placing a thermocouple above the flame. The appearance of a component in the column effluent causes the flame to lengthen and increase in temperature and the output of the thermocouple to change. This detector is sensitive and very easy to construct. Since the use of pure hydrogen leads to an unsatisfactory base-line stability, it is preferable to burn a mixture of hydrogen and nitrogen; this can be realized either by using this mixture as carrier gas or by utilizing nitrogen as such and injecting a constant current of hydrogen into the effluent just before the jet of the detector[94,177,178].

Another form of detection consists in measuring the changes in luminosity of a flame[57,179].

A detector of extremely high sensitivity, based on changes in the electric conductivity of a flame as the result of the ionization of components in the effluent, has been developed by McWilliam and Dewar[180–183]. An arrangement similar to that of Scott, described above, is used (*i.e.* a mixture of hydrogen and nitrogen is burned at a jet), but the thermocouple is replaced by an electrode and a DC potential is applied between the latter and the jet. The changes in current are converted into changes in potential, which are amplified. The flame ionization detector has a very small dead volume and appears particularly suited for use with columns of extremely high efficiency, including those of the capillary type.

(*vi*) *Ionization detectors*

A number of detectors (besides that employing a flame, as described above) are founded on the possibility of ionizing the column effluent in various ways.

By using argon as carrier gas and irradiating the column effluent with β-rays, a high degree of ionization is brought about in organic components that are present. Lovelock[184,185] has constructed a detector based on this principle; it is very sensitive, has a fairly small dead volume and, like the flame ionization detector, is particularly adapted for use with high-efficiency columns.

Ionization of the gas can also be effected by an electric discharge, either at high voltage and low gas pressure[186,187] or at low voltage and very low pressure[188,189]. The detectors so obtained also possess a high sensitivity.

(*vii*) *Other detectors*

Numerous other phenomena have been utilized for the construction of detectors. They can only be briefly mentioned here.

By oxidizing organic compounds over copper oxide they are converted into carbon dioxide, which can be determined by infrared absorption[190]. A detector based on changes in surface potential has been described[191,192], and another founded on the variation of the electrostatic capacity of a condensor having active carbon as dielectric[191]. Finally, the techniques of radioactivity have been employed for the analysis of tracer compounds[193,194]. (For a review of detectors, the reader is referred to ref. [2]).

(*k*) *Various accessories*

Various types of traps have been described, by means of which constituents of a mixture can be isolated in a high degree of purity[64,72,109,127,195-198], even at a reduced pressure[199]; they are sometimes simply U-tubes immersed in liquid nitrogen. In order to avoid the loss of substance that can occur by the formation of fine droplets or micro-crystals, it has been proposed to employ an electrostatic precipitator[200], or to entrain the solutes, after leaving the column, by a current of vapour from a boiling solvent, the vapour being then immediately condensed[201].

The operation of chromatographic apparatus has been rendered completely automatic by the use of electromagnetic valves and a time-control system; analyses can thus be carried out at regular intervals of time[196], so as to yield successive traces which can be employed, for instance, as a means of controlling manufacture[202,203].

Finally, a special form of operation is being considered, in which the stationary phase is circulated, and whereby it becomes possible to separate certain components of a mixture continuously[204].

4. Applications of gas chromatography

This subject will be dealt with relatively briefly, since it is impossible to give a detailed account of the extensive literature now existing; this should be consulted for every special type of application.

Gas chromatography has become an invaluable adjunct of numerous research techniques; it is particularly useful for determining trace components or impurities in a major constituent[205-210], for the study of the volatile components of flavours[211-213], for investigating the products of complex reactions, such as the constituents of tobacco smoke[214], the products of catalysis[215] or of an incomplete combustion[216,217], for the study of azeotropes[218], for that of atmospheric pollutants[216,219] and solvents[65,220-222], and so on.

The applications of gas chromatography can also be classified from another aspect, namely according to the type of the substances examined. A very concise review will be given to show the possibilities of the method.

Gas analysis[5,223,224]: hydrogen in the atmosphere of mines[225], nitrogen and its oxides[226-228], halogens and interhalogen compounds[175], boron hydride[229]. *Hydrocarbon analysis*: saturated hydrocarbons[230,231], olefins[55],

References p. 263

naphthenes[58], cyclanes and cyclenes[232,236]. *Halogen derivatives of hydrocarbons*[233]. *Alcohols*[139,234]. *Amines*[139,235]. *Nitro-derivatives*[235]. *Phenols* and components of tars[168,237–242]. *Sulphonated derivatives*[243]. *Organic peroxides*[244], etc.

The examination of natural substances and their derivatives will be considered in greater detail, owing to their importance in biochemistry.

In the first place, extracts of plants, essential oils and volatile vegetable substances can be submitted to the new technique. Thus it has been possible to determine the nature of the hydrocarbons and other terpenic constituents of the essential oil of hops[245], of the oils of bergamot and lemon[153], of those of eucalyptus and mint[246,247], of citronella and lemongrass[248], of yugoslavian fennel[249], of the fruit of *Litsea citrata Blume*[250], of thyme[251]. (See also refs. [252–256], and for the application of gas chromatography in perfumery [257–259].)

As a second example we can take the case of the organic acids, which are encountered either as such, or as their esters, in natural products, and frequently also result from oxidizing degradation reactions on molecules of which the structure is to be investigated.

In this field, as in many others, James and Martin[8] have led the way by separating the various isomers of the C_1 to C_5 acids over silicone oil as stationary liquid. They observed, however, that there was a considerable deformation of the peaks, due to the fact that the acids behave, in solution, as dimers, owing to the existence of intermolecular hydrogen bonds. Without altering the temperature, but by increasing the flow rate during the course of the experiment, these authors obtained a chromatogram for the acids from C_1 up to and including C_{11}. Nevertheless, because of the poor separation so obtained, it is now considered preferable to chromatograph the methyl esters, and a micro-method for preparing them has been described[260,261].

Cropper and Heywood[262,263] have succeeded in investigating the methyl esters from C_{12} to C_{22} over high-vacuum silicone grease (see also ref. [85]), whilst Beerthuis and Keppler[264] have been able to go as far as cerotic acid (C_{26}). James and Martin[265] and James and Wheatley[266] have reconsidered this important problem. Their conclusions may be summarized as follows. In the graph for log $(V_g)/(V_g)_{st} = f$ (number of carbon atoms), (see p. 245), the esters of the normal acids give a separate straight line lying above that for the esters of branched acids. The esters of acids with one and two double bonds emerge, over a paraffinic stationary liquid, before the corresponding saturated esters, and if the double bonds approach the carboxyl group the emergence is retarded. With an aromatic stationary phase a different behaviour is observed; the unsaturated esters are then retarded with respect to the corresponding saturated esters. Furthermore, the unsaturated esters may be revealed by converting them either into saturated esters, or into their dibromides or hydroxyl derivatives; the displacement or disappearance of a peak is then characteristic of an unsaturated ester. James and Martin have finally applied the chromatographic technique to an examination of the fatty matter in goat's milk, in olive oil and to the acids extracted from a culture medium of *Pseudomonas aeroginosa*. For details, the reader must be referred to the original publication.

5. Conclusion

Gas chromatography is a technique which is now at the height of its evolution, and is constantly undergoing new developments and claiming new successes. Its present trends—as far as one may risk formulating them—seem to lie in five well-defined directions:

(*i*) Its extension to low temperatures (*e.g.* $-200°$ C) and to high temperatures ($400°$ and even $500°$ C). It will then cover a temperature range of nearly $700°$ C.

(*ii*) The realization of high column efficiencies. At the time of writing, the author knows of columns whose efficiency is equivalent to hundreds of thousands of theoretical plates. Perhaps, when these lines are printed, the figure of a million will have been reached or passed.

(*iii*) In correlation with the foregoing, there will be an increase in the sensitivity of detectors, consequently also a reduction in the amount of substance that can be measured accurately and a lowering of the sample size. The ionization detectors utilizing argon as carrier gas allow a quantity of substance of but 10^{-10} grams per milliliter of carrier gas to be determined with satisfactory accuracy. In order to enable an amount of sample of but $^{1}/_{10}$ to $^{1}/_{1000}$ of a microliter to be introduced, special devices have had to be developed. The limit of size is still lower when the techniques of radioactivity are employed; in that case the sample need amount to but 10^{-15} g.

(*iv*) At the other end of the scale is the development of columns allowing appreciable weights of substance, up to 100 grams, to be separated. The scale of masses in gas chromatography hence extends over a range of 10^{17} decimal places.

(*v*) Finally, a process of automatisation, allowing the operation to be repeated regularly from the taking of the sample to a direct recording of the peak areas, such with a view, for instance, to the control of manufacturing processes.

The advances that have been made since James and Martin published their first article on gas–liquid chromatography are amazing, and one cannot help wondering how far they will still continue as the result of inventiveness and imagination on the part of investigators. It is true that the same question may be asked with respect to many sciences and tech-

References p. 263

niques, but it must be admitted that the evolution of gas chromatography is particularly spectacular and rapid. Its salient successes may tend to instil modesty in beginners in the field. Nevertheless, if the value of a technique is measured by the number of its adherents, its future is assured, and new experts will every day join the ranks of those practising the method of gas chromatography.

REFERENCES

[1] H. H. STRAIN AND T. R. SATO, *Anal. Chem.*, 28 (1956) 687.
[2] C. J. HARDY AND F. H. POLLARD, *J. Chromatog.*, 2 (1959) 1.
[3] W. RAMSAY, *Proc. Roy. Soc., (London)*, A76 (1905) 111.
[4] S. CLAESSON, *Arkiv Kemi, Mineral. Geol.*, A23 (1946) No. 1; *Ann. N.Y. Acad. Sci.*, 49 (1948) 183.
[5] J. JANÁK, *Collection Czechoslov. Chem. Communs.*, 18 (1953) 798; 19 (1954) 684, 700, 917; 20 (1955) 336, 343, 348, 923, 1199, 1241; *Chem. listy*, 48 (1954) 207; 49 (1955) 1403; *Erdöl u. Kohle*, 10 (1957) 442; *Chem. Tech., (Berlin)*, 8 (1956) 125; *Mikrochim. Acta*, 1–6 (1956) 1038;
A. I. M. KEULEMANS AND A. KWANTES, *Vapour Phase Chromatography*, Butterworths, London, 1957, p. 235 and 247;
J. JANÁK, M. NEDOROST AND V. BUBENIKOVA, *Chem. listy*, 51 (1957) 890;
J. JANÁK AND J. NOVAK, *ibid.*, 51 (1957) 1832;
J. JANÁK AND K. TESARIK, *ibid.*, 51 (1957) 2048.
[6] A. J. P. MARTIN AND R. L. M. SYNGE, *Biochem. J.* 35 (1941) 1358.
[7] A. T. JAMES AND A. J. P. MARTIN, *Biochem. J.*, 50 (1952) 679.
[8] A. T. JAMES AND A. J. P. MARTIN, *Analyst*, 77 (1952) 915.
[9] A. J. P. MARTIN, *Endeavour*, 6 (1947) 22.
[10] D. AMBROSE, A. I. M. KEULEMANS AND J. H. PURNELL, *Anal. Chem.*, 30 (1958) 1582.
[11] H. W. JOHNSON AND F. H. STROSS, *Anal. Chem.*, 30 (1958) 1586.
[12] J. BUZON, P. CHOVIN, L. FANICA, R. FERRAND, G. GUIOCHON, M. HUGUET, J. LEBBE, J. SERPINET AND J. TRANCHANT, *Bull. soc. chim. France*, (1959) 1137.
[13] Anon., *J. Chromatog. Data*, 2 (1959) D33.
[14] P. CHOVIN AND J. LEBBE, *Compt. rend.*, 247 (1958) 596.
[15] J. N. WILSON, *J. Am. Chem. Soc.*, 62 (1940) 1583.
[16] J. WEISS, *J. Chem. Soc.*, (1943) 297.
[17] D. DE VAULT, *J. Am. Chem. Soc.*, 65 (1943) 532.
[18] H. C. THOMAS, *Ann. N.Y. Acad. Sci.*, 49 (1948) 161.
[19] J. ROUBAUD-VALETTE, *J. Chim. Phys.*, 50 (1953) 117.
[20] E. GLUECKAUF, *J. Chem. Soc.*, (1949) 3280.
[21] E. WICKE, *Angew. Chem.*, 19 (1947) 15.
[22] A. KLINKENBERG AND F. SJENITZER, *Chem. Eng. Sci.*, 5 (1956) 258.
[23] J. J. VAN DEEMTER, F. J. ZUIDERWEG AND A. KLINKENBERG, *Chem. Eng. Sci.*, 5 (1956) 271.
[24] E. GLUECKAUF, *Trans. Faraday Soc.*, 51 (1955) 34.
[25] P. JAULMES AND R. MESTRES, *Compt. rend.*, 248 (1959) 2752.
[26] B. H. KETELLE AND G. E. BOYD, *J. Am. Chem. Soc.*, 69 (1947) 2800.
[27] G. E. BOYD, L. S. MYERS JR. AND A. W. ADAMSON, *J. Am. Chem. Soc.*, 69 (1947) 2849.
[28] L. LAPIDUS AND N. R. AMUNDSON, *J. Phys. Chem.*, 56 (1952) 984.
[29] E. GLUECKAUF, *Principles of Operation of Ion Exchange Columns, Mémoire présenté à la Conférence des échanges d'ions*, London, 5–7 April 1954.
[30] J. J. VAN DEEMTER, *Gas Chrom. Discuss. Group*, Cambridge, England, 4th Oct. 1957.
[31] A. I. M. KEULEMANS AND A. KWANTES, *Vapour Phase Chromatography*, Butterworths, London, 1957, p. 15.
[32] A. I. M. KEULEMANS, *Gas Chromatography*, Reinhold, New York, 1957.
[33] W. J. DE WET AND V. PRETORIUS, *Anal. Chem.*, 30 (1958) 325.
[34] J. D. CHESHIRE AND R. P. W. SCOTT, *J. Inst. Petrol.*, 44 (1958) 74.
[35] J. BOHEMEN AND J. H. PURNELL, *Gas Chromatography 1958*, Butterworths, London, 1958, p. 6.
[36] A. B. LITTLEWOOD, *Gas Chromatography 1958*, Butterworths, London, 1958, p. 23.
[37] R. P. W. SCOTT, *Gas Chromatography 1958*, Butterworths, London, 1958, p. 189.
[38] P. CHOVIN, *Bull. soc. chim. France*, (1958) 905.
[39] M. J. E. GOLAY, *Anal. Chem.*, 29 (1957) 928.
[40] E. R. GILLILAND, *Ind. Eng. Chem.*, 26 (1934) 681.
[41] F. VAN DE CRAATS, *Gas Chromatography 1958*, Butterworths, London, 1958, p. 248.
[42] D. BRENNAN AND C. KEMBALL, *J. Inst. Petrol.*, 44 (1958) 14.

[43] P. E. Porter, C. H. Deal and F. H. Stross, *J. Am. Chem. Soc.*, 78 (1956) 2999.
[44] F. H. Pollard and C. J. Hardy, *Chem. & Ind., (London)*, (1955) 1145.
[45] A. B. Littlewood, C. S. G. Phillips and D. T. Price, *J. Chem. Soc.*, (1955) 1480.
[46] C. S. G. Phillips, *Gas Chromatography*, Butterworths, London, 1956.
[47] F. H. Pollard and C. J. Hardy, *Vapour Phase Chromatography*, Butterworths, London, 1957, p. 115.
[48] G. Dijkstra and J. de Goey, *Gas Chromatography 1958*, Butterworths, London, 1958, p. 56.
[49] M. J. E. Golay, *Gas Chromatography*, Academic Press, New York, 1958, p. 1.
[50] M. J. E. Golay, *Gas Chromatography 1958*, Butterworths, London, 1958, p. 36.
[51] J. R. A. Anderson and K. H. Napier, *Australian J. Chem.*, 10 (1957) 250.
[52] A. I. M. Keulemans, A. Kwantes and P. Zaal, *Anal. Chim. Acta*, 13 (1955) 357.
[53] G. J. Pierotti, C. H. Deal, E. L. Derr and P. E. Porter, *J. Am. Chem. Soc.*, 78 (1956) 2989.
[54] A. Kwantes and G. W. A. Rijnders, *Gas Chromatography 1958*, Butterworths, London, 1958, p. 125.
[55] H. S. Knight, *Anal. Chem.*, 30 (1958) 9.
[56] C. J. Hardy, *J. Chromatog.*, 2 (1959) 490.
[57] D. W. Grant and G. A. Vaughan, *Vapour Phase Chromatography*, Butterworths, London, 1957, p. 413.
[58] F. T. Eggertsen and H. S. Knight, *Anal. Chem.*, 30 (1958) 15.
[59] M. R. Hoare and J. H. Purnell, *Trans. Faraday Soc.*, 52 (1956) 222.
[60] J. H. Purnell, *Vapour Phase Chromatography*, Butterworths,London, 1957, p. 52.
[61] J. G. Keppler, G. Dijkstra and J. A. Schols, *Vapour Phase Chromatography*, Butterworths, London, 1957, p. 222.
[62] N. H. Ray, *J. Appl. Chem.*, (London), 4 (1954) 21.
[63] H. M. Tenney, *Anal. Chem.*, 30 (1958) 2.
[64] B. T. Whitham, *Vapour Phase Chromatography*, Butterworths, London, 1957, p. 194.
[65] B. T. Whitham, *Vapour Phase Chromatography*, Butterworths, London, 1957, p. 395.
[66] B. W. Bradford, D. Harvey and D. E. Chalkley, *J. Inst. Petrol.*, 41 (1955) 80.
[67] E. Gil-Av, J. Herling and J. Shabtai, *Chem. & Ind., (London)*, (1957) 1483.
[68] D. W. Barber, C. S. G. Phillips, G. F. Tusa and A. Verdin, *J. Chem. Soc.*, (1959) 18.
[69] E. Bayer, *Gas Chromatography 1958*, Butterworths, London, 1958, p. 333.
[70] S. H. Langer, *Gas Chromatography Discussion Group*, London, 10 April, 1959.
[71] C. Lutinsky, *Appl. Spectroscopy*, 11 (1957) 100.
[72] H. E. Bellis and E. J. Slowinski, *J. Chem. Phys.*, 25 (1956) 794.
[73] W. V. E. Doering, R. G. Buttery, R. G. Laughlin and N. Chaudhuri, *J. Am. Chem. Soc.*, 78 (1956) 3224.
[74] H. N. Morrow and K. B. Buckley, *Petrol. Refiner*, 36, No. 8 (1957) 157.
[75] C. W. Munday and G. R. Primavesi, *Vapour Phase Chromatography*, Butterworths, London, 1957, p. 146.
[76] Y. R. Naves, *Perfumery Essent. Oil Record*, 48 (1958) 290.
[77] J. S. Lewis, H. W. Patton and W. I. Kaye, *Anal. Chem.*, 28 (1956) 1370.
[78] C. M. Drew, J. R. McNesby, S. R. Smith and A. S. Gordon, *Anal. Chem.*, 28 (1956) 979.
[79] M. Dimbat, P. E. Porter and F. H. Stross, *Anal. Chem.*, 28 (1956) 290.
[80] S. Dal Nogare, C. E. Bennett and J. C. Harden, *Gas Chromatography*, Academic Press, New York, 1958, p. 117.
[81] D. H. Lichtenfels, S. A. Fleck and F. H. Burrow, *Anal. Chem.*, 27 (1955) 1510.
[82] R. H. Eastman, *J. Am. Chem. Soc.*, 79 (1957) 4243.
[83] F. H. Pollard and C. J. Hardy, *Anal. Chim. Acta*, 16 (1957) 135.
[84] E. Cremer and F. Prior, *Z. Elektrochem.*, 55 (1951) 66, 217.
[85] G. Dijkstra, J. G. Keppler and J. A. Schols, *Rec. Trav. Chim.*, 74 (1955) 805.
[86] R. H. Munch, *Anal. Chem.*, 27 (1955) 271.
[87] D. M. Rosie and R. L. Grob, *Anal. Chem.*, 29 (1957) 1263.
[88] L. C. Browning and J. O. Watts, *Anal. Chem.*, 29 (1957) 24.
[89] G. Schomburg, *Z. anal. Chem.*, 164 (1958) 147.

[90] A. E. MESSNER, D. M. ROSIE AND P. A. ARGABRIGHT, *Conf. Anal. Chem.*, Pittsburg, (U.S.A.), March 1958.
[91] A. I. M. KEULEMANS, A. KWANTES AND G. W. A. RIJNDERS, *Anal. Chim. Acta*, 16 (1957) 29.
[92] M. C. SIMMONS AND L. R. SNYDER, *Anal. Chem.*, 30 (1958) 32.
[93] C. DUMAZERT AND CL. GHIGLIONE, *Bull. soc. chim. France*, (1959) 615.
[94] J. I. HENDERSON AND J. H. KNOX, *J. Chem. Soc.*, (1956) 2299.
[95] D. H. JAMES AND C. S. G. PHILLIPS, *J. Sci. Instr.*, 29 (1952) 362.
[96] D. H. DESTY, E. GLUECKAUF, A. T. JAMES, A. I. M. KEULEMANS, A. J. P. MARTIN AND C. S. G. PHILLIPS, *Vapour Phase Chromatography*, Butterworths, London, 1957, p. xi.
[97] K. WENCKE, *Chem. Tech. (Berlin)*, 8 (1956) 728.
[98] D. E. M. EVANS, W. E. MASSINGHAM, M. STACEY AND J. C. TATLOW, *Nature*, 182 (1958) 591.
[99] D. H. DESTY, J. N. HARESNAPE AND B. H. F. WHYMAN, *Anal. Chem.*, 32 (1960) 302.
[100] R. P. W. SCOTT, *Gas Chromatography Discussion Group*, London, 10 April 1959.
[101] F. VAN DE CRAATS, *Anal. Chim. Acta*, 14 (1956) 136.
[102] S. W. GREEN, *Vapour Phase Chromatography*, Butterworths, London, 1957, p. 388.
[103] D. HARVEY AND D. E. CHALKLEY, *Fuel*, 34 (1955) 191.
[104] H. W. PATTON AND G. P. TOUEY, *Anal. Chem.*, 28 (1956) 1685.
[105] W. K. HALL AND P. H. EMMETT, *J. Am. Chem. Soc.*, 79 (1957) 2091.
[106] G. F. HARRISON, *Vapour Phase Chromatography*, Butterworths, London, 1957, p. 332.
[107] W. C. PERCIVAL, *Anal. Chem.*, 29 (1957) 20.
[108] J. J. LINGANE AND S. L. JONES, *Anal. Chem.*, 22 (1950) 1220.
[109] J. G. KEPPLER, J. A. SCHOLS AND G. DIJKSTRA, *Rec. Trav. Chim.*, 75 (1956) 965.
[110] D. W. CARLE, *Gas Chromatography*, Academic Press, New York, 1958, p. 67.
[111] F. R. CROPPER AND A. HEYWOOD, *Vapour Phase Chromatography*, Butterworths, London, 1957, p. 316.
[112] R. E. DAVIS AND J. M. MCCREA, *Anal. Chem.*, 29 (1957) 1114.
[113] H. M. TENNEY AND R. J. HARRIS, *Anal. Chem.*, 29 (1957) 317.
[114] F. G. STANFORD, *Analyst*, 84 (1959) 321.
[115] S. W. S. MCCREADIE AND A. F. WILLIAMS, *J. Appl. Chem.*, *(London)*, 7 (1957) 47.
[116] D. E. M. EVANS AND J. C. TATLOW, *Vapour Phase Chromatography*, Butterworths, London, 1957, p. 256.
[117] C. J. HARDY, *Thesis*, Univ. of Bristol, England, 1955.
[118] V. T. BROOKS, W. MURRAY AND A. F. WILLIAMS, *Meeting IUPAC*, Vol. VIII, Lisbon, 1956, p. 39.
[119] J. C. HAWKES, *Vapour Phase Chromatography*, Butterworths, London, 1957, p. 266.
[120] D. E. M. EVANS AND J. C. TATLOW, *J. Chem. Soc.*, (1955) 1184.
[121] G. HESSE AND B. TSCHACHOTIN, *Naturwissenschaften*, 25/26 (1942) 387.
[122] G. K. ASHBURY, A. J. DAVIES AND J. W. DRINKWATER, *Anal. Chem.*, 29 (1957) 918.
[123] J. B. EVANS AND J. E. WILLARD, *J. Am. Chem. Soc.*, 78 (1956) 2908.
[124] S. A. GREENE, M. L. MOBERG AND E. M. WILSON, *Anal. Chem.*, 28 (1956) 1369.
[125] A. T. JAMES, *Endeavour*, 15 (1956) 73.
[126] H. W. PATTON, J. S. LEWIS AND W. I. KAYE, *Anal. Chem.*, 27 (1955) 170.
[127] C. M. DREW AND J. R. MCNESBY, *Vapour Phase Chromatography*, Butterworths, London, 1957, p. 213.
[128] G. KYRYACOS AND C. E. BOORD, *Anal. Chem.*, 29 (1957) 787.
[129] R. M. BARRER AND A. D. ROBINS, *Trans. Faraday Soc.*, 49 (1953) 807.
[130] J. JANÁK, *Collection Czechoslov. Chem. Communs.*, 20 (1955) 1241.
[131] A. T. JAMES, A. J. P. MARTIN AND G. HOWARD-SMITH, *Biochem. J.*, 52 (1952) 238.
[132] E. R. ADLARD, *Vapour Phase Chromatography*, Butterworths, London, 1957, p. 98.
[133] A. I. M. KEULEMANS AND A. KWANTES, *Proc. 4th World Petrol. Congr.*, Colombo, Rome, 1955, p. 273.
[134] D. H. DESTY, F. M. GODFREY AND C. L. A. HARBOURN, *Gas Chromatography 1958*, Butterworths, London, 1958, p. 200.
[135] R. J. CVETANOVIC AND K. O. KUTSCHKE, *Vapour Phase Chromatography*, Butterworths, London, 1957, p. 87.
[136] S. SUNNER, K. J. KARRMAN AND V. SUNDEN, *Mikrochim. Acta*, (1956) 1144.

[137] I. B. SORENSEN AND P. SOLTOFT, *Acta Chem. Scand.*, 10 (1956) 1673.
[138] J. JANÁK, *Vapour Phase Chromatography*, Butterworths, London, 1958, p. 235.
[139] H. S. KNIGHT, *Anal. Chem.*, 30 (1958) 2030.
[140] E. C. ORMEROD AND R. P. W. SCOTT, *J. Chromatog.*, 2 (1959) 65.
[141] D. H. DESTY, T. J. WARHAM AND B. H. F. WHYMAN, *Vapour Phase Chromatography*, Butterworths, London, 1957, p. 346.
[142] N. H. RAY, *Analyst*, 80 (1955) 853.
[143] W. H. MCFADDEN, *Anal. Chem.*, 30 (1958) 479.
[144] D. H. DESTY, A. GOLDUP AND B. H. F. WHYMAN, *Gas Chromatography Discussion Group*, London, 10 April 1959.
[145] A. T. JAMES, *Vapour Phase Chromatography*, Butterworths, London, 1957, p. 127.
[146] H. BOER, *Vapour Phase Chromatography*, Butterworths, London, 1957, p. 169.
[147] A. G. MCINNES, *Vapour Phase Chromatography*, Butterworths, London, 1957, p. 304.
[148] K. FRIEDRICH, *Chem. & Ind. (London)*, (1957) 47.
[149] L. BLOM AND L. EDELHAUSEN, *Anal. Chim. Acta*, 15 (1956) 569.
[150] A. LIBERTI, *Anal. Chim. Acta*, 17 (1957) 247.
[151] A. LIBERTI AND G. P. CARTONI, *Atti accad. nazl. Lincei*, 20 (1956) 787.
[152] A. LIBERTI AND G. P. CARTONI, *Chim. e ind., (Milan)*, 39 (1957) 821.
[153] A. LIBERTY AND G. P. CARTONI, *Gas Chromatography 1958*, Butterworths, London, 1958, p. 321.
[154] A. LIBERTI, G. P. CARTONI AND U. PALLOTTA, *Latte*, 30 (1956) 581.
[155] A. LIBERTI, G. P. CARTONI AND U. PALLOTTA, *Ann. Chim., (Rome)*, 48 (1958) 40.
[156] J. JANÁK, M. NEDOROST AND V. BUBENIKOVA, *Chem. listy*, 51 (1957) 890.
[157] M. NEDOROST, *Chem. listy*, 50 (1956) 317.
[158] C. ROUIT, *Vapour Phase Chromatography*, Butterworths, London, 1957, p. 291.
[159] E. LEIBNITZ, H. HRAPIA AND H. G. KÖNNECKE, *Brennstoff Chem.*, 38 (1957) 14.
[160] R. MAUREL, *Compt. rend.*, 244 (1957) 3157.
[161] W. STUVE, *Gas Chromatography 1958*, Butterworths, London, 1958, p. 178.
[162] R. PAPOULAR, *Rev. Tech. C.F.T.H.*, (1957) 9.
[163] P. CHOVIN AND J. LEBBE, *Monographies de Chimie Organique*, Vol. II, part 1, Masson et Cie, Paris, 1959.
[164] R. B. SELIGMAN, *Symposium Bethesda*, May 1956.
[165] A. D. DAVIS AND G. A. HOWARD, *J. Appl. Chem., (London)*, 8 (1958) 183.
[166] A. D. DAVIS AND G. A. HOWARD, *Chem. & Ind. B.I.F. Review*, (1956) R25.
[167] S. DAL NOGARE AND L. W. SAFRANSKI, *Anal. Chem.*, 30 (1958) 894.
[168] F. DUPIRE AND G. BOTQUIN, *Anal. Chim. Acta*, 18 (1958) 282.
[169] J. L. OGILVIE, M. C. SIMMONS AND G. P. HINDS, *Anal. Chem.*, 30 (1958) 25.
[170] H. R. FELTON AND A. A. BUEHLER, *Anal. Chem.*, 30 (1958) 1163.
[171] G. E. GREEN, *Nature*, 180 (1957) 295.
[172] S. NOREM, *Gas Chromatography*, Academic Press, New York, 1958, p. 191.
[173] A. ZLATKIS AND J. F. ORO, *Anal. Chem.*, 30 (1958) 1156.
[174] A. J. P. MARTIN AND A. T. JAMES, *Biochem. J.*, 63 (1956) 138.
[175] J. F. ELLIS AND G. IVESON, *Gas Chromatography 1958*, Butterworths, London, 1958, p. 300.
[176] R. P. W. SCOTT, *Nature*, 176 (1955) 793.
[177] M. M. WIRTH, *Vapour Phase Chromatography*, Butterworths, London, 1957, p. 154.
[178] G. R. PRIMAVESI, G. F. OLDHAM AND R. J. THOMPSON, *Gas Chromatography 1958*, Buttersworths, London, 1958, p. 165.
[179] D. W. GRANT, *Gas Chromatography 1958*, Butterworths, London, 1958, p. 153.
[180] I. G. MCWILLIAM AND R. A. DEWAR, *Nature*, 181 (1958) 760.
[181] I. G. MCWILLIAM AND R. A. DEWAR, *Gas Chromatography 1958*, Butterworths, London, 1958, p. 142.
[182] J. HARLEY, W. NEL AND V. PRETORIUS, *Nature*, 181 (1958) 177.
[183] A. E. THOMPSON. *J. Chromatog.*, 2 (1959) 148.
[184] J. E. LOVELOCK, *J. Chromatog.*, 1 (1958) 35.
[185] J. E. LOVELOCK, *Nature*, 182 (1958) 1663.
[186] R. C. PITKETHLY, *Anal. Chem.*, 30 (1958) 1309.

[187] J. Harley and V. Pretorius, *Nature*, 178 (1956) 1244.
[188] S. A. Ryce and W. A. Bryce, *Nature*, 179 (1957) 541.
[189] S. A. Ryce and W. A. Bryce, *Can. J. Chem.*, 35 (1957) 1293.
[190] A. E. Martin and J. Smart, *Nature*, 175 (1955) 422.
[191] J. H. Griffiths, D. H. James and C. S. G. Phillips, *Analyst*, 77 (1952) 897.
[192] J. H. Griffiths and C. S. G. Phillips, *J. Chem. Soc.*, (1954) 3446
[193] R. Wolfgang and F. S. Rowland, *Anal. Chem.*, 30 (1958) 903.
[194] G. Moussebois and G. Duyckaerts, *J. Chromatog.*, 1 (1958) 200.
[195] A. Weinstein, *Anal. Chem.*, 29 (1957) 1899.
[196] D. Ambrose and R. R. Collerson, *Nature*, 177 (1956) 84.
[197] D. H. Desty and B. H. F. Whyman, *Anal. Chem.*, 29 (1957) 320.
[198] J. Haslam and A. R. Jeffs, *J. Appl. Chem.*, (*London*), 7 (1957) 24.
[199] B. M. Craig, T. M. Mallard and L. L. Hoffman, *Anal. Chem.*, 31 (1959) 319.
[200] E. P. Atkinson and G. A. P. Tuey, *Gas Chromatography 1958*, Butterworths, London 1958, p. 270.
[201] J. H. Jones and C. D. Ritchie, *J. Assoc. Offic. Agr. Chemists*, 41 (1958) 753.
[202] J. Hooimeijer, A. Kwantes and F. van de Craats, *Gas Chromatography 1958*, Butterworths, London, 1958, p. 288.
[203] A. J. Miller, *Oil Gas J.*, 56 (1958) 88.
[204] H. Pichler and H. Schulz, *Brennstoff-Chem.*, 39 (1958) 148.
[205] J. Sverak and P. L. Reiser, *Mikrochim. Acta*, 1 (1958) 159.
[206] J. Sverak and P. L. Reiser, *Mikrochim. Acta*, 3 (1958) 1126.
[207] G. Nodop, *Z. anal. Chem.*, 164 (1958) 120.
[208] J. D. Boggus and N. G. Adams, *Anal. Chem.*, 30 (1958) 1471.
[209] S. J. Bodnar and S. J. Mayeux, *Anal. Chem.*, 30 (1958) 1384.
[210] C. E. Bennett, S. Dal Nogare, L. Safranski and C. D. Lewis, *Anal. Chem.*, 30 (1958) 898.
[211] W. G. Jennings, *J. Dairy Sci.*, 40 (1957) 271.
[212] K. P. Dimick and J. Corse, *Food Technol.*, 10 (1956) 360.
[213] J. W. Rhoades, *The Coffee Brewing Inst.*, Public. No. 34, July 1958.
[214] L. D. Quin and M. E. Hobbs, *Anal. Chem.*, 30 (1958) 1400.
[215] J. Marechal, I. Convent and J. van Rysselberge, *Rev. inst. franç. pétrole et Ann. combustibles liquides*, 12 (1957) 1067.
[216] F. T. Eggertsen and F. M. Nelsen, *Anal. Chem.*, 30 (1958) 1040.
[217] G. Kyryacos, H. R. Menapace and C. E. Boord, *Anal. Chem.*, 31 (1959) 222.
[218] J. F. Haskins, G. W. Warren, L. J. Priestley Jr. and V. A. Yaborough, *Anal. Chem.*, 30 (1958) 217.
[219] P. W. West, B. Sen and N. A. Gibson, *Anal. Chem.*, 30 (1958) 1390.
[220] P. Peyrot, *Chim. & ind. (Paris)*, 78 (1957) 3.
[221] F. Martin, J. Courteix and S. Vertalier, *Bull. soc. chim. France*, (1958) 494.
[222] E. G. Hoffman, *Z. anal. Chem.*, 164 (1958) 182.
[223] M. Velut and J. Jourda, *Rev. inst. franç. pétrole et Ann. combustibles liquides*, 12 (1958) 1635.
[224] K. Wencke, *Chem. Tech. (Berlin)*, 9 (1957) 404.
[225] J. R. Parkington, *Nature*, 179 (1957) 911.
[226] M. Lefort and X. Tarrago, *J. Chromatog.*, 2 (1959) 218.
[227] S. A. Greene and H. Pust, *Anal. Chem.*, 30 (1958) 1039.
[228] R. N. Smith, J. Swinehart and D. G. Lesnini, *Anal. Chem.*, 30 (1958) 1217.
[229] J. J. Kaufman, J. E. Todd and W. S. Koski, *Anal. Chem.*, 29 (1957) 1032.
[230] F. T. Eggertsen and S. Groenings, *Anal. Chem.*, 30 (1958) 20.
[231] A. Zlatkis, *Anal. Chem.*, 30 (1958) 332.
[232] E. A. M. S. Dahmen and J. D. van der Laarse, *Z. anal. Chem.*, 164 (1958) 37.
[233] T. M. Reed, *Anal. Chem.*, 30 (1958) 221.
[234] L. Maricq and L. Molle, *Bull. acad. roy. méd. Belg.*, 24 (1959) 199.
[235] J. H. Jones, C. D. Ritchie and K. S. Heine Jr., *J. Assoc. Offic. Agr. Chemists*, 41 (1958) 749.
[236] E. Gil-Av, J. Herling and J. Shabtai, *J. Chromatog.*, 1 (1958) 508.
[237] J. Janák and R. Komers, *Z. anal. Chem.*, 164 (1958) 69.

[238] J. JANÁK AND R. KOMERS, *Gas Chromatography 1958*, Butterworths, London, 1958, p. 343.
[239] G. BERGMAN AND D. JENTZSCH, *Z. anal. Chem.*, 164 (1958) 10.
[240] C. KARR JR., P. M. BROWN, P. A. ESTEP AND G. L. HUMPHREY, *Anal. Chem.*, 30 (1958) 1413.
[241] L. IRVINE AND T. J. MITCHELL, *J. Appl. Chem.*, (*London*), 8 (1958) 3.
[242] E. C. JENNINGS JR., T. D. CURRAN AND D. E. EDWARDS, *Anal. Chem.*, 30 (1958) 1946.
[243] C. F. SPENCER, F. BAUMANN AND F. J. JOHNSON, *Anal. Chem.*, 30 (1958) 1473.
[244] M. H. ABRAHAM, A. G. DAVIES, D. R. LLEWELLYN AND E. M. THAIN, *Anal. Chim. Acta*, 17 (1957) 499.
[245] G. A. HOWARD AND C. A. SLATER, *Chem. & Ind.*, (*London*), (1957) 495.
[246] L. DOMANGE AND S. LONGUEVALLE, *Compt. rend.*, 247 (1958) 209.
[247] L. DOMANGE AND S. LONGUEVALLE, *Ann. pharm. franç.*, 16 (1958) 557.
[248] Y. R. NAVES AND A. ODERMATT, *Compt. rend.*, 247 (1958) 300.
[249] Y. R. NAVES AND J. TUCAKOV, *Compt. rend.*, 248 (1959) 843.
[250] Y. R. NAVES AND A. V. GRAMPOLOFF, *Compt. rend.*, 248 (1959) 2029.
[251] Y. R. NAVES, *France et ses parfums*, No. 8 (1959) 23.
[252] Y. R. NAVES AND A. ODERMATT, *France et ses parfums*, No. 6 (1958) 10.
[253] E. BAYER, G. KUPFER AND K. H. REUTHER, *Z. anal. Chem.*, 164 (1958) 1.
[254] Y. R. NAVES, *Bull. soc. chim. France*, (1958) 1372.
[255] Y. R. NAVES AND A. ODERMATT, *Bull. soc. chim. France*, (1958) 377.
[256] Y. R. NAVES, P. ARDIZIO AND CL. FAVRE, *Bull. soc. chim. France*, (1958) 566.
[257] G. A. P. TUEY, *Soap, Perfumery & Cosmetics*, 31 (1958) 353.
[258] W. A. WISEMAN, *Perfumery Essent. Oil Record*, 48 (1957) 380.
[259] P. CHOVIN, *Parfums, cosmét. savons*, 1 (1958) 261.
[260] W. STOFFEL, F. CHU AND E. H. AHRENS JR., *Anal. Chem.*, 31 (1959) 307.
[261] H. KURZ, *Fette u. Seifen*, 44 (1937) 144.
[262] F. R. CROPPER AND A. HEYWOOD, *Nature*, 172 (1953) 1101.
[263] F. R. CROPPER AND A. HEYWOOD, *Nature*, 174 (1954) 1063.
[264] R. K. BEERTHUIS AND J. G. KEPPLER, *Nature*, 179 (1957) 731.
[265] A. T. JAMES AND A. J. P. MARTIN, *Biochem. J.*, 63 (1956) 144.
[266] A. T. JAMES AND J. R. WHEATLEY, *Biochem. J.*, 63 (1956)269.
[267] P. CHOVIN, *Bull. soc. chim. France*, (1960) 755.
[268] P. CHOVIN, *Bull. soc. chim. France*, (1961) 875.

SUBJECT INDEX

Abbreviations used: A.C., adsorption chromatography; C.C.D., countercurrent distribution; G.C., gas chromatography; G.L.C., gas–liquid chromatography; G.S.C., gas–solid chromatography; I.E.C., ion-exchange chromatography; PpC., paper chromatography; PtC., partition chromatography on columns.